INTRODUCTION TO
PROBABILITY AND
STATISTICS

INTRODUCTION TO PROBABILITY AND STATISTICS

Second Edition

William Mendenhall

University of Florida

Wadsworth Publishing Company, Inc.
Belmont, California

Fifth printing: March 1969

Introduction to Probability and Statistics, Second Edition
by William Mendenhall
(Former title: *Introduction to Statistics*)

L.C. Cat. Card No.: 67-19290

Printed in the United States of America

PREFACE

Introductory courses in statistics vary greatly, depending on the background and objectives of the students and the philosophy of the instructors. Most college students have encountered experimentation in high school, and those in the biological, social, and physical sciences as well as the business field are involved in experimental or decision-making courses early in their college careers. Consequently, students need a clear understanding of the scientific method and the role of statistics in making inferences based on observed data. That the need for statistics is not confined to science majors is apparent when one considers the published results of numerous opinion polls and other quantitative facts that bombard the average citizen in the news media and advertising. The ability to question and assess the reliability of this mass of numerical information is essential for an understanding of the world in which we live. Therefore an introductory survey course in statistics should be made available to all students majoring in the arts, sciences, and business; and it is for these students that this text was written.

Some very strong beliefs concerning the desirable characteristics of an introductory course in statistics influenced the style of presentation and content, and these beliefs make the text quite different from others designed for the same group of students. First, I think that the student should clearly see inference as the objective of statistics, should understand how statistical inference-making procedures work and why they function better than our own intuitive inference-making machinery. Thus, I believe that an elementary but clear understanding of the role of probability in making inferences and assessing their reliabilities is essential to an intelligent use of statistical methods. Consequently, a strong effort has been made to weld the theories of probability and inference throughout the book. Second, the student should see that the same statistical problems occur in business, biology, engineering, and the social sciences and should realize that the basic concepts of statistics and inferential methods apply in all fields. Only the frequency of occurrence of specific types of problems varies from one field to another. Thus, I think that a first course in statistics should stress the unity of concepts and not be field-oriented. Specialized courses can follow in the student's field of application. Finally, I believe that an introduction to probability should be presented in an organized manner that is elementary, palatable, consistent with the mathematical theory of probability, and, consequently, based on the notion of a sample space.

Three distinct points of emphasis in the text are a result of this philosophy. The objective of statistics, inference, is stated in Chapter 1, and the introduction to every subsequent chapter explains the role of the chapter material in making inferences and measuring their reliabilities. Second, not only is probability presented in a very elementary (but thorough) manner based on the concept of the sample space, but it is employed at the earliest opportunity (Chapter 6) in two very practical inferential problems as well as in subsequent discussions when the complexity of the probabilistic problem is within the grasp of the student. Finally, an attempt has been made to provide a large number of examples and exercises with practical application in a variety of fields, thereby indicating the broad applicability of statistical methodology.

The chapters on the analysis of variance and nonparametric statistics have been added in this edition to provide flexibility in the construction of the course. Students in business and in the social and biological sciences at the University of Florida take a course based on the first ten chapters of the text. This is followed by specialized courses in each student's field of application. For example, business majors follow the introductory course with a second-semester course on index numbers and time-series analysis in the College of Business Administration. A course oriented toward the social sciences might utilize some combination of Chapters 11, 12, and 13, and an elementary course in the theory of probability, with some emphasis on inference, might include Chapters 1 through 8 and Chapter 13.

Exercises are graduated in difficulty so that all students can solve some of the exercises, a substantial number can solve most, and a few of the best students are challenged to solve all without error. Unannounced quizzes are very effective in helping the student learn the new language of statistics. A thorough knowledge of definitions and concepts is essential before the students attempt the exercises.

The number of colleagues and friends who have provided their kind assistance in helping me write this text has increased over time. Particular thanks are due to William Miller and Paul Benson of Bucknell University for assistance in developing and testing the first edition and for helpful comments concerning revision; to John T. Webster, William Brelsford, and Robert Crovelli for assistance in reading rough drafts of the original manuscript and in testing and checking the problem sets; and to Douglas Chapman of the University of Washington, Arthur Coladarci of Stanford University, and Paul Meyer of Washington State University for their very helpful reviews of the original manuscript. I am particularly indebted to Fred Barnett and P. V. Rao of the Department of Statistics, the University of Florida, for their helpful comments concerning the new material included in the revision. Thanks are also due to Professors E. J. Pearson, A. Hald, W. H. Beyer, and D. L. Burkholder, and to R. A. Wilcox and C. W. Dunnett, for their kind permission to use tables reprinted in Appendix II. Particular thanks are due to the typists who have given their best and endured the worst: to Mrs. Florence Valentine, who typed the original draft of the manuscript, and to Mrs. Angie Anastasia and Mrs. Gay Midelis for preparing the material for the revision. Finally, as in the preface of the first edition, I acknowledge the forbearance and assistance of my wife and children and their partnership in this writing endeavor.

CONTENTS

13 Nonparametric Statistics

14 A Summary and Conclusion   *325*

Appendix I

Appendix II

INTRODUCTION TO PROBABILITY AND STATISTICS

1

WHAT IS
STATISTICS?

1.1 Illustrative Statistical Problems

What is statistics? How does it function? How does it help to solve certain practical problems? Rather than attempt a definition at this point, let us examine several problems which might come to the attention of the statistician. From these examples we can then select the essential elements of a statistical problem.

In predicting the outcome of a national election, pollsters interview a predetermined number of people throughout the country and record their preference. On the basis of this information a prediction is constructed. Similar problems are encountered in market research (What fraction of smokers prefer cigarette brand A?); in sociology (What fraction of rural homes are electrified?); in industry (What fraction of items purchased, or produced, are defective?).

The yield (production) of a chemical plant is dependent upon many factors. By observing these factors and the yield over a period of time, we can construct a prediction equation relating yield to the observed factors. How do we find a good prediction equation? If the equation is used to predict yield, the prediction will rarely equal the true yield; that is, the prediction will almost always be in error. Can we place a limit on the prediction error? Which factors are the most important in predicting yield? One encounters similar problems in the fields of education, sociology, psychology, and the physical sciences. For instance, colleges wish to predict the grade-point average of college students based upon information obtained *prior* to college entrance. Here, we might relate grade-point average to rank in high school class, the type of high school, college board examination scores, socio-economic status, or any number of such factors.

In addition to prediction, the statistician is concerned with decision making based upon observed data. Consider the problem of determining the effectiveness of a new cold vaccine. For simplification, let us assume that ten people have received the new cold vaccine and are observed over a winter season. Of these ten, eight survive the winter without acquiring a cold. Is the vaccine effective?

Two physically different teaching techniques are used to present a subject to two groups of students of comparable ability. At the end of the instructional period, a measure of achievement is obtained for each group. On the basis of this information, we ask, " Do the data present sufficient evidence to indicate that one method produces, on the average, higher student achievement?"

Consider the inspection of purchased items in a manufacturing plant. On the basis of such an inspection, each lot of incoming goods must be either accepted or rejected and returned to the supplier. The inspection might involve drawing a sample of ten items from each lot and recording the number of defectives. The decision to accept or reject the lot could then be based upon the number of defective items observed.

A company manufacturing complex electronic equipment produces some systems which function properly but also some which, for unknown reasons, do not. What makes good systems good and bad systems bad? In attempting to answer this question, we might make certain internal measurements on a system in order to find important factors which differentiate between an acceptable and an unacceptable product. From a sample of good and bad systems, data could then be collected that might shed light on the fundamental design or on production variables affecting system quality.

1.2   The Population and the Sample

The above examples are varied in nature and complexity, but each involves prediction or decision making. In addition, each of these examples involves *sampling*. A specified number of items (objects or bits of information)—a *sample*—is drawn from a much larger body of data which we will call the *population*. Note that the word "population" refers to data and not to people. The pollster draws a sample of opinion (those interviewed) from the *statistical population* which represents the entire voting population of the country. In predicting the fraction of smokers who prefer cigarette brand A, we assume that those interviewed yield a representative sample of the population of all smokers. The sample for the cold vaccine experiment consists of observations made on the ten individuals receiving the vaccine. The sample is presumably representative of a much larger body of people—the population—who could have received the vaccine.

Which is of primary interest, the sample or the population? In all of the examples given above, we are primarily interested in the population. We cannot interview all of the people in the United States, hence we must predict their behavior on the basis of information obtained from a representative sample. Likewise, it is practically impossible to give all possible users a cold vaccine. The manufacturer of the drug is interested in its effectiveness in preventing colds in the purchasing public (the population) and must predict this effectiveness from information extracted from the sample. Hence, the sample may be of immediate interest, but we are primarily interested in describing the population from which the sample is drawn.

1.3   The Essential Elements of a Statistical Problem

The essential elements of a statistical problem are now vaguely apparent. The objective of statistics is to make inferences (predictions, decisions) about a population based upon information contained in a sample. Essential to each of the foregoing examples is, first, the analysis of observed data and, second, the making of an inference about the population from which the sample is drawn. A third element is not so obvious. We would suppose that numerical data, or any type of observation, contain a given quantity of information. This information is purchased with time and money expended in controlled experimentation or data collection. Furthermore, we might suspect that a given expenditure would yield varying amounts of information for various methods of experimentation. Such is, in fact, the case. Hence, essential to statistical problems is the design of the experiment, or sampling procedure, which must enable the gathering of a maximum amount of information for a given expenditure. This aspect of a statistical problem is less important when data collection is inexpensive. On the other hand, in pre-election surveys, in the testing of complex electronics systems, in the inspection of new products, and in many other data-collecting situations which are very costly, the design of the experiment or sampling procedure assumes a very important role.

To summarize, a statistical problem involves: (1) the design of the experiment or sampling procedure, (2) the collection and analysis of data, and (3) the making of inferences about the population based upon information in a sample.

1.4   The Role of Statistics and the Statistician

We may now ask, "What is the role of the statistician in attaining the objective in what we have described as statistical problems?" People have been making observations and collecting data for centuries. Furthermore, they have been using the data as a basis for prediction and decision making completely unaided by statistics. What then do statisticians and statistics have to offer?

Statistics is an area of science concerned with the extraction of information from numerical data and its use in making inferences about a population from which the data are obtained. In some respects the statistician quantifies information and studies various designs and sampling procedures, searching for the procedure that yields the most information in a given situation for a fixed expenditure. We might liken data to a lemon and say that the statistician is concerned with squeezing or extracting as much information from the data as possible. Finally, we consider the matter of inference. Everyone has made many predictions and decisions, and it is clear that some people are better predictors and decision makers than others. The statistician studies various inferential procedures, looking for the best predictor or decision-making process for a given situation. Even more important, he provides information concerning the *goodness* of an inferential procedure. When we predict, we would like to know something about the error in our prediction. If we make a decision, what is the chance that our decision is incorrect? Our built-in individual prediction and decision-making systems do not provide immediate answers to these important questions and could be evaluated only by observation over a long period. In contrast, statistical procedures do provide answers to these questions.

1.5   Summary

Statistics is an area of science concerned with the design of experiments or sampling procedures, the analysis of data, and the making of *inferences* about a *population* of measurements from information contained in a *sample*. The statistician is concerned with developing and using procedures for *design, analysis,* and *inference making* which will provide the best inferences for a given expenditure. In addition to making the best inference, he is concerned with providing a quantitative measure of the *goodness* of the inference-making procedure.

1.6 A Note to the Reader

We have stated the objective of statistics and, hopefully, have answered the question, "What is statistics?" The remainder of this text is devoted to the development of the basic concepts involved in statistical methodology. In other words, we wish to explain how statistical techniques actually work and why.

Statistics is a very broad field of applied mathematics. Most of the fundamental rules (called theorems in mathematics) are developed and based upon a knowledge of the calculus or higher mathematics. Inasmuch as this is meant to be an introductory text, we omit proofs except where they can be easily derived. Where concepts or theorems can be shown to be intuitively reasonable, we will attempt to give a logical explanation. Hence we will attempt to convince the reader with the aid of examples and intuitive arguments rather than with rigorous mathematical derivations.

The reader should refer occasionally to Chapter 1 and review the objective of statistics and the elements of a statistical problem. Each of the following chapters should, in some way, be directed toward answering the questions posed here. Each is essential to completing the overall picture of statistics.

REFERENCE

Careers in Statistics. American Statistical Association and the Institute of Mathematical Statistics, 1962.

2

USEFUL
MATHEMATICAL
NOTATION

2.1 Introduction

Presuming that the reader is familiar with elementary algebra, we will omit a general review of that subject. However, two topics of elementary algebra—functional notation and summation notation— are used extensively in the following chapters and are worthy of discussion at this point.

2.2 Functional Notation

Let us consider two sets* of elements (objects, numbers, or anything we want to use) and their relation to one another. Let the symbol x represent an element of the first set and y an element of the second. One could specify a number of different rules defining *relationships* between x and y. For instance, if our elements are people, we have rules for determining whether x and y, two persons, are first cousins. Or, suppose

---

* A set is a collection of specific things.

that x and y are integers taking values 1, 2, 3, 4, ... For some reason, we might wish to say that x and y are "related" if $x = y$.

Now let us direct our attention to a specific relationship useful in mathematics called a *functional relation* between x and y.

> **Definition:** A function consists of two sets of elements and a defined correspondence between an element of the first set, x, and an element of the second set, y, such that for each element x there corresponds one, and only one, element y.

A function may be exhibited as a collection of ordered pairs of elements, written (x, y). In fact, a function is often defined as a collection of ordered pairs of elements with the property stated in the definition.

Most often, x and y will be variables taking numerical values. The two sets of elements would represent all of the possible numerical values that x and y might take and the rule defining the correspondence between them would be an equation. For example, if we state that x and y are real numbers and that

$$y = x + 2,$$

then y is a function of x. Assigning a value to x (that is, choosing an element of the set of all real numbers), there corresponds one, and only one, value of y. When $x = 1$, $y = 3$. When $x = -4$, $y = -2$, and so on.

The area, A, of a circle is related to the radius, r, by the formula,

$$A = \pi r^2.$$

Note that if we assign a value to r, the value of A can be determined from the formula. Hence A is a function of r. Likewise, the circumference of a circle, C, is a function of the radius.

As a third example of a functional relation, consider a classroom containing twenty students. Let x represent a specific body in the classroom and y represent a name. Is y a function of x? To answer the question, we examine x and y in the light of the definition. We note that each body has a name y attached to it. Hence when x is specified, y will be uniquely determined. According to our definition, y is a function of x. Note that the defining rule for functional relations does not require that x and y take numerical values. We will encounter an important functional relation of this type in Chapter 4.

Having defined a functional relation, we may now turn to *functional notation*.

Mathematical writing frequently uses the same phrase or refers to a specific object many times in the course of a discussion. Unnecessary repetition wastes the reader's time, takes up valuable space, and is cumbersome to the writer. Hence the mathematician resorts to mathematical symbolism which is in some respects a type of mathematical shorthand. Rather than state "The area of a circle, A, is a function of the radius, r," the mathematician would write $A(r)$. The expression

$$y = f(x)$$

tells us that y is a function of the variable appearing in parentheses, namely x. Note that this expression does not tell us the specific functional relation existing between y and x.

Consider the function of x,

$$y = 3x + 2.$$

In functional notation, this would be written as

$$f(x) = 3x + 2.$$

It is understood that $y = f(x)$.

Functional notation is especially advantageous when we wish to indicate the value of the function y when x takes a specific value, say $x = 2$. For the above example, we see that when $x = 2$

$$y = 3x + 2$$
$$= 3(2) + 2$$
$$= 8.$$

Rather than write this, we use the simpler notation

$$f(2) = 8.$$

Similarly, $f(5)$ would be the value of the function when $x = 5$:

$$f(5) = 3(5) + 2$$
$$= 15 + 2$$
$$= 17.$$

To find the value of the function when x equals any value, say $x = c$, we substitute the value of c for x in the equation and obtain

$$f(c) = 3c + 2.$$

Example 2.1: Given a function of x,

$$g(x) = \frac{1}{x} + 3x.$$

(1) Find $g(4)$.

$$g(4) = \frac{1}{4} + 3(4)$$

$$= .25 + 12$$

$$= 12.25.$$

(2) Find $g\left(\frac{1}{a}\right)$.

$$g\left(\frac{1}{a}\right) = \frac{1}{(1/a)} + 3\left(\frac{1}{a}\right)$$

$$= a + \frac{3}{a}$$

$$= \frac{a^2 + 3}{a}.$$

Example 2.2: Let $p(y) = (1 - a)a^y$.   Find $p(2)$ and $p(3)$.

$$p(2) = (1 - a)a^2;$$

$$p(3) = (1 - a)a^3.$$

Example 2.3: Let $f(y) = 4$.   Find $f(2)$ and $f(3)$.

$$f(2) = 4;$$

$$f(3) = 4.$$

Note that $f(y)$ always equals 4, regardless of the value of y.   Hence when a value of y is assigned, the value of the function is determined and will equal 4.

Example 2.4: Let $f(x) = x^2 + 1$ and $g(x) = x + 2$.   Find $f[g(x)]$.   We find $f[g(x)]$ by substituting $g(x)$ for x in the function $f(x)$.   Thus,

$$f[g(x)] = [g(x)]^2 + 1$$

$$= (x + 2)^2 + 1$$

$$= x^2 + 4x + 4 + 1$$

$$= x^2 + 4x + 5.$$

2.3   Numerical Sequences

In statistics we will be concerned with samples consisting of sets of measurements.   There will be a first measurement, a second, and so on. Introducing the notion of a mathematical sequence at this point will provide us with a simple notation for discussion of data and will, at the same time, supply our first practical application of functional notation. This will, in turn, be used in the summation notation introduced in Section 2.4.

A set of objects, $a_1, a_2, a_3, a_4, \ldots$, ordered in the sense that we can identify the first member of the set a_1, the second a_2, etc., is called a *sequence*.   Most often, $a_1, a_2, a_3, \ldots$, called *elements* of the sequence, are numbers but this is not a requirement.   For example, the numbers

$$1, 5, 4, 8, 7, 11, 10, \ldots$$

form a sequence moving from left to right.   Note that the elements are ordered only in their position in the sequence and need not be ordered in magnitude.   Likewise, in some card games, we are interested in a sequence of cards; for example,

$$10, \text{Jack, Queen, King, Ace.}$$

Although nonnumerical sequences are of interest, we will be concerned solely with numerical sequences.   Specifically, data obtained in a sample from a population will be regarded as a sequence of measurements.

Since sequences will form an important part of subsequent discussions, let us turn to a shortcut method of writing sequences utilizing functional notation.   Inasmuch as the elements of a sequence are ordered in position in the sequence, it would seem natural to attempt to *write a formula for a typical element of the sequence as a function of its position*. For example, consider the sequence,

$$3, 4, 5, 6, 7, \ldots,$$

where each element in the sequence is one greater than the preceding element.   Let y be a position variable for the sequence so that y can take values 1, 2, 3, 4, etc.   Then we might write a formula for the element in position y as

$$f(y) = y + 2.$$

Thus the first element in the sequence would be in position $y = 1$, and $f(1)$ would equal

$$f(1) = 1 + 2 = 3.$$

Likewise, the second element would be in position $y = 2$, and the second element of the sequence would be,

$$f(2) = 2 + 2 = 4.$$

A brief check convinces us that this formula works for all elements of the sequence. Note that finding a proper formula (function) is a matter of trial and error and requires a bit of practice.

Example 2.5: Given the sequence

$$1, 4, 9, 16, 25, \ldots,$$

find a formula expressing a typical element in terms of a position variable y.

We note that each element is the square of the position variable; hence

$$f(y) = y^2.$$

Example 2.6: The formula for the typical element of the following sequence is not so obvious:

$$0, 3, 8, 15, 24, 35, \ldots.$$

The typical element would be

$$f(y) = y^2 - 1.$$

Readers of mathematical writings (and this includes the author) prefer consistency in the use of mathematical notation. Unfortunately, this is not always practical. Writers are limited by the number of symbols available and also by the desire to make their notation consistent with some other texts on the subject. Hence x and y are very often used in referring to a variable but we could just as well use i, j, k, or z. For instance, suppose that we wish to refer to a set of measurements and denote the measurements as a variable y. We might write this sequence of measurements as

$$y_1, y_2, y_3, y_4, y_5, \ldots,$$

using a subscript to denote a particular element in the sequence. We are now forced to choose a new position variable (since y has been used). Suppose that we use the letter i. Then we could write a typical element as

$$f(i) = y_i.$$

Note that, as previously, $f(1) = y_1, f(2) = y_2$, etc.

2.4   Summation Notation

As we will observe in Chapter 3, in analyzing statistical data we will often be working with sums of numbers, and we will need a simple notation for indicating a sum.   For instance, consider the sequence of numbers

$$1, 2, 3, 4, 5, \ldots$$

and suppose that we wish to discuss the sum of the squares of the first four numbers of the sequence.   Using summation notation, this would be written as

$$\sum_{y=1}^{4} y^2.$$

Interpretation of the summation notation is relatively easy.   The Greek letter Σ (capital sigma), corresponding to "S" in the English alphabet (the first letter in the word "Sum"), tells us to *sum elements of a sequence* A typical element of the sequence is given to the right of the summation symbol, and the position variable, called the *variable of summation*, is shown beneath.   For our example, y^2 is a typical element, y is the variable of summation, and the implied sequence is

$$1, 4, 9, 16, 25, 36, \ldots.$$

Which elements of the sequence should appear in the sum?   The position of the first element in the sum is indicated below the summation sign, the last above.   The sum would include all elements proceeding *in order* from the first to last.   Thus, in our example, the sum would include the sum of the elements commencing with the first and ending with the fourth:

$$\sum_{y=1}^{4} y^2 = 1 + 4 + 9 + 16$$

$$= 30.$$

Example 2.7:

$$\sum_{y=2}^{4} (y - 1) = (2 - 1) + (3 - 1) + (4 - 1)$$

$$= 6.$$

Example 2.8:

$$\sum_{x=2}^{5} 3x = 3(2) + 3(3) + 3(4) + 3(5)$$

$$= 42.$$

We emphasize that the typical element is a function only of the variable of summation.   All other symbols are regarded as constants.

Example 2.9:

$$\sum_{i=1}^{3} (y_i - a) = (y_1 - a) + (y_2 - a) + (y_3 - a).$$

In this example, note that i is the variable of summation and that it appears as a subscript in the typical element.

Example 2.10:

$$\sum_{i=1}^{2} (x - i + 1) = (x - 1 + 1) + (x - 2 + 1)$$

$$= 2x - 1.$$

Example 2.11:

$$\sum_{y=2}^{4} y - 1 = (2 + 3 + 4) - 1$$

$$= 8.$$

Note the difference between Example 2.7 and Example 2.11.   The quantity $(y - 1)$ is the typical element in Example 2.7, while y is the typical element in Example 2.11.

2.5   Useful Theorems Relating to Sums

Consider the summation

$$\sum_{y=1}^{3} 5.$$

The typical element is 5 and it does not change.   The sequence is, therefore,

$$5, 5, 5, 5, \ldots,$$

and

$$\sum_{y=1}^{3} 5 = 5 + 5 + 5$$

$$= 15.$$

Theorem 2.1: Let c be a constant (an element which does not involve the variable of summation) and y be the variable of summation. Then,

$$\sum_{y=1}^{n} c = nc.$$

Proof:

$$\sum_{y=1}^{n} c = c + c + c + \ldots + c,$$

where the sum involves n elements.
Then,

$$\sum_{y=1}^{n} c = nc.$$

Example 2.12:

$$\sum_{y=1}^{4} 3a = 4(3a) = 12a.$$

Example 2.13:

$$\sum_{i=1}^{3} (3x - 5) = 3(3x - 5).$$

(Note that i is the variable of summation.)
    A second theorem is illustrated using Example 2.8. We note that 3 is a common factor in each term. Therefore,

$$\sum_{y=2}^{5} 3y = 3(2) + 3(3) + 3(4) + 3(5)$$

$$= 3(2 + 3 + 4 + 5)$$

$$= 3 \sum_{y=2}^{5} y.$$

Thus it would appear that the summation of a constant times a variable is equal to the constant times the summation of the variable.

Theorem 2.2: Let c be a constant. Then

$$\sum_{i=1}^{n} c y_i = c \sum_{i=1}^{n} y_i.$$

Proof:

$$\sum_{i=1}^{n} cy_i = cy_1 + cy_2 + cy_3 + \ldots + cy_n$$

$$= c(y_1 + y_2 + \ldots + y_n)$$

$$= c \sum_{i=1}^{n} y_i.$$

Theorem 2.3:

$$\sum_{i=1}^{n} (x_i + y_i + z_i) = \sum_{i=1}^{n} x_i + \sum_{i=1}^{n} y_i + \sum_{i=1}^{n} z_i.$$

Proof:

$$\sum_{i=1}^{n} (x_i + y_i + z_i) = x_1 + y_1 + z_1 + x_2 + y_2 + z_2$$

$$+ x_3 + y_3 + z_3 + \ldots + x_n + y_n + z_n.$$

Regrouping, we have

$$\sum_{i=1}^{n} (x_i + y_i + z_i) = (x_1 + x_2 + \ldots + x_n) + (y_1 + y_2 + \ldots + y_n)$$

$$+ (z_1 + z_2 + \ldots + z_n)$$

$$= \sum_{i=1}^{n} x_i + \sum_{i=1}^{n} y_i + \sum_{i=1}^{n} z_i.$$

In words we would say that the summation of a typical element which is itself a sum of a number of terms is equal to the sum of the summations of the terms.

Theorems 2.1, 2.2, and 2.3 can be used jointly to simplify summations. Consider the following examples:

Example 2.14:

$$\sum_{x=1}^{3} (x^2 + ax + 5) = \sum_{x=1}^{3} x^2 + \sum_{x=1}^{3} ax + \sum_{x=1}^{3} 5$$

$$= \sum_{x=1}^{3} x^2 + a \sum_{x=1}^{3} x + 3(5)$$

$$= (1 + 4 + 9) + a(1 + 2 + 3) + 15$$

$$= 6a + 29.$$

Example 2.15:

$$\sum_{i=1}^{4}(x^2 + 3i) = \sum_{i=1}^{4}x^2 + \sum_{i=1}^{4}3i$$

$$= 4x^2 + 3\sum_{i=1}^{4}i$$

$$= 4x^2 + 3(1 + 2 + 3 + 4)$$

$$= 4x^2 + 30.$$

2.6 Summary

Two types of mathematical notations have been presented, functional notation and summation notation. The former is used in summation notation to express the typical element as a function of the variable of summation. Other uses for functional notation will be discussed in Chapter 4. Summation notation will be employed in Chapter 3 and succeeding chapters.

EXERCISES

1. Given $f(y) = 4y + 3$, find

   (a) $f(0)$,   (b) $f(1)$,   (c) $f(2)$,
   (d) $f(-1)$,   (e) $f(-2)$,   (f) $f(a^2)$,
   (g) $f(-a)$,   (h) $f(1 - y)$.

2. Given $f(y) = \dfrac{y^2 - 1}{y}$, find

   (a) $f(2)$,   (b) $f(-3)$,   (c) $f(-1)$,
   (d) $f(x)$,   (e) $f(a - 1)$.

3. Given $f(x) = x^2 - x + 1$, find
   (a) $f(-2)$,   (b) $f(a + b)$.

4. If $g(y) = \dfrac{y^2 - 1}{y + 1}$, find

   (a) $g(1)$,   (b) $g(-1)$,   (c) $g(4)$,
   (d) $g(-a^2)$.

5. If $p(x) = (1 - a)^x$, find $p(0)$ and $p(1)$.

6. If $f(x) = 3x^2 - 3x + 1$ and $g(x) = x - 3$, find
   (a) $f(1/2)$,   (b) $g(-3)$,   (c) $f(1/x)$,
   (d) $f[g(x)]$.

7. If $h(x) = 2$, find
   (a) $h(0)$,   (b) $h(1)$,   (c) $h(2)$.

Utilize Theorems 2.1, 2.2, and 2.3 to simplify and evaluate the following summations.

8. $\sum_{y=1}^{3} y^3$.

9. $\sum_{y=1}^{3} 6$.

10. $\sum_{x=2}^{3} (1 + 3x + x^2)$.

14. $\sum_{x=1}^{4} (x + xy^2)$.

11. $\sum_{i=1}^{5} (x^2 + 2i)$.

15. $\sum_{i=1}^{2} (y_i - i)$.

12. $\sum_{y=0}^{5} (x^2 + y^2)$.

16. $\sum_{i=1}^{n} (y_i - a)$.

13. $\sum_{x=0}^{2} (x^3 + 2ix)$.

17. $\sum_{i=1}^{n} (y_i - a)^2$.

SUPPLEMENTARY EXERCISES

Verify the following identities. Each of them is a shortcut formula which will be used in later chapters. The symbols $\bar{x}$ and $\bar{y}$ appearing in these identities have the following definitions:

$$\bar{x} = \frac{\sum_{i=1}^{n} x_i}{n}; \quad \bar{y} = \frac{\sum_{i=1}^{n} y_i}{n}.$$

1. $\sum_{i=1}^{n} (x_i - \bar{x})^2 = \sum_{i=1}^{n} x_i^2 - \frac{\left(\sum_{i=1}^{n} x_i\right)^2}{n}$.

2. $\sum_{i=1}^{n} (x_i - \bar{x})(y_i - \bar{y}) = \sum_{i=1}^{n} x_i y_i - \frac{\left(\sum_{i=1}^{n} x_i\right)\left(\sum_{i=1}^{n} y_i\right)}{n}$.

3. $\frac{\sum_{i=1}^{n} (y_i - \bar{y})^2}{n-1} = \frac{1}{n-1}\left\{\sum_{i=1}^{n} y_i^2 - \frac{1}{n}\left(\sum_{i=1}^{n} y_i\right)^2\right\}$.

$$4.\ \frac{\sum\limits_{i=1}^{n} (x_i - \bar{x})(y_i - \bar{y})}{\sum\limits_{i=1}^{n} (x_i - \bar{x})^2} = \frac{n \sum\limits_{i=1}^{n} x_i y_i - \left(\sum\limits_{i=1}^{n} x_i\right)\left(\sum\limits_{i=1}^{n} y_i\right)}{n \sum\limits_{i=1}^{n} x_i^2 - \left(\sum\limits_{i=1}^{n} x_i\right)^2}$$

3

DESCRIBING
DISTRIBUTIONS OF
MEASUREMENTS

3.1 Introduction

After a brief detour in Chapter 2, we return to the main objective of our study—making inferences about a large body of data, the population, based upon information contained in a sample. A most peculiar difficulty arises, namely, how will the inferences be phrased? How do we describe a set of measurements, whether they be the sample or the population? If the population were before us, how could we describe this large set of measurements?

Numerous texts have been devoted to the methods of descriptive statistics—that is, the methods of describing sets of numerical data. Essentially, these methods can be categorized as *graphical methods* and *numerical methods*. In this text we will restrict our discussion to a few graphical and numerical methods which are useful not only for descriptive purposes but also for statistical inference. The reader interested in descriptive statistics should refer to the references listed on page 45.

3.2 A Graphical Method

It would seem natural to introduce appropriate graphical and numerical methods of describing sets of data through consideration of a set of real data.   The data presented in Table 3.1 represent the grade-point averages of thirty Bucknell University freshmen recorded at the end of the freshman year.

A cursory examination indicates that the lowest grade-point average in the sample is 1.4, the largest, 2.9.   How are the other twenty-eight measurements distributed?   Do most lie near 1.4, near 2.9, or are they

Table 3.1.   Grade-Point Averages of Thirty
Bucknell University Freshmen

1.5	2.6	1.4	2.0	1.4
1.8	2.1	2.6	2.0	1.6
2.4	2.5	2.2	2.0	1.9
2.2	2.0	1.9	2.5	2.9
2.1	2.3	2.0	2.2	2.4
2.2	2.3	1.7	2.2	1.6

evenly distributed over the interval from 1.4 to 2.9?   To answer this question, we divide the interval into an arbitrary number of equal sub-intervals, the number depending upon the amount of data available.   (As a rule of thumb, the number of sub-intervals chosen would range from five to twenty, the larger the amount of data available, the more sub-intervals employed.)   For instance we might use the sub-intervals 1.35 to 1.55, 1.55 to 1.75, 1.75 to 1.95, etc.   Note that the points dividing the sub-intervals have been chosen so that it is impossible for a measurement to fall on the point of division, thus eliminating any ambiguity regarding the disposition of a particular measurement.   The sub-intervals, called *classes* in statistical language, form cells or pockets similar to the pockets of a billiard table.   We wish to determine the manner in which the measurements are distributed in the pockets, or classes.   A tally of the data from Table 3.1 is presented in Table 3.2.

The thirty measurements fall in one of eight classes which, for purposes of identification, we shall number.   The identification number appears in the first column of Table 3.2 and the corresponding class boundaries are given in the second column.   The third column of the table is used for the tally, a mark entered opposite the appropriate class for each measurement falling in the class.   For example, three of the thirty measurements fall in class 1, three in class 2, three in class 3, seven in class 4, etc. The number of measurements falling in a particular class, say class i, is called the *class frequency* and is designated by the symbol f_i.

Table 3.2.   *Tabulation of Relative Frequencies for a Histogram*

CLASS i	CLASS BOUNDARIES	TALLY	TABULATION FREQUENCY f_i	RELATIVE FREQUENCY
1	1.35–1.55	I I I	3	3/30
2	1.55–1.75	I I I	3	3/30
3	1.75–1.95	I I I	3	3/30
4	1.95–2.15	⊬⊬ I I	7	7/30
5	2.15–2.35	⊬⊬ I I	7	7/30
6	2.35–2.55	I I I I	4	4/30
7	2.55–2.75	I I	2	2/30
8	2.75–2.95	I	1	1/30
		Total $n = 30$		1

The class frequency is given in the fourth column of Table 3.2. The last column of this table presents the fraction of the total number of measurements falling in each class. We call this the *relative frequency*. If we let n represent the total number of measurements, for instance, in our example $n = 30$, then the relative frequency for the ith class would equal f_i divided by n:

$$\text{Relative frequency} = f_i/n.$$

The resulting tabulation can be presented graphically in the form of a frequency histogram, Figure 3.1. Rectangles are constructed over each interval, their height being proportional to the number of measurements (class frequency) falling in each class interval. Viewing the frequency histogram, we see at a glance the manner in which the grade point averages are distributed over the interval.

It is often more convenient to modify the frequency histogram by plotting class relative frequency rather than class frequency. A relative frequency histogram is presented in Figure 3.2. Statisticians rarely make a distinction between the frequency histogram and the relative frequency histogram and refer to either as a frequency histogram or simply a histogram. The two diagrams, when drawn to the same scale, are identical. (See Figure 3.2.)

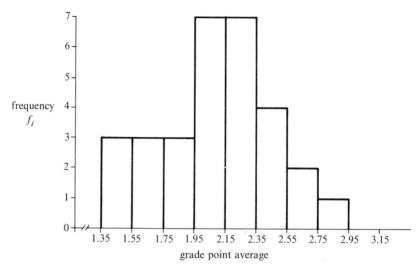

Figure 3.1.   Frequency Histogram

Although we were interested in describing the set of $n = 30$ measurements, we are much more interested in the population from which the sample was drawn.   We might view the thirty grade-point averages as a representative sample drawn from the population of grade-point averages of the freshmen currently in attendance at Bucknell University.   Or, if we are interested in the academic achievement of freshmen college students in general, we might consider our sample representative of the achievement of the population of freshmen attending Bucknell *or colleges similar to Bucknell.*   In either case, if we had the grade-point averages for the entire population, we could construct a population relative frequency histogram.

Let us consider the relative frequency histogram for the sample in greater detail.   What fraction of the students attained grade-point averages equal to 2.2 or better?   Checking the relative frequency histogram, we see that the fraction would involve all classes to the right of 2.15.   Using Table 3.2, we see that fourteen students achieved grade-point averages equal to or greater than 2.2.   Hence the fraction is 14/30 or approximately 47%.   *We note that this is also the percentage of the total area of the histogram, Figure 3.2, lying to the right of* 2.15.   Suppose we were to write each grade-point average on a piece of paper, place the thirty slips of paper in a hat, mix them, and then draw one paper from the hat.   What is the chance that this paper would contain a grade-point average equal to or greater than 2.2?   Since 14 of the 30 slips are marked with numbers equal to or greater than 2.2, we would say that we have

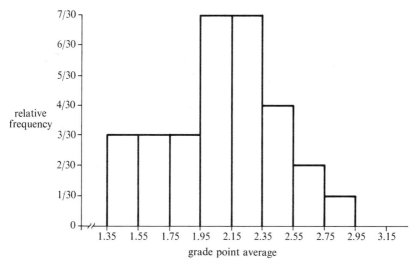

Figure 3.2.   Relative Frequency Histogram

14 chances out of 30.   Or, we might say that the probability is 14/30. The reader has undoubtedly encountered the word "probability" in ordinary conversation and we are content to defer definition and discussion of its significance until Chapter 4.

Let us now direct our attention to the population from which the sample was drawn.   What fraction of students in the *population* attained a grade point average equal to or greater than 2.2?   If we possessed the relative frequency histogram for the population, we could give the exact answer to this question by calculating the fraction of total area lying to the right of 2.15.   Unfortunately, since we do not have such a histogram we are forced to make an inference.   We must estimate the true population fraction, basing our estimate upon information contained in the sample. Our *estimate* would likely be 14/30 or 47%.   Suppose we wish to state the chance or probability that a student drawn from the population would have a grade-point average equal to or greater than 2.2.   Without knowledge of the population relative frequency histogram we would infer that the population histogram is similar to the sample histogram and that approximately 14/30 of the measurements in the population would be equal to or greater than 2.2.   Naturally, this estimate would be in error.   We will examine the magnitude of this estimation error in Chapter 8.

The relative frequency histogram is often called a *frequency distribution* because it shows the manner in which the data are distributed along the abscissa of the graph.   We note that the rectangles constructed above each class are subject to two interpretations. They represent the fraction of observations falling in a given class. Also, if a measurement is drawn from the data, a particular class relative frequency is also the chance or probability that the measurement will fall in that class. The most significant feature of the sample frequency histogram is that it provides information on the population frequency histogram which describes the population. We would expect the two frequency histograms, sample and population, to be similar. Such is the case. The degree of resemblance will increase as more and more data are added to the sample. If the sample were enlarged to include the entire population, the sample and population would be synonymous and the histograms would be identical.

3.3   Numerical Descriptive Methods

Graphical methods are extremely useful in conveying a rapid general description of collected data and in presenting data. This supports, in many respects, the saying that a picture is worth a thousand words. There are, however, limitations to the use of graphical techniques for describing and analyzing data. For instance, suppose we wish to discuss our data before a group of people and have no method of describing the data other than verbally. Unable to present the histogram visually, we would be forced to use other descriptive measures which would convey to the listeners a mental picture of the histogram. A second and not so obvious limitation of the histogram and other graphical techniques is that they are difficult to use for purposes of statistical inference. Presumably we use the sample histogram to make inferences about the shape and position of the population histogram which describes the population and is unknown to us. Our inference is based upon the correct assumption that some degree of similarity will exist between the two histograms, but we are then faced with the problem of measuring the degree of similarity. We know when two figures are identical, but this situation will not likely occur in practice. Hence, if the sample and population histograms differ, how can we measure the degree of difference or, expressing it positively, the degree of similarity? To be more specific, we might wonder about the degree of similarity between the histogram, Figure 3.2, and the frequency histogram for the population of grade-point averages from which the sample was drawn. Although these difficulties are not insurmountable, we prefer to seek other descriptive measures which readily lend themselves for use as predictors of the shape of the population frequency distribution.

The limitations of the graphical method of describing data can be overcome by the use of *numerical descriptive measures*. Thus we would like to use the sample data to calculate a set of numbers which will convey to the statistician a good mental picture of the frequency distribution and which will be useful in making inferences concerning the population.

3.4   Measures of Central Tendency

In constructing a mental picture of the frequency distribution for a set of measurements, we would likely envision a histogram similar to that shown in Figure 3.2 for the data on grade-point averages.   One of the first descriptive measures of interest would be a *measure of central tendency*, that is, a measure of the center of the distribution.   We note that the grade-point data ranged from a low of 1.4 to a high of 2.9, the center of the histogram being located in the vicinity of 2.1.   Let us now consider some definite rules for locating the center of a distribution of data.

One of the most common and useful measures of central tendency is the *arithmetic average* of a set of measurements.   This is also often referred to as the *arithmetic mean* or, simply, the *mean* of a set of measurements.

Definition: The arithmetic mean of a set of n measurements y_1, y_2, y_3, ..., y_n is equal to the sum of the measurements divided by n.

Recall that we are always concerned with both the sample and the population, each of which possesses a mean.   In order to distinguish between the two, we will use the symbol $\bar{y}$ for the mean of the sample and μ (the Greek letter mu) for the mean of the population.   The mean of the sample data can be calculated using our definition,

$$\bar{y} = \frac{\sum_{i=1}^{n} y_i}{n},$$

and can be used as a measure of central tendency for the sample.

Example 3.1: Find the mean of the set of measurements 2, 9, 11, 5, 6.

$$\bar{y} = \frac{\sum_{i=1}^{n} y_i}{n} = \frac{2 + 9 + 11 + 5 + 6}{5} = 6.6.$$

Even more important, $\bar{y}$ will be employed as an estimator (predictor) of μ, the mean of the population which is unknown.

For example, the mean of the data, Table 3.1, is equal to

$$\bar{y} = \frac{\sum\limits_{i=1}^{n} y_i}{n} = \frac{62.5}{30} = 2.08.$$

Note that this falls approximately in the center of the set of measurements. The mean of the entire population of grade-point averages, μ, is unknown to us but if we were to estimate its value, our estimate would be $\mu = 2.08$.

A second measure of central tendency is the *median*.

Definition: The median of a set of n measurements $y_1, y_2, y_3, \ldots, y_n$ is defined to be the value of y that falls in the middle when the measurements are arranged in order of magnitude.

Example 3.2: Consider the set of five measurements

$$9, 2, 7, 11, 14.$$

Arranging the measurements in order of magnitude, 2, 7, 9, 11, 14, we would choose 9 as the median. If the number of measurements is even, we choose the median as the value of y half-way between the two middle measurements.

Example 3.3: Consider the set of measurements

$$9, 2, 7\ 11, 14, 6.$$

Arranged in order of magnitude, 2, 6, 7, 9, 11, 14, we would choose the median half-way between 7 and 9, which is 8.

Our rule for locating the median may seem a bit arbitrary for the case where we have an even number of measurements, but recall that we calculate the sample median either for descriptive purposes or as an estimator of the population median. If it is used for descriptive purposes, we may be as arbitrary as we please. If it is used as an estimator of the population median, "the proof of the pudding is in the eating." A rule for locating the sample median is poor or good depending upon whether it tends to give a poor or good estimate of the population median.

The reader will note that we have not specified a symbol for the population median. This is because most of the common methods of statistical inference suitable for an elementary course in statistics are based upon the use of the sample mean rather than the median.   We say this, being wholly aware of the popularity of the median in the social sciences, but point out that it is used more often for descriptive purposes than for statistical inference.   We also note that other measures of central tendency exist which have practical application in certain situations, but limitations of time and space forbid their discussion here.   As we proceed in this text we will use the sample mean, exclusively, as a measure of central tendency.

3.5   Measures of Variability

Having located the center of a distribution of data, our next step is to provide a measure of the *variability* or *dispersion* of the data.   Consider the two distributions shown in Figure 3.3.   Both distributions are

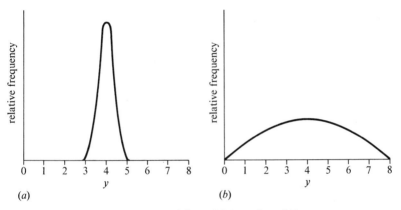

Figure 3.3.   Variability or Dispersion of Data

located with a center at $y = 4$ but there is a vast difference in the *variability of the measurements about the mean* for the two distributions.   The measurements in Figure 3.3(a) vary from 3 to 5, while in Figure 3.3(b) they vary from 0 to 8.   Variation is a very important characteristic of data.   For example, if we are manufacturing bolts, excessive variation in the bolt diameter would imply a high percentage of defective product.   On the other hand, if we are using an examination to discriminate between good and poor accountants, we would be most unhappy if the examination always produced test grades with little variation, as this would make discrimination very difficult indeed.   In addition to the practical importance of variation in data, it is obvious that a measure of this characteristic is necessary to the construction of the mental image of the frequency distribution. Numerous measures of variability exist, and we will discuss a few of the most important.

The simplest measure of variation is the *range*.

> **Definition:** The range of a set of n measurements $y_1, y_2, y_3, \ldots, y_n$ is defined to be the difference between the largest and smallest measurement.

For our grade-point data, Table 3.1, we note that the measurements varied from 1.4 to 2.9. Hence the range is equal to $(2.9 - 1.4) = 1.5$.

Unfortunately, the range is not completely satisfactory as a measure of variation. Consider the two distributions of Figure 3.4. Both distributions have the same range but the data of Figure 3.4(b) are more variable than the data of Figure 3.4(a). To overcome this limitation of the range, we introduce *quartiles* and *percentiles*. Remember that if we specify an interval along the y-axis of our histogram, the percentage of area under the histogram lying above the interval is equal to the percentage of the total number of measurements falling in that interval. Since the median is the middle measurement when the data are arranged in order of magnitude, the median would be the value of y such that half the area of the histogram would lie to its left, half to the right. Similarly, we might define *quartiles* as values of y which divide the area of the histogram into quarters.

> **Definition:** Let $y_1, y_2, \ldots, y_n$ be a set of n measurements arranged in order of magnitude. The *lower quartile* (first quartile) is the value

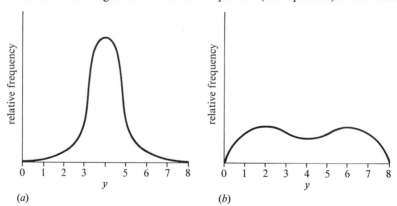

(a)   *(b)*

Figure 3.4.   Distribution with Equal Ranges
and Unequal Variability

of y that exceeds 1/4 of the measurements and is less than the remaining 3/4. The second quartile is the median. The *upper quartile* (third quartile) is the value of y that exceeds 3/4 of the measurements and is less than 1/4.

Locating the lower quartile on a histogram, Figure 3.5, we note that 1/4 of the area lies to the left of the lower quartile, 3/4 to the right. The upper quartile is the value of y such that 3/4 of the area lies to the left, 1/4 to the right.

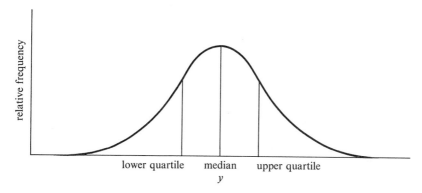

Figure 3.5.   Location of Quartiles

For some applications, it is preferable to use *percentiles.*

Definition: Let $y_1, y_2, \ldots, y_n$ be a set of n measurements arranged in order of magnitude. The pth percentile is the value of y such that $p\%$ of the measurements is less than that value of y and $(100 - p)\%$ is greater.

For example, the ninetieth percentile for a set of data would be the value of y that exceeds 90% of the measurements and is less than 10%. Just as in the case of quartiles, 90% of the area of the histogram would lie to the left of the ninetieth percentile.

The range possesses simplicity in that it can be expressed as a single number. Quartiles and percentiles, on the other hand, are more sensitive measures of variability, but several numbers must be given to provide an adequate description. Can we find a measure of variability expressible as a single number but more sensitive than the range?

Consider, as an example, the set of measurements 5, 7, 1, 2, 4. We can depict these data graphically, as in Figure 3.6, by showing the measurements as dots falling along the y-axis. Figure 3.6 is called a *dot diagram*. Calculating the mean as the measure of central tendency, we obtain

$$\bar{y} = \frac{\sum_{i=1}^{n} y_i}{n} = \frac{19}{5} = 3.8$$

and locate it on the dot diagram. We can now view variability in terms of distance between each dot (measurement) and the mean, $\bar{y}$. If the distances are large, we can say that the data are more variable than if the

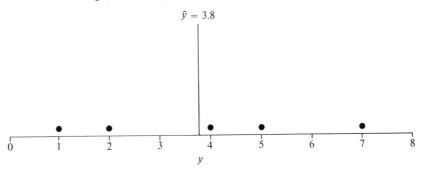

Figure 3.6. Dot Diagram

distances are small. Being more explicit, we will define the *deviation* of a measurement from its mean to be the quantity $(y_i - \bar{y})$. Note that measurements to the right of the mean represent positive deviations, and those to the left, negative deviations. The values of y and the deviations for our example are shown in columns 1 and 2 of Table 3.3.

Table 3.3.   The Computation of $\sum_{i=1}^{n} (y_i - \bar{y})^2$

y_i	$y_i - \bar{y}$	$(y_i - \bar{y})^2$	y^2
5	1.2	1.44	25
7	3.2	10.24	49
1	−2.8	7.84	1
2	−1.8	3.24	4
4	.2	.04	16
$\sum_{i=1}^{5} y_i = 19$	0	22.80	95

If we now agree that deviations contain information on variation'
our next step is to construct a formula based upon the deviations which
will provide a good measure of variation.   As a first possibility we might
choose the average of the deviations.   Unfortunately, this will not work
because some of the deviations are positive, some are negative, and the
sum is actually equal to zero.   This can easily be shown using our
summation theorems (see Chapter 2).

Given n measurements $y_1, y_2, \ldots, y_n$,

$$\sum_{i=1}^{n}(y_i - \bar{y}) = \sum_{i=1}^{n} y_i - \sum_{i=1}^{n} \bar{y}$$

$$= \sum_{i=1}^{n} y_i - n\bar{y}$$

$$= \sum_{i=1}^{n} y_i - n\frac{\sum_{i=1}^{n} y_i}{n}$$

$$= \sum_{i=1}^{n} y_i - \sum_{i=1}^{n} y_i = 0.$$

Note that the deviations, the second column of Table 3.3, sum to zero.

The reader will readily observe an easy solution to this problem.
Why not calculate the average of the *absolute values* of the deviations?
This method has, in fact, been employed as a measure of variability but
it tends to be unsatisfactory for purposes of statistical inference.   We
prefer overcoming the difficulty caused by the sign of the deviations by
working with the average of their squares,

$$\frac{\sum_{i=1}^{n}(y_i - \bar{y})^2}{n}.$$

When this quantity is large, the data will be more variable than when
it is small.

Definition: The *variance* of a set of n measurements $y_1, y_2, \ldots, y_n$ is
defined to be the average of the square of the deviations of the
measurements about their mean.

For example, we may calculate the variance for the set of $n = 5$
measurements presented in Table 3.3.   The square of the deviation of
each measurement is recorded in the third column of Table 3.3.   Adding,

we obtain

$$\sum_{i=1}^{5} (y_i - \bar{y})^2 = 22.80.$$

The variance would equal

$$\frac{\sum_{i=1}^{5} (y_i - \bar{y})^2}{n} = \frac{22.80}{5} = 4.56.$$

Let us use s'^2 to represent the sample variance and σ^2 (σ is the Greek letter sigma) to represent the population variance. Then,

$$s'^2 = \frac{\sum_{i=1}^{n} (y_i - \bar{y})^2}{n}.$$

(The reason for choosing these symbols to represent variance will be apparent as we proceed.)

At this point, the reader will be understandably disappointed with the practical significance attached to variance as a measure of variability. Large variances imply a large amount of variation but this only permits comparison of several sets of data. When we attempt to say something specific concerning a single set of data, we are at a loss. For example, what can be said about the variability of a set of data with a variance equal to 100? This question cannot be answered with the facts at hand. We will remedy this situation by introducing a new definition and, in Section 3.6, a theorem and a rule.

Definition: The standard deviation of a set of n measurements, y_1, $y_2, y_3, \ldots, y_n$, is equal to the positive square root of the variance.

The variance is measured in terms of the square of the original units of measurement. Thus, if the original measurements were in inches, the variance would be expressed in square inches. Taking the square root of the variance, we obtain the standard deviation, which, most happily, returns our measure of variability to the original units of measurement. The sample standard deviation is

$$s' = \sqrt{s'^2} = \sqrt{\frac{\sum_{i=1}^{n} (y_i - \bar{y})^2}{n}},$$

and the population standard deviation is σ. As an aid for remembering, note that the symbol s is the first letter in the word "standard."

Having defined the standard deviation, we might wonder why we bothered to define the variance in the first place. Actually, both the variance and the standard deviation play an important role in statistics, a fact which the reader must accept on faith at this stage of our discussion.

3.6   On the Practical Significance of the Standard Deviation

We now introduce an interesting and useful theorem developed by the Russian mathematician, Tchebysheff. Proof of the theorem is not difficult but we omit it from our discussion.

> **Tchebysheff's Theorem:** Given a number k greater than or equal to 1 and a set of n measurements $y_1, y_2, \ldots, y_n$, at least $(1 - 1/k^2)$ of the measurements will lie within k standard deviations of their mean.

Tchebysheff's Theorem applies to any set of measurements, and for purposes of illustration we could refer to either the sample or the population. We will use the notation appropriate for populations, but the reader should realize that we could just as easily use $\bar{y}$ and s', the mean and standard deviation for the sample.

The idea involved in Tchebysheff's Theorem is illustrated in Figure 3.7. An interval is constructed by measuring a distance of $k\sigma$ on either

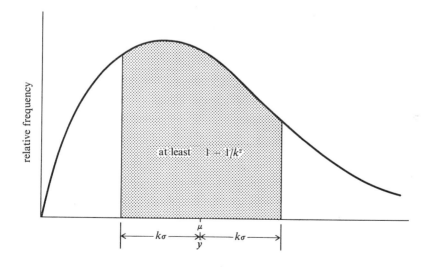

Figure 3.7.   Illustrating Tchebysheff's Theorem

side of the mean, μ. Note that the theorem is true for any number we wish to choose for k as long as it is greater than or equal to 1. Then, computing the fraction $1 - 1/k^2$, we see that Tchebysheff's Theorem states that *at least* that fraction of the total number, n, of measurements will lie in the constructed interval.

Let us choose a few numerical values for k and compute $1 - 1/k^2$. See Table 3.4. When $k = 1$, the theorem states that at least $1 - 1/(1)^2 = 0$ of the measurements lie in the interval $\mu - \sigma$ to $\mu + \sigma$, a most unhelpful and uninformative result. However, when $k = 2$, we observe that *at least* $1 - 1/(2)^2 = 3/4$ of the measurements will lie in the interval $\mu - 2\sigma$

Table 3.4.   Illustrative Values of $1 - 1/k^2$

k	$1 - 1/k^2$
1	0
2	3/4
3	8/9

to $\mu + 2\sigma$. At least 8/9 of the measurements will lie within three standard deviations of the mean. Let us consider an example where we will use the mean and standard deviation (or variance) to construct a mental image of the distribution of measurements from which the mean and standard deviation were obtained.

Example 3.4: The mean and variance of a sample of $n = 25$ measurements are 75 and 100, respectively. Use Tchebysheff's Theorem to describe the distribution of measurements.

Solution: We are given $\bar{y} = 75$ and $s'^2 = 100$. The standard deviation is $s' = \sqrt{100} = 10$. The distribution of measurements is centered about $\bar{y} = 75$, and Tchebysheff's Theorem states:

(1) *At least* 3/4 of the 25 measurements lie in the interval $\bar{y} \pm 2s' = 75 \pm 2(10)$, that is, 55 to 95.
(2) *At least* 8/9 of the measurements lie in the interval $\bar{y} \pm 3s' = 75 \pm 3(10)$, that is, 45 to 105.

We emphasize the "at least" in Tchebysheff's Theorem because the theorem is very conservative, applying to *any* distribution of measurements. In most situations, the fraction of measurements falling in the specified interval will exceed $1 - 1/k^2$.

We now state a rule which accurately describes the variability of a bell-shaped distribution and describes reasonably well the variability of other mound-shaped distributions of data. The frequent occurrence of mound-shaped and bell-shaped distributions of data in nature and hence the applicability of our rule leads us to call it the Empirical Rule.

The Empirical Rule: Given a distribution of measurements that is approximately bell-shaped (see Figure 3.9), the interval

(1) $\mu \pm \sigma$ will contain approximately 68% of the measurements,
(2) $\mu \pm 2\sigma$ will contain approximately 95% of the measurements,
(3) $\mu \pm 3\sigma$ will contain approximately 99.7% of the measurements.

The bell-shaped distribution, Figure 3.8, is commonly known as the *normal distribution* and will be discussed in detail in Chapter 7. The

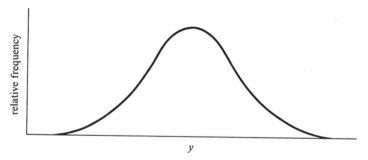

Figure 3.8. The Normal Distribution

point we wish to make here is that the Empirical Rule is extremely useful and provides an excellent description of variation for many types of data.

Example 3.5: A time study was conducted to determine the length of time necessary to perform a specified operation in a manufacturing plant. The length of time necessary to complete the operation was measured for each of $n = 40$ workmen. The mean and standard deviation were found to equal 12.8 and 1.7, respectively. To describe the data, we calculate the intervals

$$\bar{y} \pm s' = 12.8 \pm 1.7, \text{ or } 11.1 \text{ to } 14.5;$$

$$\bar{y} \pm 2s' = 12.8 \pm 2(1.7), \text{ or } 9.4 \text{ to } 16.2;$$

$$\bar{y} \pm 3s' = 12.8 \pm 3(1.7), \text{ or } 7.7 \text{ to } 17.9.$$

According to the Empirical Rule, we would expect approximately 68% of the measurements to fall in the interval 11.1 to 14.5, 95% in the interval 9.4 to 16.2, and 99.7% in the interval 7.7 to 17.9.

If we doubt that the distribution of measurements is mound-shaped or wish, for some other reason, to be conservative, we can apply Tchebysheff's Theorem and be absolutely certain of our statements.   Tchebysheff's Theorem would tell us that at least 3/4 of the measurements fell in the interval 9.4 to 16.2 and at least 8/9 in the interval 7.7 to 17.9.

Before leaving this topic, we might wonder how well the Empirical Rule applies to the grade-point data of Table 3.1.   We will show, in Section 3.7, that the mean and standard deviation for the $n = 30$ measurements is $\bar{y} = 2.09$ and $s' = 0.37$.   The appropriate intervals were calculated and the number of measurements falling in each interval recorded.   The results are shown in Table 3.5 with k in the first column and the interval,

Table 3.5.   Frequency of Measurements Lying
within k Standard Deviations of the Mean
for the Data, Table 3.1.

k	INTERVAL $\bar{y} \pm ks'$	FREQUENCY IN INTERVAL	RELATIVE FREQUENCY
1	1.71–2.45	19	.63
2	1.34–2.82	29	.97
3	.97–3.19	30	1.0

$\bar{y} \pm ks'$ in the second column, using $\bar{y} = 2.08$ and $s' = 0.37$.   The frequency or number of measurements falling in each interval is given in the third column and the relative frequency in the fourth column.

3.7   A Short Method for Calculating the Variance

The calculation of the variance and standard deviation of a set of measurements is no small task regardless of the method employed, but it is particularly tedious if one proceeds, according to the definition, by calculating each deviation individually as shown in Table 3.3.   We will use the data of Table 3.3 to illustrate a shorter method of calculation. The tabulations are presented in Table 3.6 in two columns, the first containing the individual measurements and the second containing the squares of the measurements.

Table 3.6.   Table for Simplified Calculations of

$$\sum_{i=1}^{n}(\hat{y}_i - \bar{y})^2$$

y_i	y_i^2
5	25
7	49
1	1
2	4
4	16
Totals 19	95

We now calculate

$$\sum_{i=1}^{n} y_i^2 - \frac{\left(\sum_{i=1}^{n} y_i\right)^2}{n} = 95 - \frac{(19)^2}{5}$$

$$= 95 - \frac{361}{5} = 95 - 72.2$$

$$= 22.8$$

and notice that it is exactly equal to the sum of squares of the deviations. $\sum_{i=1}^{n}(y_i - \bar{y})^2$, given in the third column of Table 3.3.

This is no accident.   We will show that the sum of squares of the deviations is always equal to

$$\sum_{i=1}^{n}(y_i - \bar{y})^2 = \sum_{i=1}^{n} y_i^2 - \frac{\left(\sum_{i=1}^{n} y_i\right)^2}{n}.$$

The proof is obtained by using the summation theorems, Chapter 2:

$$\sum_{i=1}^{n}(y_i - \bar{y})^2 = \sum_{i=1}^{n}(y_i^2 - 2\bar{y}y_i + \bar{y}^2)$$

$$= \sum_{i=1}^{n} y_i^2 - 2\bar{y}\sum_{i=1}^{n} y_i + \sum_{i=1}^{n} \bar{y}^2$$

$$= \sum_{i=1}^{n} y_i^2 - \frac{2\sum y_i}{n}\sum y_i + n\bar{y}^2$$

$$= \sum_{i=1}^{n} y_i^2 - \frac{2}{n}\left(\sum_{i=1}^{n} y_i\right)^2 + n\left(\frac{\sum_{i=1}^{n} y_i}{n}\right)^2$$

or

$$\sum_{i=1}^{n} (y_i - \bar{y})^2 = \sum_{i=1}^{n} y_i^2 - \frac{\left(\sum_{i=1}^{n} y_i\right)^2}{n}.$$

We call this formula the shortcut method of calculating the sums of squares of deviations needed in the formulae for the variance and standard deviation. Comparatively speaking, it is short because it eliminates all of the subtractions required for calculating the individual deviations. A second and not so obvious advantage is that it tends to give better computational accuracy than the method utilizing the deviations. The beginning statistics student frequently finds the variance which he has calculated at odds with the answer in the text. This is usually caused by rounding off decimal numbers in the computations. We suggest that rounding off be held at a minimum since it may seriously affect the results of computation of the variance. A third advantage is that the shortcut method is especially suitable for use of electric desk calculators, some of which accumulate $\sum_{i=1}^{n} y_i$ and $\sum_{i=1}^{n} y_i^2$ simultaneously.

Before leaving this topic, we will calculate the standard deviation for the $n = 30$ grade-point averages, Table 3.1. The student may verify the following:

$$\sum_{i=1}^{n} y_i = 62.5,$$

$$\sum_{i=1}^{n} y_i^2 = 134.19.$$

Using the shortcut formula,

$$\sum_{i=1}^{n} (y_i - \bar{y})^2 = \sum_{i=1}^{n} y_i^2 - \frac{\left(\sum_{i=1}^{n} y_i\right)^2}{n}$$

$$= 134.19 - \frac{(62.5)^2}{30} = 134.19 - 130.21$$

$$= 3.98.$$

It follows that the standard deviation is

$$s' = \sqrt{\frac{\sum_{i=1}^{n} (y_i - \bar{y})^2}{n}} = \sqrt{\frac{3.98}{30}} = 0.37.$$

3.8   Estimating the Population Variance

The reader will recall that we used the sample mean, $\bar{y}$, as an estimator of the population mean, μ. Although it was not specifically stated, we wished to convey the impression that the sample mean provides *good* estimates of μ. In the same vein, it would seem reasonable to assume that the sample variance, s'^2, would provide a good estimate of the population variance. However, it can be shown that, for small samples (n small), the sample variance tends to *underestimate* σ^2 and that the formula

$$s^2 = \frac{\sum_{i=1}^{n}(y_i - \bar{y})^2}{n-1}$$

provides better estimates. Note that s^2 and s'^2 differ only in the denominator where n is replaced by $(n-1)$ and that when n is large, s'^2 and s^2 will be approximately equal. We omit proof of these remarks and postpone discussion of estimation until Chapter 7. However, we mention that statisticians invariably calculate s^2 rather than the sample variance s'^2 and, in practice, refer to s^2 as the sample variance. Statisticians understand this misnomer but use it, lacking a better term; and, as we pointed out, s'^2 and s^2 are practically equal for large samples. Also, Tchebysheff's Theorem is still valid if we use s instead of s', and the Empirical Rule, an approximate statement applying to moderate size or large samples, retains its usefulness when s is substituted for s'. We will have numerous occasions for use of s^2 in succeeding chapters and will economize in terminology by referring to s^2 as the sample variance instead of the estimator of the population variance, which is more lengthy. Furthermore, in all of our calculations, we will use s^2 rather than s'^2.

Example 3.6: Calculate $\bar{y}$ and s for the measurements 85, 70, 60, 90, 81.

Solution:

y_i	y_i^2
85	7225
70	4900
60	360
90	8100
81	6561
386	30386

$$\bar{y} = \frac{386}{5} = 77.2.$$

$$\sum_{i=1}^{n} (y_i - \bar{y})^2 = \sum_{i=1}^{n} y_i^2 - \frac{\left(\sum_{i=1}^{n} y_i\right)^2}{n}$$

$$= 30386 - \frac{(386)^2}{5}$$

$$= 30386 - 29799.2$$

$$= 586.8.$$

$$s = \sqrt{\frac{\sum_{i=1}^{n} (y_i - \bar{y})^2}{n-1}} = \sqrt{\frac{586.8}{4}} = \sqrt{146.7}$$

$$= 12.1.$$

3.9 Summary and Comments

Methods for describing sets of measurements fall into one of two categories, graphical methods and numerical methods. The relative frequency histogram is an extremely useful graphical method for characterizing a set of measurements. Numerical descriptive measures are numbers which attempt to create a mental image of the frequency histogram (or frequency distribution). We have restricted the discussion to measures of central tendency and variation, the most useful of which are the mean and standard deviation. While the mean possesses intuitive descriptive significance, the standard deviation is significant only when used in conjunction with Tchebysheff's Theorem and the Empirical Rule. The objective of sampling is the description of the population from which the sample was obtained. This is accomplished by using the sample mean, $\bar{y}$, and the quantity, s^2, as estimators of the population mean, μ, and variance, σ^2.

Many descriptive methods and numerical measures have been presented in this chapter but these constitute only a small percentage of those which might have been discussed. In addition, many special computational techniques usually found in elementary texts have been omitted. This was necessitated by the limited time available in an elementary course and because the advent and common use of electronic computers have minimized the importance of special computational formulae. But, more important, the inclusion of such techniques would tend to detract from and obscure the main objective of modern statistics and this text—statistical inference.

EXERCISES

1. Conduct the following experiment: toss ten coins and record y, the number of heads observed. Repeat this process $n = 50$ times, thus providing fifty values of y. Construct a relative frequency histogram for these measurements.

2. The following measurements represent the grade-point average of twenty-five college freshmen:

2.6	1.8	2.6	3.7	1.9
2.1	2.7	3.0	2.4	2.3
3.1	2.6	2.6	2.5	2.7
2.7	2.9	3.4	1.9	2.3
3.3	2.2	3.5	3.0	2.5

   Construct a relative frequency histogram for this data.

3. Given the set of $n = 6$ measurements 5, 7, 2, 1, 3, 0, calculate $\bar{y}$, s^2 and s.

4. Given the set of $n = 7$ measurements 3, 0, 1, 5, 3, 0, 4, calculate $\bar{y}$, s^2, and s.

5. Calculate $\bar{y}$, s^2, and s for the data in Exercise 1.

6. Calculate $\bar{y}$, s^2, and s for the data in Exercise 2.

7. Refer to the histogram constructed in Exercise 1 and find the fraction of measurements lying in the interval $\bar{y} \pm 2s$. (Use the results of Exercise 5.) Are the results consistent with Tchebysheff's Theorem? Is the frequency histogram of Exercise 1 relatively mound-shaped? Does the Empirical Rule adequately describe the variability of the data in Exercise 1?

8. Repeat the instructions of Exercise 7 using the interval $\bar{y} \pm s$.

9. Refer to the grade point data in Exercise 2. Find the fraction of measurements falling in the intervals $\bar{y} \pm s$ and $\bar{y} \pm 2s$. Do these results agree with Tchebysheff's Theorem and the Empirical Rule?

10. The following five measurements represent the amount of milk, in ounces, discharged by an automatic milk dispenser: 7.1, 7.2, 7.0, 7.3, 7.0. Calculate $\bar{y}$, s^2, and s.

11. Refer to Exercise 10. Calculate the fraction of measurements in the intervals $\bar{y} \pm s$ and $\bar{y} \pm 2s$. Do these results agree with Tchebysheff's Theorem? Why is the Empirical Rule inappropriate for describing the variability of this data?

12. Why do statisticians prefer the use of s^2 rather than s'^2 in estimating a population variance σ^2?

13. Mathematics achievement test scores for four hundred students were found to have a mean and variance equal to 600 and 4900, respectively. Use Tchebysheff's Theorem to describe the variability of the test scores. If the distribution of scores was bell-shaped, approximately how many of the scores would fall in the interval 530 to 670? Approximately how many scores would be expected to exceed 740?

14. A machining operation produces bolts with an average diameter of .51 inches and a standard deviation of .01 inches. If the distribution of bolt diameters is approximately normal, what fraction of total production would possess diameters falling in the interval .49 to .53 inches?

15. Refer to Exercise 14. Suppose that the bolt specifications required a diameter equal to $.5 \pm .02$ inches. Bolts not satisfying this requirement are considered defective. If the machining operation functioned as described in Exercise 14, what fraction of total production would result in defective bolts?

16. An hour examination in statistics produced the following scores:

83	91	88	82	81
84	62	93	50	63
96	68	73	80	97
95	91	38	82	72
88	83	78	93	69
78	91	87	84	91

Construct a relative frequency histogram for the examination scores.

17. Compute $\bar{y}$, s^2, and s for the data in Exercise 16.

18. Refer to Exercise 16. Find the number of scores in the intervals $\bar{y} \pm s$ and $\bar{y} \pm 2s$ and compare with Tchebysheff's Theorem and the Empirical Rule.

19. Find the range for the data in Exercise 16. Find the ratio of the range to s. If one possessed a large amount of data possessing a bell-shaped distribution, the range would be expected to equal how many standard deviations? (Note that this provides a rough check for the computation of s.)

20. Find the ratio of the range to s for the data in Exercise 1.

21. The rule of thumb found in Exercise 19 for a large amount of data (more than 25 measurements) can be extended to smaller amounts of data obtained in sampling from a bell-shaped distribution. Thus, the calculated s should not be far different from range divided by the appropriate ratio found in the following table:

NUMBER OF MEASUREMENTS	5	10	25
EXPECTED RATIO OF RANGE TO s	2.5	3	4

For the data in Exercise 2, estimate s as suggested.   Compare this estimate with the calculated s.

22. Repeat the instructions of Exercise 21 using the data given in Exercises 3 and 10.

23. From the following data, a student calculated s to be .263.   On what grounds might we doubt his accuracy?   What is the correct value (nearest hundredth)?

17.2	17.1	17.0	17.1	16.9
17.0	17.1	17.0	17.3	17.2
17.1	17.0	17.1	16.9	17.0
17.1	17.3	17.2	17.4	17.1

24. A set of 128 examination scores in history produced a mean and standard deviation equal to 92% and 10%, respectively.   Would you expect the relative frequency distribution for these scores to be bell-shaped?   Why? (Note that a score cannot exceed 100%.)

REFERENCES

Freund, J. E., *Modern Elementary Statistics*.   2nd ed.   Englewood Cliffs, N.J.: Prentice-Hall, Inc., 1960.

Mode, E. B., *The Elements of Statistics*.   Englewood Cliffs, N.J.: Prentice-Hall, Inc., 1941.

Neiswanger, W. A., *Elementary Statistical Methods*.   New York: The Macmillan Company, Inc., 1956.

4

PROBABILITY

4.1 Introduction

Probability and statistics are related in a most curious way. In essence, probability is the vehicle which enables the statistician to use information in a sample to make inferences or describe the population from which the sample was obtained. We illustrate this relationship with a simple example.

Consider a balanced die with its familiar six faces. By balanced we mean that the chance of observing any one of the six sides on a single toss of the die is just as likely as any other. Tossing the die might be viewed as an experiment which could conceivably be repeated a very large number of times, thus generating a population of numbers where the measurements, y, would be either 1, 2, 3, 4, 5, or 6. Assume that the population is so large that each value of y occurs with equal frequency. Note that we do not actually generate the population; rather, it exists conceptually. Now let us toss the die once and observe the value of y. This one measurement represents a sample of $n = 1$ drawn from the population. What is the probability that the sample value of y will equal 2? Knowing the structure of the population, we realize that each value of y has an equal chance of occurring and hence the probability that $y = 2$ is $1/6$. This example illustrates the type of problem considered in probability theory. The *population* is assumed to be *known* and we are concerned with calculating the probability of observing a particular sample. Exactly the opposite is true in statistical problems where we assume the population unknown, the sample known, and we wish to make inferences about the population. Thus probability reasons from the population to the sample while statistics acts in reverse, moving from the sample to the population.

To illustrate how probability is used in statistical inference, consider the following example. Suppose that a die is tossed $n = 10$ times and the number of dots, y, appearing is recorded after each toss. This represents a sample of $n = 10$ measurements drawn from a much larger body of tosses, the population, which could be generated if we wished. Suppose that all ten measurements resulted in $y = 1$. We wish to use this information to make an inference concerning the population of tosses; specifically, we wish to infer that the die is or is not balanced. Having observed ten tosses, each resulting in $y = 1$, we would be somewhat suspicious of the die and would likely reject the theory that the die was balanced. We reason as follows: If the die were balanced, as we hypothesize, observing ten identical measurements is most *improbable*. Hence, either we observed a rare event or else our hypothesis is false. We would likely be inclined to the latter conclusion. Notice that the decision was based upon the probability of observing the sample, assuming our theory to be true.

The above illustration emphasizes the importance of probability in making statistical inferences. In the following discussion of the theory of probability, we will assume the population known and calculate the probability of drawing various samples. In doing so, we are really choosing a *model* for a physical situation because the actual composition of a population is rarely known in practice. Thus the probabilist models a physical situation (the population) with probability much as the sculptor models with clay.

4.2 The Sample Space

Data are obtained either by observation of uncontrolled events in nature or by controlled experimentation in the laboratory. To simplify our terminology, we seek a word which will apply to either method of data collection and hence define an *experiment* to be the process by which an observation (or measurement) is obtained. Note that the observation need not be numerical. Typical examples of experiments are:

(1) Recording a test grade.

(2) Making a measurement of daily rainfall.

(3) Interviewing a voter to obtain his preference prior to an election.

(4) Inspecting a light bulb to determine whether it is a defective or an acceptable product.

(5) Tossing a coin and observing the face which appears.

A *population* of measurements results when the experiment is repeated many times. For instance, we might be interested in the length of life of television tubes produced in a plant during the month of June. Testing a single tube to failure and measuring length of life would represent a single experiment, while repetition of the experiment for all tubes produced during this period would generate the entire population. A *sample* would represent the results of some small group of experiments selected from the population.

Let us now direct our attention to a careful analysis of an experiment and the construction of a mathematical model for a population. A by-product of our development will be a systematic and direct approach to the solution of probability problems.

We commence by noting that each experiment may result in one or more outcomes which we will call *events* and denote by capital letters. Consider the following experiment.

Example 4.1: Experiment: Toss a die and observe the number appearing on the upper face. Some events would be:

(1) Event A: observe an odd number.

(2) Event B: observe a number less than 4.

(3) Event E_1: observe a 1.

(4) Event E_2: observe a 2.

(5) Event E_3: observe a 3.

(6) Event E_4: observe a 4.

(7) Event E_5: observe a 5.

(8) Event E_6: observe a 6.

The events detailed above do not represent a complete listing of all possible events associated with the experiment but suffice to illustrate a point. The reader will readily note a difference between events A and B and the events E_1, E_2, E_3, E_4, E_5, and E_6. Event A will occur if either events E_1, E_3, or E_5 occur, that is, if we observe a 1, 3, or 5. Thus, A could be decomposed into a collection of simpler events, namely, E_1, E_3, and E_5. Likewise, event B will occur if E_1, E_2, or E_3 occur and could be viewed as a collection of smaller or simpler events. In contrast, we note that it is impossible to decompose events E_1, E_2, E_3, ..., E_6. Events E_1, E_2, ..., E_6 are called *simple* events and A and B are *compound* events.

Definition: An event which cannot be decomposed is called a simple event. Simple events will be denoted by the symbol E with a subscript.

The events $E_1, E_2, \ldots, E_6$ represent a complete listing of all simple events associated with the experiment, Example 4.1. An interesting property of simple events is readily apparent. An experiment will result in one and only one of the simple events. For instance, if a die is tossed, we will observe either a 1, 2, 3, 4, 5, or 6 but we cannot possibly observe more than one of the simple events at the same time. Hence a list of simple events provides a breakdown of all possible outcomes of the experiment. For purposes of illustration, consider the following examples:

Example 4.2: Experiment: Toss a coin. Simple events:

E_1: observe a head.
E_2: observe a tail.

Example 4.3: Experiment: Toss two coins. Simple events:

	COIN #1	COIN #2
E_1:	Head	Head
E_2:	Head	Tail
E_3:	Tail	Head
E_4:	Tail	Tail

It would be extremely convenient if we were able to construct a model for an experiment which could be portrayed graphically. We do this in terms of point sets. To each simple event we assign a point, called a *sample point*. Thus the symbol E_i will now be associated with either simple event E_i or its corresponding sample point. The resulting diagram is called a Venn diagram.

Example 4.1 may be viewed symbolically in terms of the Venn diagram shown in Figure 4.1. Six sample points are shown corresponding to the six possible simple events enumerated in Example 4.1. Likewise, the tossing of two coins, Example 4.3, is an experiment possessing four sample points. The set of all sample points for the experiment is called the *sample space* and is represented by the symbol S. We say that S is the totality of all sample points.

What is an event in terms of the sample points? We recall that event A, Example 4.1, occurred if any one of the simple events E_1, E_3, or E_5

occurred.   That is, we observe A, an odd number, if we observe either a
1, 3, or 5.   Event B, a number less than 4, occurs if E_1, E_2, or E_3 occurs.
Thus, if we designate the sample points associated with an event, the event

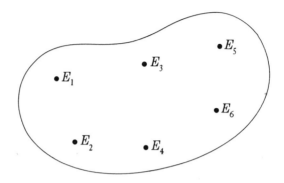

Figure 4.1.   Venn Diagram for Die Tossing

is as clearly defined as if we had presented a verbal description of it.   The
event, "observe E_1, E_3, or E_5" is obviously the same as the event, "observe
an odd number."

Definition: An event is a collection of sample points.

Keep in mind that the foregoing discussion refers to the outcome of a
single experiment and that the performance of the experiment will result in
the occurrence of one and only one sample point.   Obviously, an event
will occur if any sample point in the event occurs.

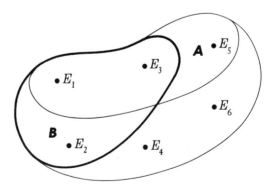

Figure 4.2.   Events A and B for Die Tossing

An event could be represented on the Venn diagram by encircling the sample points in that event. Events A and B for the die-tossing problem are shown in Figure 4.2. Note that points E_1 and E_3 are in both events A and B and that both A and B occur if either E_1 or E_3 occur.

Populations of observations are obtained by repeating an experiment a very large number of times. Some fraction of this very large number of experiments will result in E_1, another fraction in E_2, etc. From a practical point of view, we think of the fraction of the population resulting in an event A as the *probability* of A. Putting it another way, if an experiment is repeated a large number of times, N, and A is observed n times, the probability of A is

$$P(A) = \frac{n}{N}.$$

In practice, the composition of the population is rarely known and hence the desired probabilities for various events are unknown. Mathematically speaking, we ignore this aspect of the problem and take the probabilities as given, hence providing a *model* for a real population. For instance, we would assume that a large population of die tosses, Example 4.1, would yield

$$P(E_1) = P(E_2) = \ldots = P(E_6) = 1/6.$$

That is, we assume that the die is perfectly balanced. Is there such a thing as a perfectly balanced die? Probably not, but we would be inclined to think that the probability of the sample points would be so near 1/6 that our assumption is quite valid for practical purposes and provides a good model for die tossing.

We complete our model for the population by adding the following. To each point in the sample space we assign a number called the *probability of* E_i, denoted by the symbol $P(E_i)$, such that:

(1) $0 \leq P(E_i) \leq 1$, for all i;

(2) $\sum_{S} P(E_i) = 1$.

The two requirements placed upon the probabilities of the sample points are necessary in order that the model conform to our relative frequency concept of probability. Thus, we require that a probability be greater than or equal to 0 and less than or equal to 1 and that the sum of the probabilities over the entire sample space, S, be equal to 1. Furthermore, from a practical point of view, we would choose the $P(E_i)$ in a realistic way so that they agree with the observed relative frequency of occurrence of the sample points.

We are now in a position to state a simple rule for the probability of any event, say event A.

Definition: The probability of an event A is equal to the sum of the probabilities of the sample points in A.

Note that the definition agrees with our intuitive concept of probability.

Example 4.4: Calculate the probability of the event A for Example 4.1.

Solution: Event A is "observe an odd number" and includes points E_1, E_3, E_5. Hence,

$$P(A) = P(E_1) + P(E_3) + P(E_5)$$
$$= 1/6 + 1/6 + 1/6.$$

Example 4.5: Calculate the probability of observing exactly one head in a toss of two coins.

Solution: Construct the sample space letting H represent a head, T a tail.

	FIRST COIN	SECOND COIN	$P(E_i)$
E_1:	H	H	1/4
E_2:	H	T	1/4
E_3:	T	H	1/4
E_4:	T	T	1/4

It would seem reasonable to assign a probability of 1/4 to each of the sample points. We are interested in:

Event A: observe exactly one head. Sample points E_2 and E_3 are in A. Hence

$$P(A) = P(E_2) + P(E_3)$$
$$= 1/4 + 1/4$$
$$= 1/2$$

Example 4.6: Consider the following experiment involving two urns. Urn #1 contains two white balls and one black ball. Urn #2 contains one white ball.   A ball is drawn from urn #1 and placed in urn #2.   Then a ball is drawn from urn #2.   What is the probability that the ball drawn from urn #2 will be white? See Figure 4.3.

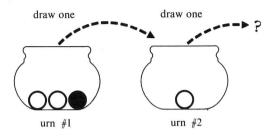

draw one   draw one

?

urn #1   urn #2

Figure 4.3.   Representation of the Experiment in Example 4.6

Solution: The problem is easily solved once we have listed the sample points.   For convenience, number the white balls 1, 2, and 3 with ball #3 residing in urn #2.   The sample points are listed below using W_i to represent the *i*th white ball.

| | DRAWN FROM | | |
	URN #1	URN #2	$P(E_i)$
E_1:	W_1	W_1	1/6
E_2:	W_1	W_3	1/6
E_3:	W_2	W_2	1/6
E_4:	W_2	W_3	1/6
E_6:	B	B	1/6
E_5:	B	W_3	1/6

Event A, drawing a white ball from urn #2, occurs if E_1, E_2, E_3, E_4, or E_6 occur.   Once again, it would seem reasonable to assume the sample points equally likely and to assign a probability of 1/6 to each.   Hence,

$$P(A) = P(E_1) + P(E_2) + P(E_3) + P(E_4) + P(E_6)$$
$$= \ 1/6 \ + \ 1/6 \ + \ 1/6 \ + \ 1/6 \ + \ 1/6$$
$$= 5/6.$$

Note that we have constructed a probabilistic model for a population which possesses, in addition to elegance, a great deal of utility.   It provides us with a simple, logical, and direct method for calculating the probability of an event or, if you like, the probability of a sample drawn from a theoretical population. The student having prior experience with probability problems will recognize the advantage of a systematic procedure for their solution. The disadvantages soon become apparent. Listing the sample points can be quite tedious and one must be certain that none has been omitted. The total number of points in S may run into the millions. Hence it behooves us to consider some mathematical theorems useful in counting sample points as well as an alternative method for calculating the probability of events.

4.3   Results Useful in Counting Sample Points

We now proceed to state three theorems falling in the realm of combinatorial mathematics which greatly simplify counting in special cases. The first we call the *mn* rule.

Theorem 4.1: With m elements a_1, a_2, a_3, ..., a_m and n elements $b_1, b_2, \ldots, b_n$ it is possible to form mn pairs containing one element from each group.

Proof: Verification of the theorem can be seen by observing the rectangular table in Figure 4.4. There will be one square in the table for each $a_i b_j$ combination—a total of mn squares.

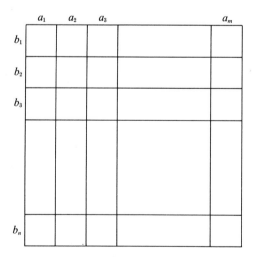

Figure 4.4.   Table Indicating the Number of Pairs (a_i, b_j)

Example 4.7: Two dice are tossed. How many sample points are associated with the experiment?

Solution: The first die can fall in one of six ways; that is, $m = 6$. Likewise, the second die can fall in $n = 6$ ways. The total number, N, of sample points is

$$N = mn = (6)\,(6) = 36.$$

Example 4.8: How many sample points are associated with the experiment, Example 4.6?

Solution: A ball can be chosen from urn #1 in one of $m = 3$ ways. After one of these ways has been chosen, a ball may be drawn from urn #2 in $n = 2$ ways. The total number of sample points is

$$N = mn = (3)\,(2) = 6.$$

The *mn* rule can be extended to any number of sets.

Example 4.9: How many sample points are in the sample space when three coins are tossed?

Solution: Each coin can land in one of two ways. Hence,

$$N = (2)\,(2)\,(2) = 8.$$

A second useful mathematical result is associated with orderings or *permutations*. For instance, suppose that we have three books, b_1, b_2, and b_3. In how many ways can the books be arranged on a shelf, taking them two at a time? We enumerate, listing all combinations of two in the first column and a reordering of each in the second column:

COMBINATIONS OF TWO	REORDERING OF COMBINATIONS
$b_1 b_2$	$b_2 b_1$
$b_1 b_3$	$b_3 b_1$
$b_2 b_3$	$b_3 b_2$

The number of permutations is six, a result easily obtained from the *mn* rule. The first book can be chosen in $m = 3$ ways, and, once selected, the second book can be chosen in $n = 2$ ways. The result is $mn = 6$.

In how many ways can three books be arranged on a shelf taking three at a time? Enumerating, we obtain

$$b_1 b_2 b_3 \qquad b_2 b_1 b_3 \qquad b_3 b_1 b_2$$
$$b_1 b_3 b_2 \qquad b_2 b_3 b_1 \qquad b_3 b_2 b_1$$

a total of six. This, again, could be obtained easily by the extension of the *mn* rule. The first book can be chosen and placed in $m = 3$ ways. After choosing the first, the second can be chosen in $n = 2$ ways, and finally the third in $p = 1$ ways. Hence, the total number of ways is

$$N = mnp = 3 \cdot 2 \cdot 1 = 6.$$

Definition: An ordered arrangement of r distinct objects is called a *permutation*. The number of ways of ordering n distinct (different) objects taken r at a time will be designated by the symbol P_r^n.

Theorem 4.2: $P_r^n = n(n - 1)(n - 2)\ldots(n - r + 1)$.

Proof: We are concerned with the number of ways of filling r positions with n distinct objects. Applying the extension of the *mn* rule, the first object can be chosen in one of n ways. After choosing the first, the second can be chosen in $(n - 1)$ ways, the third in $(n - 2)$ ways, and the rth in $(n - r + 1)$ ways. Hence the total number of ways is

$$P_r^n = n(n - 1)(n - 2)\ldots(n - r + 1).$$

Expressed in terms of factorials,

$$P_r^n = \frac{n!}{(n - r)!}$$

[The reader should recall that $n! = n(n - 1)(n - 2)\ldots 3 \cdot 2 \cdot 1$ and $0! = 1$. Thus, $4! = 4 \cdot 3 \cdot 2 \cdot 1 = 24$.]

Example 4.10: Three lottery tickets are drawn from a total of fifty. Assume that order is of importance. How many sample points are associated with the experiment?

Solution: The total number of sample points is

$$P_3^{50} = \frac{50!}{47!} = (50)(49)(48) = 117{,}600.$$

Example 4.11: A piece of equipment is composed of five parts which may be assembled in any order. A test is to be conducted to determine the length of time necessary for each order of assembly.   If each order is to be tested once, how many tests must be conducted?

Solution: The total number of tests would equal

$$P_5^5 = \frac{5!}{0!} = (5)(4)(3)(2)(1) = 120.$$

The enumeration of the permutations of books in the previous discussion was performed in a systematic manner, first writing the combinations of n books taken r at a time and then writing the rearrangements of each combination.   In many situations, ordering is unimportant and we are interested solely in the number of possible combinations.   For instance, in how many ways can we select a committee of five men from a total of 20 candidates?   Obviously, permutations are irrelevant.   We are interested in the number of combinations of $n = 20$ things taken $r = 5$ at a time.

Definition: The number of combinations of n objects taken r at a time will be denoted by the symbol, C_r^n.   [Note: Some authors prefer the symbol $\binom{n}{r}$.]

Theorem 4.3:

$$C_r^n = \frac{P_r^n}{r!} = \frac{n!}{r!\,(n-r)!}.$$

Proof: The number of combinations of n objects taken r at a time is apparently related to the number of permutations since it was used in enumerating P_r^n.   The relationship can be developed using the *mn* rule. (We will use different symbols since n is used in P_r^n and C_r^n.)

Let $a = C_r^n$ and let b the number of ways of rearranging each combination once chosen, or P_r^r.   Then,

$$P_r^n = ab$$

$$= (C_r^n)(b).$$

Note that $b = P_r^r = r!$ Therefore,

$$P_r^n = C_r^n(r!)$$

or

$$C_r^n = \frac{P_r^n}{r!} = \frac{n!}{r!\,(n-r)!}.$$

Example 4.12: A radio tube may be purchased from five suppliers. In how many ways can three suppliers be chosen from the five?

Solution:

$$C_3^5 = \frac{5!}{3!\,2!} = \frac{(5)\,(4)}{2} = 10.$$

The following example illustrates the use of the counting rules in the solution of a probability problem.

Example 4.13: Five manufacturers, of varying but unknown quality, produce a certain type of electronic tube. If we were to select three manufacturers at random, what is the chance that the selection would contain exactly two of the best three?

Solution: Without enumerating the sample points, we would likely agree that each point, that is, any combination of three, would be assigned equal probability. If N points are in S, then each point receives probability

$$P(E_i) = \frac{1}{N}.$$

Let n be the number of points in which two of the best three manufacturers are selected. Then the probability of including two of the best three manufacturers in a selection of three is

$$P = \frac{n}{N}.$$

Our problem is to use the counting rules to find n and N.

Since a selection is a combination,

$$N = C_3^5 = \frac{5!}{3!\,2!} = 10.$$

Determination of n is more difficult but can be obtained using the *mn* rule. Let a be the number of ways of selecting exactly two from the best three, or

$$C_2^3 = \frac{3!}{2!\,1!} = 3,$$

and let b be the number of ways of choosing the remaining manufacturer from the two poorest, or

$$C_1^2 = \frac{2!}{1!\,1!} = 2.$$

Then the total number of ways of choosing the two of the best three in a selection of three is $n = ab = 6$.

Hence the probability, P, is equal to

$$P = \frac{6}{10}.$$

Note that use of the counting rules eliminated the need for enumeration of the sample points in this example. We will not always be so fortunate.

4.4 Calculating the Probability of an Event: Sample Point Approach

The procedure for calculating the probability of an event by summing the probabilities of the sample points requires the following steps:

(1) Define the experiment.

(2) List the simple events associated with the experiment and test each to make certain that they cannot be decomposed. This defines the sample space, S.

(3) Assign reasonable probabilities to the sample points in S, making certain that $\sum_S P(E_i) = 1$.

(4) Define the event of interest, A, as a specific collection of sample points. (A sample point is in A if A occurs when the sample point occurs. Test *all* sample points in S to locate those in A.)

(5) Find $P(A)$ by summing the probabilities of the sample points in A.

The combinatorial formulae of Section 4.3 are pertinent to the above procedure because they are useful in counting sample points. They assist in determining the total number of sample points in S so that none are accidently omitted in step (2). When the sample points are equiprobable, summation of the probability of the sample points in A, step (5), can be acquired by counting the points in A and multiplying by the probability per sample point.

Calculating the probability of an event by using the five-step procedure described above is systematic and will lead to the correct solution if all of the steps are correctly followed. A major source of error occurs in failing to define the experiment clearly (step 1) and then to specify simple events (step 2). A second source of error is the failure to assign valid probabilities to the sample points. The method becomes tedious (and, for all practical purposes, unmanagable) when the number of sample points in S is large, except in some special cases where sets of sample points are equiprobable. When this occurs, summation sometimes can be accomplished by using the counting rules of Section 4.3.

4.5   Compound Events

Most events of interest in practical situations are compound events requiring enumeration of a large number of sample points. Actually, we find a second approach available for calculating the probability of events which obviates the listing of sample points and is therefore much less tedious and time consuming. It is based upon the classification of events, event relations, and two probability laws which will be discussed in Sections 4.5, 4.6, and 4.7 respectively.

Compound events, as the name suggests, are formed by some composition of two or more events. Composition takes place in one of two ways, or in some combination of the two, namely, a *union* or an *intersection*.

> **Definition:** Let A and B be two events in a sample space, S. The *union of A and B* is defined to be the event containing all sample points in A or B or both. We denote the union of A and B by the symbol $(A + B)$. (Note: some authors use the symbol $A \cup B$.)

Defined in ordinary terms, a union is the event that *either* event A or event B or both A and B occur. For instance, in Example 4.1,

$$A: E_1, E_3, E_5,$$

$$B: E_1, E_2, E_3.$$

The union $(A + B)$ would be the collection of points, E_1, E_2, E_3, and E_5. This is shown diagrammatically in Figure 4.5.

> **Definition:** Let A and B be two events in a sample space, S. The *intersection of A and B* is the event composed of all sample points

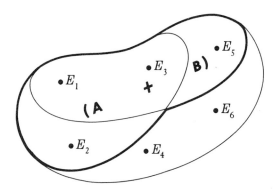

Figure 4.5.   The Event $(A + B)$ in Example 4.1

which are in both A and B. An intersection of events A and B is represented by the symbol AB. (Some authors use $A \cap B$.)

The intersection AB is the event that *both* A and B occur. It would appear in a Venn diagram as the overlapping area between A and B. The intersection AB for Example 4.1 would be the event consisting of points E_1 and E_3. If either E_1 or E_3 occur, both A and B occur. This is shown diagrammatically in Figure 4.6.

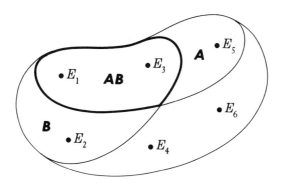

Figure 4.6.   The Intersection AB

Example 4.14: Refer to the experiment, Example 4.3, where two coins are tossed, and define:

> Event A: at least one head,
> Event B: at least one tail.

Define event A, B, AB, and $(A + B)$ as collections of sample points.

Solution: Recall that the sample points for this experiment were:

> E_1: HH (head on first coin, head on second),
> E_2: HT
> E_3: TH,
> E_4: TT.

The occurrence of sample points E_1, E_2, and E_3 implies and hence defines event A. The other events could similarly be defined:

> Event B: E_2, E_3, E_4,
> Event AB: E_2, E_3,
> Event $(A + B)$: E_1, E_2, E_3, E_4.

Note that $(A + B) = S$, the sample space, and is thus certain to occur.

4.6 Event Relations

We will define three relations between events: complementary, independent, and mutually exclusive events. The student will have many occasions to inquire whether two or more events bear a particular relationship to one another. The test for each relationship is inherent in the definition, as we will illustrate, and their use in the calculation of the probability of an event will become apparent in Section 4.7.

> **Definition:** The complement of an event A is the collection of all sample points in S and not in A. The complement of A is denoted by the symbol, $\bar{A}$.
> Since
>
> $$\sum_{S} P(E_i) = 1,$$
>
> $$P(A) + P(\bar{A}) = 1$$

and

$$P(A) = 1 - P(\bar{A}),$$

which is a useful relation for obtaining $P(A)$ when $P(\bar{A})$ is known or easily calculated.

Two events are often related in such a way that the probability of occurrence of one depends upon whether the second has or has not occurred. For instance, suppose that one experiment consists in observing the weather on a specific day. Let A be the event " observe rain " and B be the event "observe an overcast sky." Events A and B are obviously related. The probability of rain, $P(A)$, is not the same as the probability of rain given prior information that the day is cloudy. The probability of A, $P(A)$, would be the fraction of the entire population of observations which result in rain. Now let us look only at the subpopulation of observations resulting in B, a cloudy day, and the fraction of these which result in A. This fraction, called the *conditional probability of A given B*, may equal $P(A)$ but we would expect the chance of rain, given that the day is cloudy, to be larger. The conditional probability of A, given that B has occurred, is denoted as

$$P(A/B),$$

where the slant in the parentheses is read " given " and events appearing to the right of slant are the events that have occurred.

We will define the conditional probabilities of B given A and A given B as follows.

Definition:

$$P(B/A) = \frac{P(AB)}{P(A)},$$

and

$$P(A/B) = \frac{P(AB)}{P(B)}.$$

The fact that this definition is consistent with our relative frequency concept of probability is obvious after a bit of thought but is perhaps more easily seen by viewing the following construction. Suppose that an experiment is repeated a large number of times, N, resulting in both A and B, AB, n_{11} times; A and not B, $A\bar{B}$, n_{21} times; B and not A, $\bar{A}B$, n_{12} times, and neither A nor B, $\bar{A}\bar{B}$, n_{22} times. We present these results in a two-way table, Table 4.1. Note that

Table 4.1.   *Two-way Table for Events A and B*

	A	$\bar{A}$
B	n_{11}	n_{12}
$\bar{B}$	n_{21}	n_{22}

$n_{11} + n_{12} + n_{21} + n_{22} = N$. It follows that

$$P(A) = \frac{n_{11} + n_{21}}{N},$$

$$P(B) = \frac{n_{11} + n_{12}}{N},$$

$$P(A/B) = \frac{n_{11}}{n_{11} + n_{12}},$$

$$P(B/A) = \frac{n_{11}}{n_{11} + n_{21}},$$

$$P(AB) = \frac{n_{11}}{N}.$$

Using these probabilities, it is easy to see that

$$P(B/A) = \frac{P(AB)}{P(A)},$$

and

$$P(A/B) = \frac{P(AB)}{P(B)}.$$

Example 4.15: Calculate $P(A/B)$ for the die tossing in Example 4.1.

Solution: Given that B has occurred, we are concerned only with sample points E_1, E_2, and E_3, which occur with equal frequency. Of these, E_1 and E_3 imply event A. Hence

$$P(A/B) = 2/3.$$

Or, we could obtain $P(A/B)$ by substituting into the equation,

$$P(A/B) = \frac{P(AB)}{P(B)} = \frac{(1/3)}{(1/2)} = 2/3.$$

Note that $P(A/B) = 2/3$ while $P(A) = 1/2$, indicating that A and B are *dependent* upon each other.

Definition: Two events, A and B, are said to be *independent* if either

$$P(A/B) = P(A)$$

or

$$P(B/A) = P(B).$$

Otherwise, the events are said to be *dependent*.

We will note that if $P(A/B) = P(A)$, then $P(B/A)$ will also equal $P(B)$. Similarly, if $P(A/B)$ and $P(A)$ are unequal, then $P(B/A)$ and $P(B)$ will be unequal.

A third useful event relation was observed but not specifically defined in our discussion of simple events. Recall that an experiment could result in one and only one simple event. No two could occur at exactly the same time. Two events, A and B, are said to be *mutually exclusive*, if, when one occurs, it excludes the possibility of occurrence of the other. Another way to say this is to state that the intersection, AB, will contain no sample points. It would then follow that $P(AB) = 0$.

Definition: Two events, A and B, are said to be mutually exclusive if the event AB contains no sample points.

Mutually exclusive events have no overlapping area in a Venn diagram. (See Figure 4.7.)

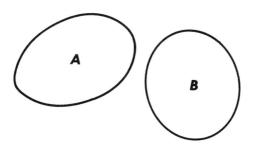

Figure 4.7. Mutually Exclusive Events

Example 4.16: Are events A and B, Example 4.1, mutually exclusive? Are they complementary?

Solution:

$$\text{Event } A: E_1, E_3, E_5,$$
$$\text{Event } B: E_1, E_2, E_3.$$

It is obvious that event AB includes points E_1 and E_3 and that $P(AB)$ is not equal to zero. Therefore, A and B are not mutually exclusive. They are not complementary because B does not contain all points in S which are not in A.

Example 4.17: Given two mutually exclusive events, A and B, with $P(A)$ and $P(B)$ not equal to zero, are A and B independent events?

Solution: Since A and B are mutually exclusive, if A occurs, B cannot occur and vice versa. Then $P(B/A) = 0$. But $P(B)$ was said to be greater than zero. Hence $P(B/A)$ is not equal to $P(B)$ and according to the definition the events are dependent.

4.7 Two Probability Laws and Their Use

As previously stated, a second approach to the solution of probability problems is based upon the classification of compound events, event relations, and two probability laws which we now state and illustrate. The "laws" can be simply stated and taken as fact as long as they are consistent with our model and with reality. The first is called the Additive Law of Probability and applies to unions.

> **The Additive Law of Probability:** The probability of a union $(A + B)$ is equal to
>
> $$P(A + B) = P(A) + P(B) - P(AB).$$
>
> If A and B are mutually exclusive, $P(AB) = 0$ and
>
> $$P(A + B) = P(A) + P(B).$$

The Additive Law conforms to reality and our model. The sum, $P(A) + P(B)$, contains the sum of the probabilities of all sample points in $(A + B)$ but includes a double counting of the probabilities of all points in the intersection, AB. Subtracting $P(AB)$ gives the correct result.

The second law of probability is called the Multiplicative Law and applies to intersections.

> **The Multiplicative Law of Probability:** Given two events, A and B, the probability of the intersection, AB, is
>
> $$P(AB) = P(A)P(B/A)$$
> $$= P(B)P(A/B).$$
>
> If A and B are *independent*, $P(AB) = P(A)P(B)$.

The Multiplicative Law follows from the definition of conditional probability.

The use of the probability laws for calculating the probability of a compound event is less direct than the listing of sample points and requires a bit of experience and ingenuity. The approach involves the expression of the event of interest as a union or intersection (or combination of both) of two or more events whose probabilities are known or easily calculated. This can often be done in many ways. The trick to find the right combination, a task requiring no little amount of creativity in some cases. The usefulness of event relations is now apparent. If the event of interest is expressed as a union of mutually exclusive events, the probabilities of the intersection need not be known. If they are independent, we need not know the conditional probabilities to calculate the probability of an intersection. Examples 4.18, 4.19, and 4.20 illustrate the use of the probability laws and the technique described above.

Example 4.18: Calculate $P(AB)$ and $P(A + B)$ for Example 4.1.

Solution: Recall that $P(A) = P(B) = 1/2$ and $P(A/B) = 2/3$. Then

$$P(AB) = P(B)P(A/B)$$

$$= (1/2)(2/3)$$

$$= 1/3,$$

$$P(A + B) = P(A) + P(B) - P(AB)$$

$$= 1/2 + 1/2 - 1/3$$

$$= 2/3.$$

The student will readily observe that these solutions agree with those obtained using the sample point approach.

Example 4.19: Two cards are drawn from a deck of fifty-two cards. Calculate the probability that the draw will include an ace and a ten.

Solution: Event A: Draw an ace and a ten. Then $A = B + C$, where

B: Draw the ace on the first draw and the ten on the second.
C: Draw the ten on the first draw and the ace on the second.

Note that B and C were chosen so as to be mutually exclusive and also intersections of events with known probabilities. Thus

$$B = B_1 B_2 \quad \text{and} \quad C = C_1 C_2$$

where

B_1: draw an ace on the first draw,
B_2: draw a ten on the second draw,
C_1: draw a ten on the first draw,
C_2: draw an ace on the second draw.

Applying the Multiplicative Law,

$$P(B_1 B_2) = P(B_1)P(B_2/B_1)$$

$$= (4/52)(4/51)$$

and

$$P(C_1 C_2) = (4/52)(4/51).$$

Then, applying the Additive Law,

$$P(A) = P(B) + P(C)$$
$$= (4/52)(4/51) + (4/52)(4/51)$$
$$= \frac{8}{663}.$$

The student is cautioned to check carefully each composition to be certain it is actually equal to the event of interest.

Example 4.20: Use the laws of probability to solve the "two urns" problem, Example 4.6.

Solution: Define the event of interest as:
Event A: ball drawn from urn $\#2$ is white.

Then

$$A = (B + C),$$

where:

B: draw a white ball from urn $\#1$ and a white ball from urn $\#2$,
C: draw a black ball from urn $\#1$ and a white ball from urn $\#2$.

Note that B and C were chosen to be mutually exclusive and that both are intersections. Thus,

$$B = B_1 A$$

and

$$C = C_1 A,$$

where:

B_1: draw a white ball from urn $\#1$,
C_1: draw a black ball from urn $\#1$.

Then

$$P(A) = P(B + C)$$
$$= P(B) + P(C) - P(BC).$$

Since B and C are mutually exclusive, $P(BC) = 0$. Then

$$P(A) = P(B) + P(C)$$
$$= P(B_1 A) + P(C_1 A).$$

Applying the Multiplicative Law,

$$P(B_1 A) = P(B_1)P(A/B_1)$$
$$= (2/3)(1)$$
$$= 2/3,$$
$$P(C_1 A) = P(C_1)P(A/C_1)$$
$$= (1/3)(1/2)$$
$$= 1/6.$$

Substituting,

$$P(A) = P(B_1 A) + P(C_1 A)$$
$$= 2/3 + 1/6$$
$$= 5/6.$$

4.8 Calculating the Probability of an Event: Event-Composition Approach

The steps for calculating the probability of an event using the event-composition approach are as follows:

(1) Define the experiment.
(2) Clearly visualize the nature of the sample points.   Identify a few to clarify your thinking.
(3) Write an equation expressing the event of interest, say A, as a composition of two or more events using either or both of the two forms of composition (unions and intersections).   Note that this equates point sets.   Make certain that the event implied by the composition and event A represent the same set of sample points.
(4) Apply the Additive and Multiplicative Laws of Probability to step (3) and find $P(A)$.

Step (3) is the most difficult because one can form many compositions that will be equivalent to event A.   The trick is to form a composition in which all the probabilities appearing in step (4) will be known.   Thus, one must visualize the results of step (4) for any composition and select the one for which the component probabilities are known.

The event-composition approach to the calculation of the probability of an event is often more powerful than the method of Section 4.4 because it avoids the necessity of actually listing the sample points in S and therefore can be used when the number of sample points is very large.   However, it is less direct and requires considerably more creative ability.

4.9   Random Variables

Observations generated by an experiment fall into one of two categories, quantitative or qualitative. For example, the daily production in a manufacturing plant would be a quantitative or numerically measurable observation, while weather descriptions, such as rainy, cloudy, sunny, would be qualitative. Statisticians are concerned with both quantitative and qualitative data although the former are perhaps more common.

In some instances it is possible to convert qualitative data to quantitative by assigning a numerical value to each category to form a scale. Industrial production is often scaled according to first grade, second grade, etc. Cigarette tobaccos are graded and foods ranked according to preference by persons employed as taste testers.

In this text we will be primarily concerned with quantitative observations such as the grade-point data discussed in Chapter 3 (Example 3.1). The events of interest associated with the experiment are the values that the data may take and are, therefore, *numerical events*. Suppose that the variable measured in the experiment is denoted by the symbol y. Recalling that an event is a collection of sample points, it would seem that certain sample points would be associated with one numerical event, say $y = 2$, another set associated with $y = 3$, etc., covering all possible values of y. Such is, in fact, the case. The variable, y, is called a *random variable* because the value of y observed for a particular experiment is a chance (or random) event associated with a probabilistic model, the sample space.

Note that each sample point implies one and only one value of y, although many sample points may imply the same value of y. For example, consider the experiment which consists of tossing two coins. Suppose we are interested in $y =$ number of heads. The random variable, y, can take three values, $y = 0$, $y = 1$, or $y = 2$. The sample points for the experiment are listed below.

$$E_1: HH,$$
$$E_2: HT,$$
$$E_3: TH,$$
$$E_4: TT.$$

The numerical event $y = 0$ includes sample point E_4; $y = 1$ includes sample points E_2 and E_3; and $y = 2$ includes sample point E_1. Note that one and only one value of y corresponds to each sample point, but the converse is not true. Two sample points, E_2 and E_3, are associated with the same value of y. Two conclusions may be drawn from this example. We note that the relationship between the random variable, y, and the sample points satisfies the definition of a functional relation presented in Chapter 2. Choose any point in the sample space, S, and there corresponds one and only one value of y. Hence, we choose the following definition for a random variable.

> **Definition:** A random variable is a numerical valued function defined over a sample space.

We also note that the numerical events associated with the random variable, y, are mutually exclusive events. The outcome of a single experiment can result in one and only one value of y. At this point we have almost completed our probabilistic model, the theoretical frequency distribution for a population of numerical measurements discussed in Chapter 3.

It would seem appropriate to recapitulate. Recalling Chapter 3, populations are described by frequency distributions. Areas under the frequency distribution are associated with the fraction of measurements in the population falling in a particular interval or they may be interpreted as probabilities. The purpose of Chapter 4 was to construct a theoretical model for the frequency distribution, or *probability distribution* as it is called in probability theory, for the population. Preceding sections of this chapter provide both the model and the machinery for achieving this result. To complete the picture, we need to calculate the probabilities associated with each value of y. These probabilities, presented in the form of a table or a formula, are called the *probability distribution* for the random variable, y. In reality, the probability distribution is the theoretical frequency distribution for the population. Random variables and probability distributions form the topic of Chapter 5.

4.10 Summary

The theories of both probability and statistics are concerned with samples drawn from populations. Probability assumes the population known and calculates the probability of observing a particular sample. Statistics assumes the sample to be known and, with the aid of probability, attempts to describe the frequency distribution of the population which is unknown. Chapter 4 is directed toward the construction of a model, the sample space, for the frequency distribution of a population of observations. The theoretical frequencies, representing probabilities of events, can be obtained by one of two methods:

(1) the summation of the probabilities of the sample points in the event of interest;

(2) the joint use of event composition (compound events) and the laws of probability.

EXERCISES

1. An experiment involves tossing a single die. Specify the sample points in the events:

A: Observe a 4.
B: Observe an even number.
C: Observe a number less than three.
D: Observe both A and B.
E: Observe either A or B or both.
F: Observe both A and C.

2. Two LSD tablets are accidentally placed in a box containing two aspirin tablets. The four tablets are identical in appearance. One tablet is selected at random from the box and is swallowed by patient A. A tablet is then selected at random from the three remaining tablets and is swallowed by patient B. Define the following events as specific collections of sample points:

(a) The sample space S.
(b) The event A that patient A obtained an LSD tablet.
(c) The event B that exactly one of the two patients obtained an LSD tablet.
(d) The event C that neither patient obtained an LSD tablet.

3. A popular test to control the quality of brand-name food products is obtained by presenting three specimens identical in appearance to each member of a panel of tasters. In each case, two of the specimens are from batches of stock known to possess the desired taste, while the third specimen is from the latest batch. Each panelist is told to select the specimen that is different from the other two. Suppose there are four tasters (designated T_1, T_2, T_3, and T_4) on the panel. Define the following events as specific collections of sample points:

(a) The sample space S.
(b) The event A that T_1, T_2, and T_3 are each " successful " in identifying the specimen from the latest batch.
(c) The event B that exactly three of the four tasters are successful.
(d) The event C that at least three of the four tasters are successful.

4. Refer to Exercise 1 and calculate the probabilities of the events D, E, and F by summing the probabilities of the appropriate sample points.

5. Two dice are tossed. Let A be the event that the first die shows an odd number and let B be the event that the second die shows a number greater than 2. Find $P(A)$ and $P(B)$. (Solve by listing the sample points.) Find the

probability that both A and B will occur. Find the probability that either A or B or both occur.

6. A die is tossed two times; what is the probability that the sum of the numbers observed will be greater than 9?

7. If three coins are tossed, what is the probability of getting exactly two heads? At least two heads?

8. Suppose that two of the six spark plugs on a six-cylinder automobile engine require replacement. If the mechanic removes two plugs at random, what is the probability that he will select the two defective plugs? At least one of the two defective plugs?

9. A pair of dice is thrown. What is the probability of getting a 2? A 7?

10. Two seeds are chosen from a packet containing seven seeds, two that will produce blue flowers, three that will produce white, and two that will produce red. What is the probability that both seeds produce flowers of the same color? (Solve by listing the sample points.)

11. Two dice are tossed. Use the mn rule to count the total number of sample points in the sample space, S.

12. Three coins are tossed. Use the mn rule to count the total number of sample points in S.

13. Refer to the experiment in Exercise 25 below, and use the mn rule to count the number of points in S.

14. How many different telephone numbers of five digits can be formed if the first digit must be a 3 or a 4?

15. Prove that $C_r^n = C_{n-r}^n$.

16. Use combinatorial methods to count the number of sample points in the sample space defined for Exercise 10. Solve Exercise 10 by using combinatorial methods.

17. A piece of equipment can be assembled in three operations, which may be arranged in any sequence.

   (a) Give the total number of ways that the equipment can be assembled.
   (b) Comparative tests are to be conducted to determine the best assembly procedure. If each assembly procedure is to be tested and compared with every other procedure exactly once, how many tests must be conducted?

18. Use combinatorial methods to count the number of sample points in the sample space for the experiment described in Exercise 8. Solve Exercise 8 by using combinatorial methods.

19. A chemist wishes to observe the effect of temperature, pressure, and the amount of catalyst on the yield of a particular chemical in a chemical

reaction. If the experimenter chooses to use two levels of temperature, three of pressure, and two of catalyst, how many experiments must be conducted in order to run each temperature-pressure-catalyst combination exactly once?

20. How many four-digit numbers can be formed from the digits 5, 6, 7, 8, 9 if each digit can be used only once? If the digits may be repeated?

21. How many ways can the letters in the word "charm" be arranged? In the word "church"?

22. If there are ten players on a basketball squad, how many different five-man teams can be organized if each player can play any position?

23. An airline has six flights from New York to California and seven flights from California to Hawaii per day. How many different flight arrangements can the airline offer from New York to Hawaii?

24. A man is in the process of buying a new car. He has a choice of 3 engine makes, 7 body styles, and 14 colors. How many different cars does he have to choose from?

25. Toss a die and a coin. If event A is the occurrence of a head and an even number and event B is the occurrence of a head and a 1, find $P(A)$, $P(B)$, $P(AB)$, and $P(A + B)$. (Solve by listing the sample points.)

26. Refer to Exercise 5. Let C be the event that the sum of the numbers appearing on the dice is even. Find $P(C), P(AC), P(BC), P(A + C), P(B + C)$ $P(ABC)$, and $P(A + B + C)$.

27. Five cards are drawn from an ordinary 52-card bridge deck. Given two events A and B as follows:

A: All five cards are spades.
B: The five cards include an Ace, King, Queen, Jack, and Ten, all of the *same* suit.

(a) Define the event AB
(b) Define the event $A + B$
(c) Give the probability of the event A
(d) Give the probability of the event B
(e) Give the probability of the event AB
(f) Give the probability of the event $(A + B)$

(Solve by summing probabilities of the sample points.)

28. A supermarket is having a sale of unlabeled cans. Included in the sale are 200 cans of corn, 300 cans of beets, and 500 cans of peaches. What is the probability that the first housewife will get a can of vegetables? Of corn? Are these two events independent? Mutually exclusive? Given that she draws a can of vegetables, what is the probability that it will be corn?

29. Refer to Exercise 2. Find each of the following by summing probabilities of sample points. $P(A), P(B), P(AB), P(A + B), P(C), P(AC)$, and $P(A + C)$.

30. Refer to Exercise 3. Suppose that the latest batch does actually possess the desired taste so that the three specimens for each taster are identical. Use the Multiplicative Law of Probability to find the probabilities attached to the sample points. Find each of the following by summing probabilities of sample points. $P(A), P(B), P(AB), P(A + B), P(C), P(AC)$, and $P(A + C)$.

31. Refer to Exercise 1. Find $P(A/B)$, $P(A/C)$, and $P(B/C)$. Calculate the probabilities of the events AB, AC, BC, and $(A + B)$ using the Additive and Multiplicative Laws of Probability. Are A and B independent? Mutually exclusive? Are B and C independent? Mutually exclusive?

32. Refer to Exercise 2. Answer the same questions as those given in Exercise 31.

33. Refer to Exercise 3. Answer the same questions as those given in Exercise 31.

34. Suppose that independent events A and B have nonzero probabilities. Show that A and B cannot be mutually exclusive.

35. Refer to Exercise 5 and find $P(A/B)$ and $P(B/A)$. Then calculate $P(AB)$, and $P(A + B)$ using the Laws of Probability.

36. Refer to Exercise 25 and calculate $P(AB)$ and $P(A + B)$ using the Laws of Probability.

37. A certain article is visually inspected successively by two different inspectors. When a defective article comes through, the probability that it gets by the first inspector is 0.1. Of those that do get past the first inspector, the second inspector will "miss" five out of ten. What fraction of the defectives will get by both inspectors?

38. Eight colleges join to form a basketball league. If each team is required to play every other team twice during the season, answer the following questions:

(a) What is the total number of league games that will be played?
(b) How many games will be played in which the contestants are two of the best three teams?
(c) For any given game, what is the probability that two of the best three teams will be playing?

39. Two ambulances are kept in readiness for emergencies. Due to the demand on their time as well as the chance of mechanical failure, the probability that a specific ambulance will be available when needed is 9/10. The availability of one ambulance is independent of the other.

(a) In the event of a catastrophe, what is the probability that both ambulances will be available?

(b) What is the probability that neither will be available?

(c) If an ambulance is needed in an emergency, what is the probability that it will be available?

40. The failure rate for a guided missile control system is 1 in 1000. Suppose a duplicate but completely independent control system is installed in each missile so that if the first fails the second can still take over. The reliability of a missile is the probability it does not fail. What is the reliability of the modified missile?

41. Consider the following fictitious problem. Suppose that it is known that at a particular supermarket, the probability of waiting five minutes or longer for checkout at the cashier's counter is 1/6. On a given day, a man and his wife decide to shop individually at the market, each checking out separately at different cashier counters. If they both reach cashier counters at the same time, answer the following questions:

(a) What is the probability that the man will wait less than five minutes for checkout?

(b) What is the probability that both the man and his wife will be checked out in less than five minutes? Assume that the checkout times for the two are independent events.

(c) What is the probability that one or the other, or both, will wait five minutes or more?

42. A basketball player hits on 60% of his shots from the floor. What is the probability that he makes exactly two of his next three shots?

43. A quality control plan calls for accepting a large lot of crankshaft bearings if a sample of seven is drawn and none is defective. What is the probability of accepting the lot if none in the lot is defective? If 1/10 are defective? If 1/2 are defective?

44. How many ways may a student choose two physics courses from six being given at different times?

45. A rat in a maze may go left, right, or straight ahead as he comes to each of four intersections in the maze. What is the probability that the rat correctly threads the maze on his first try if there is only one correct path?

46. The Senate has decided to form three committees to investigate price fixing in a particular industry. If there are 84 Senators present at the time, how many ways can three committees of sizes 17, 19, and 27 be formed if no Senator is asked to serve on more than one committee?

47. A monkey is given twelve blocks—three shaped like squares, three like rectangles, three like triangles, and three like circles. If he draws three of each kind in order—say, three triangles, then three squares, etc.—would you suspect that the monkey associates identically shaped figures? Calculate the probability of this event.

48. Refer to Exercise 27. Find $P(B/A)$. Then calculate $P(AB)$ and $P(A + B)$ using the Laws of Probability.

49. An individual is selected at random from a community in which 1% are afflicted with tuberculosis. Let T be the event that this individual has tuberculosis. An X-ray examination is not perfectly reliable. In fact, if E is the event that an individual's X-ray examination indicates the presence of tuberculosis, then $P[E \mid T] = .90$ and $P[E \mid \bar{T}] = .01$. What is the probability of T given the occurrence of E? Hint: $E = ET + E\bar{T}$.

50. An employer plans to interview ten men for possible employment. Two people are to be hired. Five of the men are affiliated with fraternities and five are not.

   (a) In how many ways could the employer select two men, disregarding fraternal affiliations?
   (b) In how many ways could he select two fraternity men?
   (c) Assuming that the employer has no preference regarding fraternal affiliations and that the men have equal qualifications, what is the probability that two fraternity men will be hired?

51. An accident victim will die unless he receives in the next ten minutes an amount of type A Rh-positive blood which can be supplied by a single donor. It requires two minutes to "type" a prospective donor's blood and two minutes to complete the transfer of blood. A large number of untyped donors are available and 40% of them have type A Rh-positive blood. What is the probability that the accident victim will be saved if there is only one blood-typing kit available?

52. Each of two packages of six flashlight batteries contain exactly two inoperable batteries. If two batteries are selected from each package, what is the probability that all four batteries will function?

53. Refer to Exercise 52. Suppose that two batteries were randomly selected from package #1 and mixed with those in package #2. Then, two were randomly drawn from the eight in package #2 What is the probability that both will function?

54. An assembler of electric fans uses motors from two sources. Company A supplies 90% of the motors and Company B supplies the other 10% of the motors. Suppose it is known that 5% of the motors supplied by Company A are defective while 3% of the motors supplied by Company B are defective. An assembled fan is found to have a defective motor. What is the probability that this motor was supplied by Company B?

55. How many times should a coin be tossed in order that the probability of observing at least one head be equal to or greater than .9?

56. An oil prospector will drill a succession of holes in a given area to find a productive well. The probability that he is successful on a given trial is .2.

(a) What is the probability that the third hole drilled is the first which locates a productive well?

(b) If his total resources allow the drilling of no more than three holes, what is the probability that he locates a productive well?

57. Suppose that two defective refrigerators have been included in a shipment of six refrigerators. The buyer begins to test the six refrigerators one at a time.

(a) What is the probability that the last defective refrigerator is found on the fourth test?

(b) What is the probability that no more than four refrigerators need be tested before both of the defective refrigerators are located?

(c) Given that one of the two defective refrigerators has been located in the first two tests, what is the probability that the remaining refrigerator is found in the third or fourth test?

REFERENCES

Cramer, H., *The Elements of Probability Theory and Some of Its Applications.* New York: John Wiley & Sons, Inc., 1955. Stockholm: Almqvist and Wiksell, 1954.

Feller, W., *An Introduction to Probability Theory and Its Applications*, Vol. 1. 2nd ed. New York: John Wiley & Sons, Inc., 1960.

Munroe, M. E., *Theory of Probability.* New York: McGraw-Hill Book Co., Inc., 1951.

5

RANDOM VARIABLES
AND PROBABILITY
DISTRIBUTIONS

5.1   In Retrospect

As we enter Chapter 5 the reader may experience a difficulty familiar to most beginning students.   The broad picture of statistics, its objective and how it works, becomes lost in a maze of detail.   Unfortunately, because of the nature of the subject, the sketch developed in introductory texts is completed only at the end of the book.   The student possesses an ever-growing fragment of the picture as he progresses from chapter to chapter, but he does not have the meaningful whole until the end.   We would attempt to alleviate this problem in two ways.   First, we suggest that the student construct the complete picture for one or two examples for ready reference as we proceed through the text.   Visualize an experiment—for instance, counting the number of insects on a particular type of leaf.   Visualize a repetition of the experiment and hence the generation of the sample.   Obviously, the sample has been drawn for a purpose—to obtain information concerning a larger body of measurements, the population of interest to the experimenter.   Specify a population parameter of interest, for example, the average number of insects per leaf, μ, and then estimate or make a decision concerning its value.   How good is the estimate or decision? The response to this question concludes the picture but unfortunately is not easily obtained at this stage. As a second example the reader might refer to the die-throwing problem described in Section 4.1. Although simple and impractical, the example gives a clear picture of the relation between probability and statistics and how probability is used to make an inference concerning the population of die-throws. Equipped with these examples, the student will more readily relate various subject areas to each other and to the whole.

Second, as we proceed through the text we will attempt to give a reason for the study of each subject area and to refocus the student's attention on an overall picture of statistics, much as we are doing in this section. Some may view such repetition as wasteful but we think it not only desirable but, for most readers, essential. Begging the student's indulgence, we will proceed to do just that.

5.2   Random Variables

Recall that an experiment is the process of collecting a measurement or observation. Most experiments of interest yield a numerical measurement which varies from sample point to sample point and hence is called a random variable. Restating the definition presented in Section 4.9, a random variable is a numerical valued function defined over a sample space. The daily closing price of an industrial stock is a *numerical event*. Observing the number of defects on a piece of new furniture or recording the grade-point average of a particular student are other examples of experiments yielding numerical events. The population associated with the experiment results when the experiment is repeated a number of times and a relatively large body of data is obtained. As previously noted, we never actually measure each member of the population but we can certainly conceive of doing so. In lieu of this, we wish to obtain a small set of these measurements, called the sample, and use the information in the sample to describe the population.

We have stated that a measurement obtained from an experiment results in a specific value of the random variable of interest and represents a measurement drawn from a population. How can a single measurement or a larger sample of, say, n measurements be used to make inferences about the population of interest? With the die-tossing example, Section 4.1, firmly in mind, *we would suggest that we calculate the probability of the observed numerical event—the sample—for a large set of possible populations and choose the one which gives the highest probability of observing the sample.*

The author would like to think that the method of inference described above appears reasonable and intuitively appealing to the reader. Note that it is not claimed to be the best, however "best" might be defined. We only suggest that it is intuitively reasonable. (In defense of the procedure, we might add that it is the basis for one of the more important methods for the statistical estimation of the parameters of a population and can be shown to provide "good" inferences in many situations.) For those who fail to grasp the argument, we defer further discussion of inference until Chapter 6. *At this point it is sufficient to note that the procedure requires a knowledge of the probability associated with each value of the random variable.* In other words, we require the *probability distribution* for the random variable which represents the theoretical frequency histogram for the population of numerical measurements. The theory of probability presented in Chapter 4 provides the mechanism for calculating these probabilities for some random variables.

5.3 A Classification of Random Variables

The observant student may have noticed a flaw in the preceding discussion, a flaw which he may or may not have resolved to his satisfaction. What is the sample space associated with the measurement of daily rainfall? Observing the rainfall on a specific day constitutes an experiment which results in a numerical measurement. If a one-foot ruler were used, the observed inches of rainfall would correspond to some point on the ruler, which, in turn, might be viewed as a point on a line. Theoretically, with measuring equipment possessing perfect accuracy, we could associate each measurement with one of an infinitely large number of points lying on the ruler, that is, on a line interval. The mathematician would prefer not to use the word "infinite" to describe the number points but we will do so, keeping in mind that no such number exists and that we simply imply that the number is so large as to exceed all bounds. Thus, to answer our question, we would state that the sample space for the rainfall measurement consists of the infinitely large set of points corresponding to the points on a line interval.

Let us now proceed to assign probability to each point in the sample space. Can we apportion probability to an infinite number of points and, at the same time, satisfy the requirement that the probabilities of the sample points sum to one? Oddly enough, the answer is yes, but only when the infinite number of points can be counted. An example of this situation will be given in Section 5.4. In all other cases, the answer is no.

The reader will quickly verify the impossibility of identifying and counting the infinite number of points associated with a line interval.

Without further discussion, let us make a distinction between sample spaces in which the number of points is finite or, in any case, is countable, and those consisting of an infinite number of points associated with points on a line interval.   Random variables defined over a countable infinity of points are called *discrete random variables*.   Those defined over and assuming the infinitely large number of values associated with the points on a line interval are called *continuous random variables*.   We will give examples of each type in succeeding sections.   At this point it is sufficient to emphasize the reason for the classification.   Probabilities can be assigned to the sample space associated with discrete random variables in such a way that the probabilities sum to one.   This is impossible with continuous random variables.   The end result is that we must develop a new and different probabilistic model for continuous random variables.

5.4   Discrete Random Variables and Their Probability Distributions

A discrete random variable is easily identified by examining the number and nature of the values which it may assume.   If the variable may assume only a *finite* or a *countable infinity* of values, it must be discrete.   In most practical problems, discrete random variables represent count (or enumeration) data such as the number of bacteria per cubic centimeter of water, the number of defective bolts in a sample of ten drawn from industrial production, the number of rural electrified homes in a township, or the number of malfunctions of an aircraft engine over a given period of time.

The number of defective bolts, y, in a sample of ten is a discrete random variable which may take a finite number (eleven) of values, namely, 0, 1, 2, 3, ... , 10.   The number of bacteria, y, in a cubic centimeter of water is undoubtedly limited but we would suppose that the limit would be extremely large.   Thus y may take values 0, 1, 2, 3, ... , n, where n may be a very large number.

The probability distribution for a discrete random variable is a formula, table, or graph providing the probability associated with each value of the random variable.   Since each value of the variable y is a numerical event, we may apply the methods of Chapter 4 to obtain the appropriate probabilities. It is interesting to note that the events cannot overlap because one and only one value of y is assigned to each sample point, and hence that the values of y represent mutually exclusive numerical events.   Summing $p(y)$ over all values of y would equal the sum of the probabilities of all

sample points and, hence, equal 1.   We may therefore state two requirements for a probability distribution,

(1) $0 \le p(y) \le 1$,

(2) $\sum\limits_{\text{all } y} p(y) = 1$.

Example 5.1: Consider an experiment which consists of tossing two
coins and let y equal the number of heads observed.   The sample points
for this experiment with their respective probabilities are given below.

SAMPLE POINT	COIN #1	COIN #2	$P(E_i)$	y
E_1	H	H	1/4	2
E_2	H	T	1/4	1
E_3	T	H	1/4	1
E_4	T	T	1/4	0

We would assign the value $y = 2$ to point E_1, $y = 1$ to point E_2, etc.
The probability of each value of y may be calculated by adding the
probabilities of the sample points in that numerical event.   The numerical event $y = 0$ contains one sample point, E_4 ; $y = 1$ contains two
sample points, E_2 and E_3 ; and $y = 2$ contains one point, E_1.   The
values of y with respective probabilities are given in Table 5.1.   Observe
that $\sum\limits_{y=0}^{2} p(y) = 1$.

Table 5.1.   The Probability Distribution for y,
y=Number of Heads

y	SAMPLE POINTS IN y	$p(y)$
0	E_4	1/4
1	E_2, E_3	1/2
2	E_1	1/4

$$\sum_{y=0}^{2} p(y) = 1$$

Noting that $p(y)$ is a function of y, according to the definition of a
functional relation given in Section 2.2, we might look for a simple
mathematical equation to replace Table 5.1.   While it is not particularly

obvious, a casual check will confirm that the equation

$$p(y) = \frac{C_y^2}{4}$$

provides exactly the same information as does Table 5.1, that is,

$$p(0) = \frac{C_0^2}{4} = 1/4,$$

$$p(1) = \frac{C_1^2}{4} = 1/2,$$

and

$$p(2) = \frac{C_2^2}{4} = 1/4.$$

The origin of our particular equation is not essential at this point.   Let us accept the fact that it *is* the probability distribution for y, as can be verified, and defer further discussion on this point until Chapter 6.

We have presented $p(y)$ in tabular form and as a formula.   We complete the discussion of this example by giving $p(y)$ in graphical form, that is, in the form of a frequency histogram discussed in Section 3.2.   The histogram for the random variable y would contain three classes corresponding to $y = 0$, $y = 1$, and $y = 2$.   Since $p(0) = 1/4$, the theoretical relative frequency for $y = 0$ is $1/4$; $p(1) = 1/2$ and hence the theoretical frequency for $y = 1$ is $1/2$, etc.   The histogram is given in Figure 5.1.

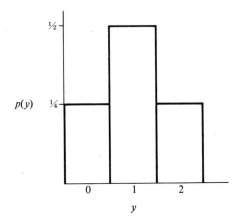

Figure 5.1.   Probability Histogram for p(y) in Example 5.1

If the reader were to draw a sample from this population—that is, if he were to throw two balanced coins, say $n = 100$ times, and each time record the number of heads observed, y, and then construct a histogram using the 100 measurements on y—he would find that the histogram for his sample would appear very similar to that for $p(y)$, Figure 5.1. If he were to repeat the experiment $n = 1000$ times, the similarity would be much more pronounced.

Example 5.2: Let y equal the number observed on the throw of a single die. The sample points are given in Table 5.2.

Table 5.2.   *Tossing a Die.   The Probability
Distribution for y*

SAMPLE POINT	NUMBER ON UPPER FACE	$P(E_i)$	y	$p(y)$
E_1	1	1/6	1	1/6
E_2	2	1/6	2	1/6
E_3	3	1/6	3	1/6
E_4	4	1/6	4	1/6
E_5	5	1/6	5	1/6
E_6	6	1/6	6	1/6

Obviously, $y = 1$ would be assigned to E_1, $y = 2$ to E_2, etc. Each value of y contains only one sample point and hence $p(y)$, the probability distribution for y, may be written in the fifth column of Table 5.2. It is also easily observed that

$$p(y) = 1/6$$

gives the probability distribution as a formula. The corresponding histogram is given in Figure 5.2.

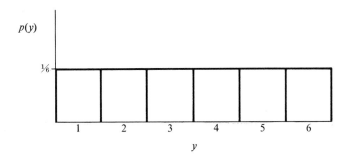

Figure 5.2.   *Probability Histogram for $p(y) = 1/6$
in Example 5.2*

Example 5.3: As a final example, we will consider a random variable which may assume a countable infinity of values. The experiment consists of tossing a coin until the first head appears. Let y equal the number of tosses. The sample points, infinite in number, are given below. Let the symbol *TTTH* represent the results of the first four tosses proceeding from left to right with H representing a head and T a tail.

$$
\begin{aligned}
E_1 &: \quad H \\
E_2 &: \quad TH \\
E_3 &: \quad TTH \\
E_4 &: \quad TTTH \\
E_5 &: \quad TTTTH \\
&\;\;\vdots \qquad \vdots \\
&\text{etc.} \quad \text{etc.}
\end{aligned}
$$

It is obvious that E_{65} would be the sample point associated with the event that each of the first 64 tosses resulted in a tail and the 65th resulted in a head. Conceivably, the experiment might never end. Let us now calculate the probability of each sample point and assign values of y to each of these points. The probability of E_1, a head on the first toss, is $1/2$. The probability of E_2, a tail and then a head, is an intersection of two independent events and can be obtained using the Multiplicative Law of Probability. Hence, $P(E_2) = (1/2)(1/2)$. Likewise, $P(E_3) = (1/2)(1/2)(1/2) = (1/2)^3$. It would seem obvious at this point that $P(E_{50}) = (1/2)^{50}$. The appropriate probability distribution would be given in the fourth column of Table 5.3, or by the equation $p(y) = (1/2)^y$. The frequency histogram is omitted.

Table 5.3. Tossing a Coin until the First Head
Appears. $y = $ Number of Tosses

SAMPLE POINT	$P(E_i)$	y	$p(y)$
E_1	1/2	1	1/2
E_2	1/4	2	1/4
E_3	1/8	3	1/8
E_4	1/16	4	1/16
E_5	1/32	5	1/32
$\vdots$	$\vdots$	$\vdots$	$\vdots$
etc.			

Will $p(y)$ satisfy the second requirement of a probability distribution; that is, will $\sum\limits_{y=1}^{\infty} p(y) = 1$?

Summing, we obtain

$$\sum_{y=1}^{\infty} p(y) = p(1) + p(2) + p(3) + \cdots$$

$$= 1/2 + 1/4 + 1/8 + \cdots.$$

The reader familiar with high school algebra will recognize this as the sum of an infinite geometric progression with common ratio equal to 1/2. A college algebra book or mathematical handbook will verify that this sum is equal to (or, correctly, approaches as a limit) one.   Thus we observe a sample space containing an infinite number of sample points, each receiving a small amount of probability, and the sum of the probabilities over the infinite number of points is equal to 1.

5.5 Continuous Random Variables

The word continuous, an adjective, means proceeding without interruption. It, in itself, provides the key for identifying continuous random variables.   Look for a measurement with a set of values which form points on a line with no interruptions or intervening spaces between them.   Heights, weights, strengths and measurements of student aptitude are examples of continuous random variables.   Unfortunately, measuring equipment and methods are such that we rarely measure the exact value of the variable.   The grade-point averages, Table 3.1, presumably a measure of student achievement, are accurate to the nearest tenth.   The length of life of a television tube is measured to the nearest hour or minute depending upon the accuracy of the measuring equipment.   Nevertheless, we would regard both as examples of continuous random variables.   Recall that we cannot assign probabilities to the sample points associated with a continuous random variable and that a completely different population model is required.   We invite the reader to refocus his attention on the discussion of the relative frequency histogram, Section 3.2, and specifically to the histogram for the thirty student grade-point averages, Figure 3.2.   If more and more measurements were obtained, we might reduce the width of the class interval.   The outline of the histogram would change slightly, for the most part becoming less and less irregular.   When the number of measurements becomes very large and the intervals very small, the relative frequency would appear, for all practical purposes, as a smooth curve.   (See Figure 5.3.)

The relative frequency associated with a particular class in the population *is* the fraction of measurements in the population falling in that interval and, also, is the probability of drawing a measurement in that class.

If the total area under the relative frequency histogram were adjusted to equal 1, then areas under the frequency curve would correspond to probabilities.   Indeed, this was the basis for the application of the Empirical Rule in Chapter 3.

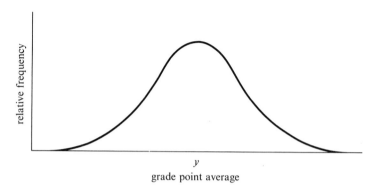

relative frequency

y
grade point average

*Figure 5.3.   The Relative Frequency Histogram for
a Population*

Let us now construct a model for the probability distribution for a continuous random variable.   Assume that the random variable, y, may take values on a real line as in Figure 5.3.   We will then distribute one unit of probability along the line much as a person might distribute a handful of sand, each measurement in the population corresponding to a single grain.   The probability, grains of sand or measurements, will pile up in certain places, and the result will be the probability distribution as in Figure 5.4.   The depth or density of probability, which varies with y, may be represented by a mathematical equation $f(y)$, called the probability distribution (or the probability density function) for the random variable y.   The function, $f(y)$, represented graphically in Figure 5.4, provides a mathematical model for the population relative frequency histogram which exists in reality.   The total area under the curve, $f(y)$, is equal to 1 and the area lying above a given interval will equal the probability that y will fall in that interval.   Thus, the probability that $a < y < b$ (a is less than y and y is less than b) is equal to the shaded area under the density function between the two points a and b.

Two puzzling questions remain.   How do we choose the model, that is, the probability distribution, $f(y)$, appropriate for a given physical situation?   And then, how can we calculate the areas under the curve corresponding to a given interval?   The first question is the more difficult because the answer will depend upon the type of measurement involved.

To grasp the reasoning better, let us consider the model for the discrete random variable. Using *good judgment*, we assigned realistic probabilities to the sample points associated with the experiment and then, applying the techniques of Chapter 4, derived the probability distribution for the

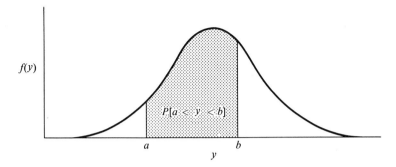

Figure 5.4.   The Probability Distribution, $f(y)$

random variable of interest. A similar approach is available for some continuous random variables but it is, unfortunately, beyond the scope of this course. The important thing to note, however, is that good judgment was required in assigning the probabilities to the sample points and that, although inexact, the probabilities were sufficiently accurate for practical purposes. Thus they provided a model for reality. Similarly, for continuous random variables, we utilize all available information and then use our best judgment in choosing the model, $f(y)$. In some cases, the approximate distribution may be derived using the theory of mathematical statistics. In others, we may rely on the frequency histograms for samples drawn from the population or histograms for data drawn from similar populations. The form of the sample histogram will often suggest a reasonable choice for $f(y)$.

Once the model, $f(y)$, has been chosen, we may calculate areas under the curve by using the integral calculus or by applying rectangular approximations, or, as a last resort, we could make an approximation of the area by visual inspection. We will leave this problem to the mathematician. The areas associated with most useful probability distributions have been calculated and appear in tabular form. (See Appendix II.)

We conclude with a comment to the "doubting Thomas" concerned because of the lack of agreement between $f(y)$ and the true relative frequency curve for the population. Can useful results be obtained from an inaccurate population model? We need only look to the physicist, the chemist, and the engineer. The equations, formulae, and various numerical expressions used in all of the sciences are simply mathematical models which, fortunately, provide good approximations to reality. The engineer uses his equations to determine the size and location of members in a bridge or an airplane wing and is concerned only that the resulting structure perform the task for which it was designed. Similarly, in statistics the attainment of the end result is the criterion by which we measure the worth of a statistical technique. Does the technique provide good inferences, that is, predictions or decisions, concerning the population from which the sample was drawn? Many statistical techniques possess this desirable property, a fact which can be shown experimentally and confirmed by the many extremely useful applications of statistics in industry and in the physical and social sciences.

5.6 Mathematical Expectation

The probability distribution, described in Sections 5.4 and 5.5, provides a model for the theoretical frequency distribution of a random variable and hence must possess a mean, variance, standard deviation, and other descriptive measures associated with the theoretical population which it represents. Recalling that both the mean and variance are averages (Sections 3.4 and 3.5), we will confine our attention to the problem of calculating the average value of a random variable defined over a theoretical population. This average is called the *expected value* of the random variable.

The method for calculating the population mean or expected value of a random variable can be more easily understood by considering an example. Let y equal the number of heads observed in the toss of two coins. For convenience, we give $p(y)$ below.

y	$p(y)$
0	1/4
1	1/2
2	1/4

Let us suppose that the experiment is repeated a large number of times, say $n = 4{,}000{,}000$ times. Intuitively, we would expect to observe approximately one million zeros, two million ones, and one million twos.

Then the average value of y would equal

$$\frac{\text{sum of measurements}}{n} = \frac{1,000,000(0) + 2,000,000(1) + 1,000,000(2)}{4,000,000}$$

$$= \frac{1,000,000(0)}{4,000,000} + \frac{2,000,000(1)}{4,000,000} + \frac{1,000,000(2)}{4,000,000}$$

$$= (1/4)(0) + (1/2)(1) + (1/4)(2).$$

Note that the first term in this sum is equal to $(0)p(0)$, the second is equal to $(1)p(1)$, and the third is equal to $(2)p(2)$.   The average value of y is then equal to

$$\sum_{y=0}^{2} yp(y) = 1.$$

The reader will observe that this result was not an accident and that it would be intuitively reasonable to define the expected value of y for a discrete random variable as follows.

Definition: Let y be a discrete random variable with probability distribution $p(y)$ and let $E(y)$ represent the expected value of y.   Then

$$E(y) = \sum_{y} yp(y),$$

where the elements are summed over all values of the random variable y.

The method for calculating the expected value of y for a continuous random variable is rather similar from an intuitive point of view, but, in practice, it involves the use of the calculus and is therefore beyond the scope of this text.

Example 5.4: Consider the random variable y representing the number observed on the toss of a single die.   The probability distribution for y is given in Example 5.2.   Then the expected value of y would be

$$E(y) = \sum_{y=1}^{6} yp(y) = (1)p(1) + (2)p(2) + \ldots + (6)p(6)$$

$$= (1)(1/6) + (2)(1/6) + \ldots + (6)(1/6)$$

$$= \frac{1}{6} \sum_{y=1}^{6} y = \frac{21}{6} = 3.5.$$

Example 5.5: Eight thousand tickets are to be sold at \$1.00 each in a lottery conducted to benefit the local fire company. The prize is a \$3000.00 automobile. If Ed Smith has purchased two tickets, what is his expected gain?

Solution: Smith's gain, y, may take one of two values. Either he will lose \$2.00 (that is, his gain will be $-$ \$2.00) or will win \$2998.00 with probabilities 7998/8000 and 2/8000, respectively. The probability distribution for the gain, y, is given below.

y	$p(y)$
-2.00	$\dfrac{7998}{8000}$
\$2998.00	$\dfrac{2}{8000}$

The expected gain will be

$$E(y) = \sum_y yp(y)$$

$$= (-2.00)\left(\frac{7998}{8000}\right) + (\$2998.00)\left(\frac{2}{8000}\right)$$

$$= -\$1.25.$$

Recall that the expected value of y is the average of the theoretical population which would result if the lottery were repeated an infinitely large number of times. If this were done, Smith's average or expected gain per lottery would be a loss of \$1.25.

Example 5.6: As a third example, consider the problem of determining the yearly premium for a \$1000.00 insurance policy covering an event which, over a long period of time, has occurred at the rate of two times in one hundred. Let y equal the yearly financial gain to the insurance company resulting from the sale of the policy and let C equal the unknown yearly premium. We will calculate the value of C such that the expected gain, $E(y)$, will equal zero. Then C is the premium required to break even. To this the company would add administrative costs and profit. The solution is, no doubt, apparent to the reader. We would suppose that the expected gain, $E(y)$, would depend upon C. Then, using the requirement that the expected gain must equal zero, we have

$$E(y) = \sum_y y p(y) = 0,$$

for which we could solve for C.

The first step in the solution is to determine the values which the gain, y, may take and then to determine $p(y)$. If the event does not occur during the year, the insurance company will gain the premium or $y = C$ dollars. If the event does occur, the gain will be negative—will be a loss—amounting to $y = -(1000 - C)$ dollars. The probabilities associated with these two values of y are 98/100 and 2/100, respectively. The probability distribution for the gain would be:

$y = $ gain	$p(y)$
C	$\dfrac{98}{100}$
$-(1000 - C)$	$\dfrac{2}{100}$

Setting the expected value of y equal to zero and solving for C, we have

$$E(y) = \sum_y y p(y)$$

$$= C\left(\frac{98}{100}\right) + [-(1000 - C)](2/100) = 0$$

or

$$\frac{98}{100}C + \frac{2}{100}C - 20 = 0$$

and

$$C = \$20.$$

Concluding, if the insurance company were to charge a yearly premium of $20, the average gain calculated for a large number of similar policies would equal zero. The actual premium would equal $20 plus administrative costs and profit.

We have learned how to find the mathematical expectation for a random variable. Let us now consider the problem of finding the mathematical average or expectation for some function of y, for instance, y^2, or the quantity $(y - \mu)^2$. The average value of $(y - \mu)^2$ is, by definition, the population variance, σ^2.

The rule for finding the expected value of a function of y, say $g(y)$, is readily obtained by considering the coin-tossing problem, Example 5.1, where y equals the number of heads observed in two tosses. Suppose that we wish to find the expected value of $g(y) = y^2$.

In accordance with the definition of a function, Section 2.2, only one value of the function corresponds to each value of y. Hence the quantity y^2 would represent a numerical event which varies over the sample space with only one value of y^2 being assigned to each sample point. Without proceeding further, it is reasonably clear that any function of a random variable, y, will itself be a random variable. The probability distribution for y, with associated values of y^2, is given below.

y	y^2	$p(y)$
0	0	1/4
1	1	1/2
2	4	1/4

Repeating the experiment a large number of times, say $n = 4,000,000$, we would expect approximately, 1,000,000 values of $y^2 = 0$, 2,000,000 values of $y^2 = 1$, and 1,000,000 values of $y^2 = 4$. The average value for y^2 would be

$$\frac{\text{sum of measurements}}{n} = \frac{1,000,000(0) + 2,000,000(1) + 1,000,000(4)}{4,000,000}$$

$$= (1/4)(0) + (1/2)(1) + (1/4)(4)$$

$$= \sum_{y=0}^{2} y^2 p(y).$$

The reader may obtain the expected value for other functions of y and other random variables using the technique employed above. The results will agree with the following definition.

Definition: Let y be a discrete random variable with probability distribution $p(y)$, and let $g(y)$ be a numerical valued function of y. Then the expected value of $g(y)$ is

$$E[g(y)] = \sum_{y} g(y)p(y).$$

We conclude with two examples.

Example 5.7: Find the variance, σ^2, for the population associated with Example 5.1, the tossing of two coins. The expected value of y, μ, was shown to equal one.

The variance is equal to the expected value of $(y - \mu)^2$ or

$$\sigma^2 = E[(y - \mu)^2] = \sum_y (y - \mu)^2 p(y)$$

$$= (0 - 1)^2 p(0) + (1 - 1)^2 p(1) + (2 - 1)^2 p(2)$$

$$= (1)(1/4) + 0(1/2) + 1(1/4)$$

$$= 1/2.$$

Example 5.8: Let y be a random variable with probability distribution, given by the following table.

y	$p(y)$
-1	1/8
0	1/4
1	3/8
2	1/4

Find the expected value of $(y^2 - 1)$.

Solution:

$$E(y^2 - 1) = \sum_y (y^2 - 1)p(y)$$

$$= [(-1)^2 - 1]p(-1) + [(0)^2 - 1]p(0)$$

$$+ [(1)^2 - 1]p(1) + [(2)^2 - 1]p(2)$$

$$= (0)(1/8) + (-1)(1/4) + (0)(3/8) + (3)(1/4)$$

$$= 1/2.$$

5.7 Summary

Random variables, representing numerical events defined over a sample space, may be classified as *discrete* or *continuous* random variables depending upon whether the number of sample points in the sample space is or is not countable. The theoretical population frequency distribution for the discrete random variable is called a probability distribution and may be derived using the technique of Chapter 4. The model for the frequency distribution for a continuous random variable is a mathematical function, $f(y)$, called a probability distribution or probability density function. This function, usually a smooth curve, is defined over a line interval and is chosen such that the total area under the curve is equal to one. The probabilities associated with a continuous random variable are given as areas under the probability distribution, $f(y)$.

A mathematical expectation is the average of a random variable calculated for the theoretical population defined by its probability distribution.

EXERCISES

1. Construct a probability histogram for the probability distribution derived in Example 5.3.

2. Toss three coins and let y equal the number of heads observed. Calculate the probability distribution for y. Construct a probability histogram for the distribution. Find the expected value and variance of y.

3. Suppose that a radio contains six transistors, two of which are defective. Three transistors are selected at random, removed from the radio, and inspected. Let y equal the number of defectives observed where $y = 0$, 1, or 2. Find the probability distribution for y. Express your results graphically as a probability histogram.

4. Let y be a random variable with probability distribution given by the following table:

y	$p(y)$
0	1/8
1	1/4
2	1/2
3	1/8

Find the expected value and variance of y. Construct a graph of the probability distribution.

5. Simulate the experiment described in Exercise 3 by marking six marbles, or coins, so that two represent defectives and four represent non-defectives. Place the marbles in a hat, mix, draw three, and record y, the number of "defectives observed." Replace the marbles and repeat the process until a total of $n = 100$ observations on y have been recorded. Construct a relative frequency histogram for this sample and compare it with the population probability distribution, Exercise 3.

6. Refer to Exercise 2. Using the probability histogram, find the fraction of the total population lying within two standard deviations of the mean. Compare with Tchebysheff's Theorem.

7. Refer to Exercise 3. Find μ, the expected value of y, for the theoretical population by using the probability distribution obtained in Exercise 3. Find the sample mean, $\bar{y}$ for the $n = 100$ measurements generated in Exercise 5. Does $\bar{y}$ provide a good estimate of μ?

8. Find the variance of y the number of dots observed on the throw of a single die. (Refer to Example 5.2). Use the probability histogram to compute the fraction of the population lying within two standard deviations of the mean.

9. Find the population variance, σ^2, for Exercise 3 and the sample variance, s^2, for Exercise 5. Compare.

10. Draw a sample of $n = 50$ measurements from the die-throw population of Example 5.2 by tossing a die fifty times and recording y after each toss. Calculate $\bar{y}$ and s^2 for the sample. Compare $\bar{y}$ with the expected value of y, Example 5.4, and s^2 with the variance of y obtained in Exercise 8. Do $\bar{y}$ and s^2 provide good estimates of μ and σ^2?

11. Using the probability distribution obtained in Exercise 3, find the fraction of the total population of measurements lying within two standard deviations of the mean. Compare with Tchebysheff's Theorem. Repeat for the sample in Exercise 5.

12. A personnel director wishes to select three out of five candidates interviewed. Although all five candidates appear to be equally desirable, there likely exists a " best " candidate, a second best, etc. Refer to the three, and unknown, best candidates as "successes" and let y equal the number of " successes " appearing in the personnel director's selection; that is, $y = 1, 2,$ or 3. Find the probability distribution for y. Construct a probability histogram for y. What is the probability that he selects at least two of the three best?

13. A heavy-equipment salesman can contact either one or two customers per day with probability 1/3 and 2/3, respectively. Each contact will result in either no sale or a $50,000 sale with probability 9/10 and 1/10, respectively. What is the expected value of his daily sales?

14. Refer to Exercise 12. Find the expected value and variance, μ and σ^2, for y.

15. A county containing a large number of rural homes is thought to have 60% insured against a fire. Four rural home owners are chosen at random from the entire population and y are found to be insured against a fire. Find the probability distribution for y. What is the probability that at least three of the four will be insured?

16. A fire detection device utilizes three temperature-sensitive cells acting independently of each other in such a manner that any one or more may actuate the alarm. Each cell possesses a probability of $p = .8$ of actuating the alarm when the temperature reaches 100 degrees or more. Let y equal the number of cells actuating the alarm when the temperature reaches 100 degrees. Find the probability distribution for y. Find the probability that the alarm will function when the temperature reaches 100 degrees.

17. Express the probability distribution, Exercise 3, as a formula. (The distribution is known to statisticians as a *hypergeometric* probability distribution.)

18. Find the expected value and variance for the random variable y defined in Exercise 16.

19. The Poisson probability distribution provides a good model for count data when y, the count, represents the number of "rare events" observed in a given unit of time, distance, area or volume. The number of bacteria per small volume of fluid and the number of traffic accidents at a given intersection during a given period of time possess, approximately, a Poisson probability distribution which is given by the formula

$$p(y) = \frac{\mu^y e^{-\mu}}{y!},$$

where $y = 0, 1, 2, 3, \ldots$; $e = 2.718 \ldots$; and μ is the population mean. If the average number of accidents over a specified section of highway is two per week, calculate the probability that no accidents will occur during a given week. (Use Table 2, Appendix II, to evaluate $e^{-\mu}$.)

20. Suppose that a random system of police patrol is devised so that a patrolman may visit a given location on his beat $y = 0, 1, 2, 3, \ldots$ times per half-hour period and that the system is arranged so that he visits each location on an average of once per time period. Assume that y possesses, approximately, a Poisson probability distribution. Calculate the probability that the patrolman will miss a given location during a half-hour period. What is the probability that he will visit it once? Twice? At least once?

21. A potential customer for a $20,000 fire insurance policy possesses a home in an area, which, according to experience, may sustain a total loss in a given year with probability of .001 and a 50% loss with probability .01. Ignoring all other partial losses, what premium should the insurance company charge for a yearly policy in order to break even?

22. The manufacturer of a low-calorie dairy drink wishes to compare the taste appeal of a new formula (formula B) with that of the standard formula (formula A). Each of four judges is given three glasses in random order, two containing formula A and the other containing formula B. Each judge is asked to state which glass he most enjoyed. Suppose that the two formulae

are equally attractive. Let y be the number of judges stating a preference for the new formula.

(a) Find the probability function for y.

(b) What is the probability that at least three of the four judges state a preference for the new formula?

(c) Find the expected value of y.

(d) Find the variance of y.

23. A fisherman has probability 1/3 of catching a fish before a given worm must be replaced. He never uses the same worm to catch more than one fish. Suppose he has three worms in his bait can. Let y be the number of fish he catches before running out of worms.

(a) Find the probability function for y.

(b) What is the probability that this fisherman catches more than one fish?

(c) What is the expected number of fish caught?

(d) What is the variance of the number of fish caught?

24. Continuing Exercise 23, we shall assume that if a fish is caught, it is (with probability 1/2) too small and must be released. If a fish is caught and it is not too small, imagine that it weighs one pound. Let w be the total weight of the fish actually kept.

(a) Find the probability function for w.

(b) What is the probability that the total weight of the fish retained exceeds one pound?

(c) What is the expected weight of the fish retained?

(d) Find the variance of w.

25. To test the willow-wand theory of water dowsing, each of ten men is asked to explore a given terrain and specify a single spot at which water can be found. Exactly five of these men will use the willow wand. Let y be the number out of the five willow-wand users who are successful in locating water. Suppose that exactly four men out of the ten are successful in locating water and that the willow-wand theory is a fraud.

(a) Find the probability function for y.

(b) Find the probability that at least three of the four successful men used the willow wand.

(c) What is the expected number of successful willow-wand users?

(d) Find the variance of y.

REFERENCES

Fraser, D. A. S., *Statistics: An Introduction.* New York: John Wiley & Sons, Inc., 1958. Chapters 3 and 4.

Freund, J. E., *Mathematical Statistics.* Englewood Cliffs, N.J.: Prentice-Hall, Inc., 1962. Chapters 3 and 4.

Mood, A. M., *Introduction to the Theory of Statistics.*   New York: McGraw-Hill Book Co., Inc., 1950.   Chapters 3 and 4.

Mosteller, F., R. E. K. Rourke, and G. B. Thomas, Jr., *Probability with Statistical Applications.*   Reading, Massachusetts: Addison-Wesley Publishing Co., Inc., 1961.   Chapter 5.

6

THE BINOMIAL
PROBABILITY
DISTRIBUTION

6.1 The Binomial Experiment

One of the most elementary, useful, and interesting discrete random variables is associated with the coin tossing experiment described in Examples 4.3, 4.5, and 5.1. In an abstract sense, numerous coin-tossing experiments of practical importance are conducted daily in the social sciences, physical sciences, and industry.

To illustrate, we might consider a sample survey conducted to predict voter preference in a political election. Interviewing a single voter bears a similarity, in many respects, to tossing a single coin because the voter's response may be in favor of our candidate—a "head"—or it may be opposition (or indicate indecision)—a "tail." In most cases, the fraction of voters favoring a particular candidate will not equal one-half but even this similarity to the coin-tossing experiment is satisfied in national presidential elections. History demonstrates that the fraction of the total vote favoring the winning presidential candidate in most national elections is very near one-half.

Similar polls are conducted in the social sciences, in industry, in education. The sociologist is interested in the fraction of rural homes that have been electrified; the cigarette manufacturer desires knowledge concerning the fraction of smokers who prefer his brand; the teacher is interested in the fraction of students who pass his course. Each person sampled is analogous to the toss of an unbalanced (since the probability of a "head" is usually not 1/2) coin.

Firing a projectile at a target is similar to a coin-tossing experiment if a "hit the target" and a "miss the target" are regarded as a head and a tail, respectively. A single missile will result in either a successful or unsuccessful launching. A new drug will prove either effective or non-effective when administered to a single patient, and a manufactured item selected from production will be either defective or non-defective. Although dissimilar in some respects, the experiments described above will often exhibit, to a reasonable degree of approximation, the characteristics of a *binomial experiment*.

> **Definition:** A binomial experiment is one which possesses the following properties:
>
> (1) The experiment consists of n identical trials.
> (2) Each trial results in one of two outcomes. For lack of a better nomenclature, we will call the one outcome a success, S, and the other a failure, F.
> (3) The probability of success on a single trial is equal to p and remains the same from trial to trial. The probability of a failure is equal to $(1 - p) = q$.
> (4) The trials are independent.
> (5) We are interested in y, the number of successes observed during the n trials.

Very few real-life situations will perfectly satisfy the requirements stated above but this is of little consequence as long as the lack of agreement is moderate and does not affect the end result. For instance, the probability of drawing a voter favoring a particular candidate in a political poll remains approximately constant from trial to trial as long as the population of voters is relatively large in comparison with the sample. If 50% of a population of one thousand voters prefer candidate A, then the probability of drawing an A on the first interview will be 1/2. The probability of an A on the second draw will equal 499/999 or 500/999, depending upon whether the first draw was favorable or unfavorable to A. Both numbers are near 1/2, for all practical purposes, and would continue to be for the third, fourth, and nth trial as long as n is not too large. On the other hand, if the number in the population is ten, and five favor candidate A, then the probability of A on the first trial is $1/2$; the probability of A on the second trial is $4/9$ or $5/9$ depending upon whether A was, or was not, drawn on the first trial. Thus, for small populations, the probability of A will vary appreciably from trial to trial and the resulting experiment will not be a binomial experiment.

6.2   The Binomial Theorem

In this section we digress from the main topic of discussion to refresh the reader's memory concerning binomials and the binomial theorem. A binomial, as defined in ordinary algebra, is an algebraic expression containing two terms. Thus, $(a + b)$, $(x - 3y)$, and $(4x^3 - 3a^2b)$ are examples of binomials. The binomial theorem concerns the power of a binomial, for example $(x + y)^n$, and in particular provides a simple formula for multiplying the binomial by itself n times.

The binomial theorem can be most easily seen by observing the pattern obtained in calculating $(x + y)^n$ for $n = 1, 2, 3,$ and 4. The reader may verify that

$$(x + y)^1 = x + y,$$
$$(x + y)^2 = x^2 + 2xy + y^2,$$
$$(x + y)^3 = x^3 + 3x^2y + 3xy^2 + y^3,$$
$$(x + y)^4 = x^4 + 4x^3y + 6x^2y^2 + 4xy^3 + y^4.$$

In each case, the expansion contains $n + 1$ terms; proceeding from left to right, we note that the exponent of x commences with n and is decreased by one as we move from term to term. At the same time, the exponent of y commences with zero and proceeds to n in the last term. The resultant pattern suggests the following formula, which is called the *binomial theorem*:

$$(x + y)^n = x^n + nx^{n-1}y + \frac{n(n - 1)}{2!} x^{n-2}y^2$$

$$+ \frac{n(n - 1)(n - 2)}{3!} x^{n-3}y^3 + \ldots + y^n,$$

a result which can be easily proved by mathematical induction.

The coefficient of a particular term in the expansion, say $x^{n-r}y^r$, would be

$$\frac{n(n - 1)(n - 2) \ldots (n - r + 1)}{r!}.$$

Multiplying numerator and denominator by $(n - r)!$, we obtain,

$$\frac{n(n - 1)(n - 2) \ldots (n - r + 1)(n - r)!}{r!(n - r)!} = \frac{n!}{r!(n - r)!} = C_r^n,$$

the number of combinations of n things taken r at a time studied in Chapter 4. Thus, the binomial theorem may be written

$$(x + y)^n = C_0^n x^n + C_1^n x^{n-1} y + C_2^n x^{n-2} y^2 + \ldots + C_n^n y^n,$$

where a general term will be of the form $C_r^n x^{n-r} y^r$. As an interesting sideline we might state that the formula may be derived directly by considering a typical term in the expansion of $(x + y)^n$ as a combination of x's and y's obtained from n identical factors of the type $(x + y)$.

For example, the coefficient of $x^2 y$ in the expansion of $(x + y)^3$ would equal $C_1^3 = 3!/1!2! = 3$, a result which the reader may quickly verify. Likewise, the coefficient of $x^2 y^2$ in the expansion of $(x + y)^4$ would equal $C_2^4 = 4!/2!2! = 6$.

Example 6.1: Expand $(x + y)^5$.

Solution:

$$(x + y)^5 = C_0^5 x^5 + C_1^5 x^4 y + C_2^5 x^3 y^2 + C_3^5 x^2 y^3 + C_4^5 xy^4 + C_5^5 y^5$$
$$= x^5 + 5x^4 y + 10x^3 y^2 + 10x^2 y^3 + 5xy^4 + y^5.$$

Example 6.2: Expand $(a - 3b)^3$.

Solution:

$$(a - 3b)^3 = [a + (-3b)]^3$$
$$= C_0^3 a^3 + C_1^3 a^2(-3b) + C_2^3 a(-3b)^2 + C_3^3(-3b)^3$$
$$= a^3 - 9a^2 b + 27ab^2 - 27b^3.$$

The usefulness of the binomial theorem as well as its relation to the binomial experiment will be readily apparent as we proceed to Section 6.3.

6.3 The Binomial Probability Distribution

Having defined the binomial experiment and suggested several practical applications, we now turn to a derivation of the probability distribution for the random variable, y, the number of successes observed in n trials. Rather than attempt a direct derivation, we will obtain $p(y)$ for experiments containing $n = 1$, 2, and 3 trials and leave the general formula to the reader's intuition.

For $n = 1$ trial, we have two sample points, E_1 representing a success, S, and E_2 representing a failure, F, with probabilities p and $q = (1 - p)$, respectively. The values $y = 1$ would be associated with E_1 and $y = 0$ with E_2. The resulting probability distribution for y is given in Table 6.1.

Table 6.1. $p(y)$ for a Binomial Experiment, $n = 1$

SAMPLE POINTS		$P(E_i)$	y		y	$p(y)$
E_1	S	p	1		0	q
E_2	F	q	0		1	p

$$\sum_{y=0}^{1} p(y) = q + p = 1$$

The probability distribution for an experiment consisting of $n = 2$ trials is derived in a similar manner and is presented in Table 6.2. The four sample points associated with the experiment are presented in the first column with the notation SF implying a success on the first trial and a failure on the second.

Table 6.2. $p(y)$ for a Binomial Experiment, $n = 2$

SAMPLE POINTS		$P(E_i)$	y		y	$p(y)$
E_1	SS	p^2	2		0	q^2
E_2	SF	pq	1		1	$2pq$
E_3	FS	qp	1		2	p^2
E_4	FF	q^2	0			

$$\sum_{y=0}^{2} p(y) = (q + p)^2 = (1)^2 = 1$$

The probabilities of the sample points are easily calculated because each point is an intersection of two independent events, namely, the outcomes of the first and second trials. Thus $P(E_i)$ can be obtained by applying the Multiplicative Law of Probability:

$$P(E_1) = P(SS) = P(S)P(S) = p^2,$$

$$P(E_2) = P(SF) = P(S)P(F) = pq,$$

$$P(E_3) = P(FS) = P(F)P(S) = qp,$$

$$P(E_4) = P(FF) = P(F)P(F) = q^2.$$

The value of y assigned to each sample point is given in the third column. The reader will note that the numerical event $y = 0$ contains sample point E_4, the event $y = 1$ contains sample points E_2 and E_3, and $y = 2$ contains sample point E_1. The probability distribution $p(y)$, presented to the right of Table 6.2, reveals a most interesting consequence; the probabilities, $p(y)$, are terms of the expansion $(q + p)^2$.

Summing, we obtain

$$\sum_{y=0}^{2} p(y) = q^2 + 2pq + p^2$$

$$= (q + p)^2 = 1.$$

The point which we wish to make is now quite clear; the probability distribution for the binomial experiment consisting of n trials is obtained by expanding $(q + p)^n$. The proof of this statement is omitted but may be obtained by using combinations to count the appropriate sample points or can be rather easily proved by mathematical induction, a task which we leave to the student of mathematics. Those more easily convinced may acquire further evidence of the truth of our statement by observing the derivation of the probability distribution for a binomial experiment consisting of $n = 3$ trials presented in Table 6.3.

Table 6.3. $p(y)$ for a Binomial Experiment, $n = 3$

	SAMPLE POINTS	$P(E_i)$	y		y	$p(y)$
E_1	SSS	p^3	3		0	q^3
E_2	SSF	p^2q	2		1	$3\,pq^2$
E_3	SFS	p^2q	2		2	$3\,p^2q$
E_4	SFF	pq^2	1		3	p^3
E_5	FSS	p^2q	2			
E_6	FSF	pq^2	1			
E_7	FFS	pq^2	1		$\sum_{y=0}^{3} p(y) = (q+p)^3 = 1$	
E_8	FFF	q^3	0			

Since the probability associated with a particular value of y is simply the term involving p to the power y in the expansion of $(q + p)^n$, we may write the probability distribution for the binomial experiment as

$$p(y) = C_y^n p^y q^{n-y},$$

where y may take values 0, 1, 2, 3, 4, ..., n.

Let us now consider a few examples.

Example 6.3: Over a long period of time it has been observed that a given rifleman can hit a target on a single trial with probability equal to .8. If he fires four shots at the target,

(a) What is the probability that he will hit the target exactly two times?

Solution: Assuming that the trials are independent and that p remains constant from trial to trial, $n = 4$, $p = .8$, and

$$p(y) = C_y^4(.8)^y(.2)^{4-y},$$

$$p(2) = C_2^4(.8)^2(.2)^{4-2}$$

$$= \frac{4!}{2!2!}(.64)(.04)$$

$$= .1536.$$

(b) What is the probability that he will hit the target at least two times?

Solution:

$$P(\text{at least two}) = p(2) + p(3) + p(4)$$

$$= 1 - p(0) - p(1)$$

$$= 1 - C_0^4(.8)^0(.2)^4 - C_1^4(.8)(.2)^3$$

$$= 1 - .0016 - .0256$$

$$= .9728.$$

(c) What is the probability he will hit the target exactly four times?

Solution:

$$p(4) = C_4^4(.8)^4(.2)^0$$

$$= \frac{4!}{4!0!}(.8)^4(1)$$

$$= .4096.$$

Note that these probabilities would be incorrect if the rifleman could observe the location of each hit on the target; in that case, the trials would be dependent and p would likely increase from trial to trial.

Example 6.4: Large lots of incoming product at a manufacturing plant are inspected for defectives by means of a sampling scheme. Ten items are to be examined and the lot rejected if two or more defectives are observed.   If a lot contains exactly 5% defectives, what is the probability that the lot will be accepted?   Rejected?

Solution: If y equals the number of defectives observed, then $n = 10$ and the probability of observing a defective on a single trial will be $p = .05$.   Then,

$$p(y) = C_y^{10}(.05)^y(.95)^{10-y}$$

and

$$p(\text{accept}) = p(0) + p(1) = C_0^{10}(.05)^0(.95)^{10} + C_1^{10}(.05)^1(.95)^9$$

$$= .914,$$

$$p(\text{reject}) = 1 - p(\text{accept})$$

$$= 1 - .914$$

$$= .086.$$

Example 6.5: A new serum was tested to determine its effectiveness in preventing the common cold.   Ten people were injected with the serum and observed for a period of one year.   Eight survived the winter without a cold.   Suppose it is known that when a serum is *not* used, the probability of surviving a winter without a cold is .5.   What is the probability of observing eight or more survivors, given that the serum is ineffective in increasing the bodily resistance to colds?

Solution: Assuming the vaccine is ineffective, the probability of surviving the winter without a cold is $p = .5$.   The probability distribution for y, the number of survivors, is

$$p(y) = C_y^{10}(.5)^y(.5)^{10-y} = C_y^{10}(.5)^{10},$$

$$p(8 \text{ or more}) = p(8) + p(9) + p(10)$$

$$= C_8^{10}(.5)^{10} + C_9^{10}(.5)^{10} + C_{10}^{10}(.5)^{10}$$

$$= .055.$$

Examples 6.3, 6.4, and 6.5 illustrate the use of the binomial probability distribution in calculating the probability associated with values of y, the number of successes in n trials defined for the binomial experiment. Thus we note that the probability distribution, $p(y) = C_y^n p^y q^{n-y}$, provides a simple formula for calculating the probabilities of numerical events, y, applicable to a broad class of experiments which occur in everyday life. This statement must be accompanied by a word of caution.   The important point, of course, is that each physical application must be carefully checked against the defining characteristics of the binomial experiment, Section 6.1, to determine whether the binomial experiment is a valid model for the application of interest.

The reader will note that Examples 6.3, 6.4, and 6.5 were problems in probability rather than statistics. The composition of the binomial population, characterized by p, the probability of a success on a single trial, was assumed known and we were interested in calculating the probability of certain numerical events. Let us now reverse the procedure; that is, let us assume that we possess a sample from the population and wish to make inferences concerning p. The physical settings for Examples 6.4 and 6.5 supply excellent practical situations in which the ultimate objective was statistical inference. We will consider these two problems in greater detail in the succeeding sections.

6.4   The Mean and Variance for the Binomial Variable

Having derived the theoretical frequency distribution for the population associated with the binomial random variable, y, it would seem desirable to find formulae for its expected value and variance. Specifically, we would like to describe this theoretical distribution utilizing the mean and variance (or standard deviation) as measures of central tendency and variation. We will have further use for these quantities in Chapter 7.

Our approach to the acquisition of formulae for μ and σ^2 will be similar to that employed in Section 6.3 for the determination of the probability distribution, $p(y)$. We will use the methods of Chapter 5 to obtain these expectations; that is, $E(y)$ and $E(y - \mu)^2$, for the simple cases $n = 1$, 2, and 3, and then give the formulae for the general case without proof. The interested reader may derive the formulae for the general case involving n trials by using the summation theorems of Chapter 2, some algebraic manipulation, and a bit of ingenuity.

The expected value of y for $n = 1$ and 2 can be derived using the probabilities given in Tables 6.1 and 6.2 along with the definition of an expectation presented in Section 5.6. Thus, for $n = 1$ we obtain

$$\mu = E(y) = \sum_{y=0}^{1} yp(y) = (0)(q) + (1)(p) = p.$$

For $n = 2$,

$$\mu = E(y) = \sum_{y=0}^{2} yp(y) = (0)(q^2) + (1)(2pq) + (2)(p^2)$$

$$= 2p(q + p) = 2p.$$

The reader using Table 6.3 can quickly show that $E(y)$ for $n = 3$ trials is equal to $3p$ and would surmise that this pattern would hold in general. Indeed, it can be shown that the expected value of y for a binomial experiment consisting of n trials is

$$E(y) = np.$$

Similarly, we may obtain the variance of y for $n = 1$ and 2 trials as follows. For $n = 1$,

$$\sigma^2 = E(y - \mu)^2 = \sum_{y=0}^{1} (y - \mu)^2 p(y) = (0 - p)^2(q) + (1 - p)^2(p)$$

$$= p^2 q + q^2 p = pq(q + p)$$

$$= pq.$$

For $n = 2$,

$$\sigma^2 = E(y - \mu)^2 = \sum_{y=0}^{2} (y - \mu)^2 p(y)$$

$$= (0 - 2p)^2(q^2) + (1 - 2p)^2(2pq) + (2 - 2p)^2(p^2)$$

$$= 4p^2 q^2 + (1 - 4p + 4p^2)(2pq) + 4(1 - p)^2 p^2.$$

Using the substitution $q = 1 - p$ and a bit of algebraic manipulation, we find that the above reduces to

$$\sigma^2 = 2pq.$$

The reader may verify that the variance of y for $n = 3$ trials is $3pq$. In general, for n trials it can be shown that the variance of y is

$$\sigma^2 = npq.$$

As we have previously mentioned, these formulae can now be employed to compute the mean and variance for the binomial variable, y. Thus we can say something concerning the center of the distribution as well as the variability of y.

6.5   Lot Acceptance Sampling for Defectives

A manufacturing plant may be regarded as an operation which transforms raw materials into a finished product, the raw materials entering the rear door of the plant and the product moving out the front. In order to operate efficiently, a manufacturer desires to minimize the amount of defective raw material received and, in the interest of quality, minimize the number of defective product shipped to his customers. To accomplish this objective, he will erect a "screen" at both doors in an attempt to prevent defectives from passing through.

To simplify our discussion, consider only the screening of incoming raw materials consisting of large lots (boxes) of items such as bolts, nails, and bearings. Diagrammatically, the screen would function in the manner indicated in Figure 6.1. The lots would proceed to the rear door of the plant, would be accepted if the fraction defective were small, and would be returned to the supplier if the fraction defective were large.

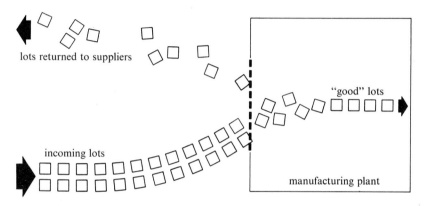

lots returned to suppliers

"good" lots

incoming lots

manufacturing plant

Figure 6.1.   Screening for Defectives

A screen could be constructed in a number of ways, the most obvious and seemingly perfect solution being a complete and careful inspection of each single item received. Unfortunately, the cost of total inspection is often enormous and hence economically unfeasible. A second disadvantage, not readily apparent, is that, even with complete inspection, defective items seem to slip through the screen. Humans become bored and lose perception when subjected to long hours of inspecting, particularly when the operation is conducted at high speed. Thus nondefective items are often rejected and defective items accepted.

A final disadvantage of total inspection is that some tests are by their very nature destructive. Testing a photoflash bulb to determine the quantity of light produced destroys the bulb. If all bulbs were tested in this manner, the manufacturer would have none left to sell.

A second type of screen, relatively inexpensive and lacking the tedium of total inspection, involves the use of a statistical sampling plan similar to the plan described in Example 6.4. A sample of *n* items is chosen at random from the lot of items and inspected for defectives. If the number of defectives, y, is less than or equal to some predetermined number, a, called the *acceptance number*, the lot is accepted. Otherwise the lot is rejected and returned to the supplier. The acceptance number for the plan described in Example 6.4 was $a = 1$.

The reader will note that this sampling plan operates in a completely objective manner and results in an inference concerning the population of items contained in the lot. If the lot is rejected, we infer that the fraction defective, p, is too large; if the lot is accepted, we infer that p is small and acceptable for use in the manufacturing process. Lot acceptance sampling plans provide an example of a statistical decision process which is, indeed, a method of statistical inference.

Our discussion of lot acceptance sampling plans would be incomplete if we were to neglect some comment concerning the "goodness" of our inference-making procedure. Although the sampling plan described above is a decision-making process, it is not unique. We could change the number in the sample, n, change a, the acceptance number, or, for that matter, we could use some non-statistical decision-making process, a procedure which is not uncommon in practice. In actuality, each individual is a decision maker relying on individual whims, preferences, and tastes. How can we compare these decision-making processes? The answer is immediately at hand; we choose the decision-making process which makes the correct decision most frequently or, alternatively, makes the incorrect decision the smallest fraction of the time.

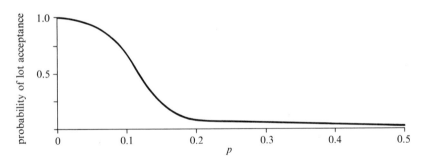

*Figure 6.2.   A Typical Operating Characteristic
Curve for a Sampling Plan*

Quality control engineers characterize the goodness of a sampling plan by calculating the probability of lot acceptance for various lot fractions defective. The result is presented in a graphic form and is called the *operating characteristic curve* for the sampling plan. A typical operating characteristic curve is shown in Figure 6.2.   In order for the screen to operate satisfactorily, we would like the probability of accepting lots with a low fraction defective to be high and the probability of accepting lots with a high fraction defective to be low.   The reader will note that the probability of acceptance always drops as the fraction defective increases, a result which is in agreement with our intuition.

For instance, suppose that the supplier guarantees that lots will contain less than 1% defective and that the manufacturer can operate satisfactorily with lots containing less than 5% defective.   Then the probability of accepting lots with less than 1% defective should be high. Otherwise the supplier will raise his price to cover the cost of "good lots" (less than 1% defective) which have been returned or will charge the manufacturer a fee for reinspection.   On the other hand, the probability of accepting lots with 5% or more should be very low.

Example 6.6: Calculate the probability of lot acceptance for a sampling plan with sample size $n = 5$ and acceptance number $a = 0$ for lot fraction defective $p = .1, .3,$ and $.5$.   Sketch the operating characteristic curve for the plan.

Solution:

$$P(\text{accept}) = p(0) = C_0^5 p^0 q^5 = q^5,$$

$$P(\text{accept}/p = .1) = (.9)^5 = .590,$$

$$P(\text{accept}/p = .3) = (.7)^5 = .168,$$

$$P(\text{accept}/p = .5) = (.5)^5 = .031.$$

A sketch of the operating characteristic curve can be obtained by plotting the three points obtained from the above calculation.   In addition, we know that the probability of acceptance must equal one when $p = 0$ and must equal zero when $p = 1$.   The operating characteristic curve is given in Figure 6.3.

Calculating the binomial probabilities is a tedious task when n is large. To simplify our calculations, the sum of the binomial probabilities from $y = 0$ to $y = a$ is presented in Appendix II, Table I, for sample sizes $n = 5, 10, 15, 20,$ and 25.   We will use Table I in the following example.

Example 6.7: Construct the operating characteristic curve for a sampling plan with $n = 15, a = 1$.

Solution: The probability of lot acceptance will be calculated for $p = .1, .2, .3, .5$.

$$P(\text{accept}) = p(0) + p(1) = \sum_{y=0}^{a=1} p(y),$$

$$P(\text{accept}/p = .1) = .549,$$

$$P(\text{accept}/p = .2) = .167,$$

$$P(\text{accept}/p = .3) = .035,$$

$$P(\text{accept}/p = .5) = .000.$$

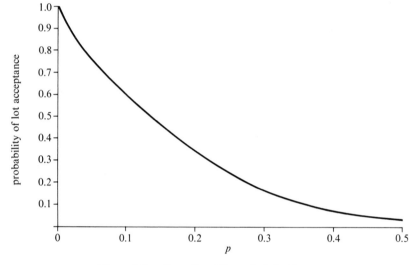

Figure 6.3. Operating Characteristic Curve,
$n = 5, a = 0$

The operating characteristic curve for the sampling plan is given in Figure 6.4.

Sampling inspection plans are widely used in industry. Each sampling plan possesses its own unique operating characteristic curve which characterizes the plan and, in a sense, describes the size of the holes in the screen. The quality control engineer will choose the plan which satisfies the requirements of his situation. Increasing the acceptance number increases the probability of acceptance and hence increases the size of the holes in the screen. Increasing the sample size provides more information upon which to base the decision and hence improves the discriminatory power of the decision procedure. Thus, when n is large the operating characteristic curve will drop rapidly as p increases. The reader may verify these remarks by working the exercises at the end of this chapter.

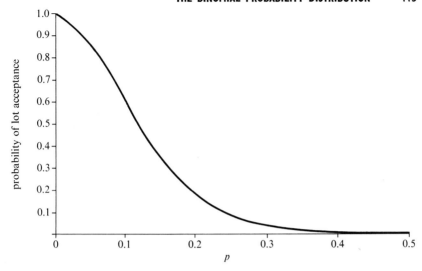

Figure 6.4.   Operating Characteristic Curve,
$n = 15, a = 1$

6.6   A Test of an Hypothesis

The cold vaccine problem, Example 6.5, is illustrative of a statistical test of an hypothesis.   The practical question to be answered concerns the effectiveness of the vaccine.   Do the data contained in the sample present sufficient evidence to indicate that the vaccine is effective?

The reasoning employed in testing an hypothesis bears a striking resemblance to the procedure used in a court trial.   In trying a man for theft, the court assumes the accused innocent until proven guilty.   The prosecution collects and presents all available evidence in an attempt to contradict the "not-guilty" hypothesis and hence to obtain a conviction. The statistical problem portrays the vaccine as the accused.   The hypothesis to be tested, called the *null hypothesis*, is that the vaccine is ineffective. The evidence in the case is contained in the sample drawn from the population of potential vaccine customers.   The experimenter, playing the role of the prosecutor, believes that his vaccine is really effective and hence attempts to use the evidence contained in a sample to reject the null hypothesis and thereby to support his contention that the vaccine is, in fact, a very successful cold vaccine.   The reader will recognize this procedure as an essential feature of the scientific method where all theories proposed must be compared with reality.

Intuitively, we would select the number of survivors, y, as a measure of the quantity of evidence in the sample.   If y were large, we would be inclined to reject the null hypothesis and conclude that the vaccine is effective. On the other hand, a small value of y would provide little evidence to support the rejection of the null hypothesis. As a matter of fact, if the null hypothesis were true and the vaccine were ineffective, the probability of surviving a winter without a cold would be $p = 1/2$ and the average value of y would be

$$E(y) = np = 10(1/2) = 5.$$

Most individuals utilizing their own built-in decision makers would have little difficulty arriving at a decision for the case $y = 10$ or $y = 5$, 4, 3, 2, or 1, which, on the surface, appear to provide substantial evidence to support rejection or acceptance, respectively. But what can be said concerning less obvious results, say $y = 7$, 8, or 9? Clearly, whether we employ a subjective or an objective decision-making procedure, we would choose the procedure which gave the smallest probability of making an incorrect decision.

The statistician would test the null hypothesis in an objective manner similar to our intuitive procedure. A decision maker, commonly called a test *statistic*, is calculated from information contained in the sample. In our example, the number of survivors, y, would suffice for a test statistic. We would then consider all possible values which the test statistic may assume, for example, $y = 0$, 1, 2, ..., 9, 10. These values would be divided into two groups, one called the *rejection region* and the other the *acceptance region*. An experiment is then conducted and the decision maker, y, observed. If y takes a value in the rejection region, the hypothesis is rejected. Otherwise, it is accepted. For example, we might choose $y = 8$, 9, or 10 as the rejection region and assign the remaining values of y to the acceptance region. Since we observed $y = 8$ survivors, we would reject the null hypothesis that the vaccine is ineffective and conclude that the probability of surviving the winter without a cold is greater than $p = 1/2$ when the vaccine is used. What is the probability that we will reject the null hypothesis when, in fact, it is true? The probability of falsely rejecting the null hypothesis is the probability that y will equal 8, 9, or 10, given that $p = 1/2$, and this is indeed the probability computed in Example 6.5 and found to equal .055. Since we have decided to reject the null hypothesis and note that this probability is small, we are reasonably confident that we have made the correct decision.

Upon reflection, the reader will observe that the manufacturer is faced with two possible types of error. On the one hand he might reject the null hypothesis and falsely conclude that the vaccine was effective. Proceeding with a more thorough and expensive testing program or a pilot plant production of the vaccine would result in a financial loss. On the other hand, he might decide not to reject the null hypothesis and falsely conclude that the vaccine was ineffective. This error would result in the loss of potential profits which could be derived through the sale of a successful vaccine.

Rejecting the null hypothesis when it is true is called the type I error for a statistical test. The probability of making a type I error is denoted by the symbol α. The probability, α, will increase or decrease as we increase or decrease the size of the rejection region. Inasmuch as α measures the risk of falsely rejecting, we might ask why we do not choose the rejection region as small as possible. For example, why not choose $y = 10$ as the rejection region? Unfortunately, decreasing α increases the probability of not rejecting when the null hypothesis is false and some alternative hypothesis is true. This second type of error is called the type II error for the statistical test and its probability is denoted by the symbol β. For a fixed sample size, n, α, and β are inversely related; as one increases, the other decreases. Increasing the sample size provides more information upon which to base the decision and hence reduces both α and β. In an experimental situation, the probabilities of the type I and type II errors for a test measure the risk of making an incorrect decision. The experimenter selects values for these probabilities, and the rejection region and sample size are chosen accordingly.

A discussion of the theory of tests of hypotheses may seem a bit premature at this point, but it provides an introduction to a line of reasoning that is sometimes difficult to grasp and which is best presented when it is allowed to incubate in the mind of the student over a period of time. Thus, some of the exercises at the end of Chapter 6 involve the use of the binomial probability distribution and, at the same time, lead the student to utilize the reasoning involved in statistical tests of hypotheses. We will take occasion to expand upon these ideas through examples and exercises in Chapter 7 and will discuss in detail the topic of statistical tests of hypotheses in Chapter 8 and succeeding chapters.

In closing, we direct the reader's attention to the similarity of the lot acceptance sampling problem and the statistical test of an hypothesis. Theoretically, they are equivalent because each involves an inference, formulated as a decision, concerning the value of p, the unknown parameter of a binomial population.

6.7 Summary

A binomial experiment is typical of a large class of useful experiments encountered in real life which satisfy, to a reasonable degree of approximation, the five defining characteristics stated in Section 6.1. The number of successes, y, observed in n trials is a discrete random variable with probability distribution

$$p(y) = C_y^n p^y q^{n-y},$$

where $q = 1 - p$ and $y = 0, 1, 2, 3, \ldots, n$. Statistically speaking, we are interested in making inferences concerning p, the parameter of a binomial population, as exemplified by the lot acceptance sampling, Section 6.4, and the test of the effectiveness of the cold vaccine, Section 6.5.

EXERCISES

1. List the five identifying characteristics of the binomial experiment.

2. A balanced coin is tossed three times. Let y equal the number of heads observed.
   (a) Use the formula for the binomial probability distribution to calculate the probabilities associated with $y = 0, 1, 2$, and 3.
   (b) Construct a probability distribution similar to Figure 5.1.
   (c) Find the expected value and standard deviation of y, using the formulae

$$E(y) = np,$$

$$\sigma = \sqrt{npq}.$$

   (d) Using the probability distribution, (b), find the fraction of the population measurements lying within one standard deviation of the mean. Repeat for two standard deviations. How do your results agree with Tchebysheff's Theorem and the Empirical Rule?

3. Suppose that a coin was definitely unbalanced and that the probability of a head was equal to $p = .1$. Follow instructions (a), (b), (c), and (d) as stated in Exercise 2. Note that the probability distribution loses its symmetry and becomes skewed when p is not equal to $1/2$.

4. The probability that a single radar set will detect an enemy plane is .9. If we have 5 radar sets, what is the probability that exactly 4 sets will detect the plane? (Assume that the sets operate independently of each other.) At least one set?

5. It is known that 10% of a brand of television tubes will burn out before their guarantee has expired. If 1000 tubes are sold, find the expected value and variance of y, the number of original tubes that must be replaced. Within what limits would y be expected to fall? (Hint: use Tchebysheff's Theorem.)

6. Suppose that the four engines of a commercial aircraft were arranged to operate independently and that the probability of in-flight failure of a single engine is .01.   What is the probability that, on a given flight,
(a) no failures are observed?
(b) no more than one failure is observed?

7. Suppose that 90% of the students taking English pass the course.   What is the probability that at least two students in a class of 20 will fail the course?   (Use Table I, Appendix II.)

8. Referring to Exercise 7, what is the expected value and standard deviation of y, the number of failures in a class of twenty?   Within what limits would y be expected to fall?

9. Suppose that it is known that one out of ten undergraduate college textbooks is an outstanding financial success.   A publisher has selected ten new textbooks for publication.   What is the probability that
(a) exactly one will be an outstanding financial success?
(b) at least one?
(c) at least two?

10. A buyer and seller agree to use a sampling plan with sample size $n = 5$ and acceptance number $a = 0$.   What is the probability that the buyer would accept a lot having fraction defective
(a) $p = .1$,   (b) $p = .3$,   (c) $p = .5$,
(d) $p = 0$,   (e) $p = 1$?
Construct the operating characteristic curve for this plan.

11. Repeat Exercise 10 for $n = 5$, $a = 1$.

12. Repeat Exercise 10 for $n = 10$, $a = 0$.

13. Repeat Exercise 10 for $n = 10$, $a = 1$.

14. Graph the operating characteristic curves for the four plans given in Exercises 10, 11, 12, and 13 on the same sheet of graph paper.   What is the effect of increasing the acceptance number, a, when n is held constant? What is the effect of increasing the sample size, n, when a is held constant?

15. A quality control engineer wishes to study the alternative sampling plans $n = 5$, $a = 1$ and $n = 25$, $a = 5$.   On the same sheet of graph paper, construct the operating characteristic curves for both plans, making use of acceptance probabilities at $p = .05$, $p = .10$, $p = .20$, $p = .30$, and $p = .40$ in each case.
(a) If you were a seller producing lots with fraction defective ranging from $p = 0$ to $p = .10$, which of the two sampling plans would you prefer?
(b) If you were a buyer wishing to be protected against accepting lots with fraction defective exceeding $p = .30$, which of the two sampling plans would you prefer?

16. A manufacturer of floor wax has developed two new brands, A and B, which he wishes to subject to a housewife evaluation to determine which

of the two is superior. Both waxes, A and B, are applied to floor surfaces in each of fifteen homes.

    (a) If there is actually no difference in the quality of the brands, what is the probability that ten or more housewives would state a preference for brand A?

    (b) For either brand A or brand B?

17. Define the type I error for a statistical test.

18. Define the type II error for a statistical test.

19. An experiment is conducted to test the hypothesis that a coin is balanced. To test the hypothesis, a coin will be tossed four times and the number of heads observed. The hypothesis will be rejected if zero or four heads appear.

    (a) What is the probability of the type I error for this test?

    (b) If the coin really is biased and the probability of observing a head on a single trial is .7, what is the probability of the type II error for the test?

20. A pair of beetles is expected to produce blackeyed offspring 30% of the time. To test this theory, three are observed and it is found that all three possess blue eyes. Does this result present sufficient evidence to contradict the theory? Justify your answer statistically.

21. A number of psychological experiments are conducted as follows: A rat is attracted to the end of a ramp that divides, leading to one of two doors. The objective of the experiment, essentially, is to determine whether the rat possesses or acquires a preference for one of the two paths. For a given experiment consisting of 6 runs, the following results were observed:

RUN	DOOR CHOSEN
1	2
2	1
3	2
4	2
5	2
6	2

    (a) State the null hypothesis to be tested.

    (b) Let y equal the number of times the rat chose the second door. What is the value of α for the test if the rejection region includes $y = 0$ and $y = 6$?

    (c) What is the value of β for the alternative, $p = .8$?

22. The number of defective electrical fuses proceeding from each of two production lines, A and B, was recorded daily for a period of 10 days with the following results:

DAY	A	B
1	172	201
2	165	179
3	206	159
4	184	192
5	174	177
6	142	170
7	190	182
8	169	179
9	161	169
10	200	210

Assume that both production lines produced the same daily output. Compare the number of defectives produced by A and B each day and let y equal the number of days when B exceeded A. Do the data present sufficient evidence to indicate that production line B produces more defectives, on the average, than A? State the null hypothesis to be tested and use y as a test statistic.

23. Continuing Exercise 16, let p equal the probability that a housewife will choose brand B in preference to A and suppose that we wish to test the hypothesis that there is no observable difference between the brands—in other words, that $p = 1/2$. Let y, the number of times that A is preferred to B, be the test statistic.
    (a) Calculate the value of α for the test if the rejection region is chosen to include $y = 0$, 1, 14, and 15.
    (b) If p is really equal to .8, what is the value of β for the test defined in (a)? (Note that this is the probability that $y = 2, 3, \ldots, 12, 13$ given that $p = .8$.)

24. Continuing Exercise 23, suppose that the rejection region is enlarged to include $y = 0$, 1, 2, 13, 14, 15.
    (a) What is the value of α for the test? Should this probability be larger or smaller than the answer given in Exercise 23?
    (b) If p is really equal to .8, what is the value of β for the test? Compare with your answer to part (b), Exercise 23.

25. A chemist wishes to determine if a new type of alloy is less susceptible to corrosion than alloys of two standard types. He makes up seven specimen strips of each type of alloy and forms seven groups of three dissimilar strips each. The strips in each group are subjected to attack by an acid and the number (y) of times that the new alloy is the least corroded is recorded. Let p be the probability that in a given group the strip of the new alloy suffers less corrosion than the other two strips.
    (a) State the appropriate hypothesis in the form of a statement about p.

(b) Find α if the rejection region is $y = 5, 6, 7$.

(c) Find β if $p = .5$.

(d) If $p = .7$, would β be more than or less than the answer to part (c)?

SUPPLEMENTARY EXERCISES

1. Derive the formula for the binomial probability distribution by using mathematical induction.

2. Derive the formula for the binomial probability distribution using the sample point approach and combinatorial mathematics.

3. Use the formula for the binomial probability distribution along with Theorems 2.1, 2.2, and 2.3 to prove

$$E(y) = np$$

variance of $y = npq$

4. Prove that the binomial probabilities always sum to 1; that is,

$$\sum_{y=0}^{n} p(y) = 1.$$

5. The manager of a large motor pool wished to compare the wearing qualities of two different types (type A and type B) of automobile tires. On each of 400 cars he replaced one rear tire with a new tire of type A and the other rear tire with a new tire of type B. When a given car had been driven 10,000 miles, he determined which of the two rear tires experienced the greater wear. Let y be the number of cars out of the 400 cars on which tire A showed the greater wear. Let p be the probability that on a given car the tire of type A will experience the greater wear. Using Tchebysheff's Theorem, find an upper bound to α for a test of the hypothesis that $p = 1/2$ if the rejection region includes the outcomes $y = 0, 1, 2, \ldots, 150, 250, 251, \ldots 400$.

6. The "power" of a test is defined to be $1 - \beta$. Find a lower bound to the power of the test given in Exercise 5 if $p = .8$.

REFERENCES

Feller, W., *An Introduction to Probability Theory and Its Applications*, Vol. 1. 2nd ed.   New York: John Wiley & Sons, Inc., 1960.   Chapter 6.

Mosteller, F., R. E. K. Rourke, and G. B. Thomas, Jr., *Probability with Statistical Applications.* Reading, Massachusetts: Addison-Wesley Publishing Co., Inc., 1961. Chapter 7.

National Bureau of Standards, *Tables of the Binomial Probability Distribution.* Washington, D.C.: U.S. Government Printing Office, 1949.

7

THE NORMAL
PROBABILITY
DISTRIBUTION

7.1 Introduction

Continuous random variables, as noted in Section 5.5, are associated with sample spaces representing the infinitely large number of sample points contained on a line interval. The heights and weights of humans, laboratory experimental measurement errors, and the length of life of light bulbs are typical examples of continuous random variables. Reviewing Section 5.5, we note that the probabilistic model for the frequency distribution of a continuous random variable involves the selection of a curve, usually smooth, called the probability distribution or probability density function. While these distributions may assume a variety of shapes, it is interesting to note that a very large number of random variables observed in nature possess a frequency distribution which is approximately bell-shaped or, as the statistician would say, is approximately a *normal probability distribution*.

Mathematically speaking, the normal probability density function,

$$f(y) = \frac{e^{-\frac{(y-\mu)^2}{2\sigma^2}}}{\sqrt{2\pi}\,\sigma}, \qquad (-\infty < y < \infty),$$

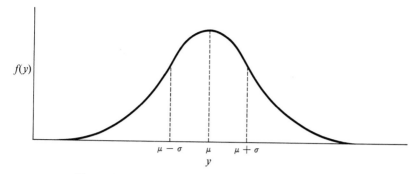

Figure 7.1. *The Normal Probability Density Function*

is the equation of the bell-shaped curve which is shown in Figure 7.1.

The symbols e and π represent irrational numbers whose values are approximately 2.7183 and 3.1416, respectively, while μ and σ are the population mean and standard deviation. The equation for the density function is constructed such that the area under the curve will represent probability. Hence the total area is equal to one.

In practice, we seldom encounter variables which range in value from "minus infinity" to "plus infinity," whatever meaning we may wish to attach to these phrases. Certainly the height of humans, the weight of a specie of beetle, or the length of life of a light bulb do not satisfy this requirement. Nevertheless, a relative frequency histogram plotted for many types of measurements will generate a bell-shaped figure which may be approximated by the function shown in Figure 7.1. Why this particular phenomenon exists is a matter for conjecture. However, one explanation is provided by the Central Limit Theorem, a theorem which may be regarded as the most important in statistics.

7.2 The Central Limit Theorem

The Central Limit Theorem states that under rather general conditions, sums and means of samples of random measurements drawn from a population tend to possess, approximately, a bell-shaped distribution in *repeated* sampling. The significance of this statement is perhaps best illustrated by an example.

Consider a population of die throws generated by tossing a die an infinitely large number of times with resulting probability distribution given by Figure 5.2. Draw a sample of $n = 5$ measurements from the population by tossing a die five times and record each of the five observations as indicated in Table 7.1 (page 126). Note that the numbers observed in the first sample were $y = 3, 5, 1, 3, 2$. Calculate the sum of the five

Table 7.1. Sampling from the Population of Die
Throws

SAMPLE NUMBER	SAMPLE MEASUREMENTS	Σy_i	$\bar{y}$	SAMPLE NUMBER	SAMPLE MEASUREMENTS	Σy_i	$\bar{y}$
1	3, 5, 1, 3, 2	14	2.8	51	2, 3, 5, 3, 2	15	3.0
2	3, 1, 1, 4, 6	15	3.0	52	1, 1, 1, 2, 4	9	1.8
3	1, 3, 1, 6, 1	12	2.4	53	2, 6, 3, 4, 5	20	4.0
4	4, 5, 3, 3, 2	17	3.4	54	1, 2, 2, 1, 1	7	1.4
5	3, 1, 3, 5, 2	14	2.8	55	2, 4, 4, 6, 2	18	3.6
6	2, 4, 4, 2, 4	16	3.2	56	3, 2, 5, 4, 5	19	3.8
7	4, 2, 5, 5, 3	19	3.8	57	2, 4, 2, 4, 5	17	3.4
8	3, 5, 5, 5, 5	23	4.6	58	5, 5, 4, 3, 2	19	3.8
9	6, 5, 5, 1, 6	23	4.6	59	5, 4, 4, 6, 3	22	4.4
10	5, 1, 6, 1, 6	19	3.8	60	3, 2, 5, 3, 1	14	2.8
11	1, 1, 1, 5, 3	11	2.2	61	2, 1, 4, 1, 3	11	2.2
12	3, 4, 2, 4, 4	17	3.4	62	4, 1, 1, 5, 2	13	2.6
13	2, 6, 1, 5, 4	18	3.6	63	2, 3, 1, 2, 3	11	2.2
14	6, 3, 4, 2, 5	20	4.0	64	2, 3, 3, 2, 6	16	3.2
15	2, 6, 2, 1, 5	16	3.2	65	4, 3, 5, 2, 6	20	4.0
16	1, 5, 1, 2, 5	14	2.8	66	3, 1, 3, 3, 4	14	2.8
17	3, 5, 1, 1, 2	12	2.4	67	4, 6, 1, 3, 6	20	4.0
18	3, 2, 4, 3, 5	17	3.4	68	2, 4, 6, 6, 3	21	4.2
19	5, 1, 6, 3, 1	16	3.2	69	4, 1, 6, 5, 5	21	4.2
20	1, 6, 4, 4, 1	16	3.2	70	6, 6, 6, 4, 5	27	5.4
21	6, 4, 2, 3, 5	20	4.0	71	2, 2, 5, 6, 3	18	3.6
22	1, 3, 5, 4, 1	14	2.8	72	6, 6, 6, 1, 6	25	5.0
23	2, 6, 5, 2, 6	21	4.2	73	4, 4, 4, 3, 1	16	3.2
24	3, 5, 1, 3, 5	17	3.4	74	4, 4, 5, 4, 2	19	3.8
25	5, 2, 4, 4, 3	18	3.6	75	4, 5, 4, 1, 4	18	3.6
26	6, 1, 1, 1, 6	15	3.0	76	5, 3, 2, 3, 4	17	3.4
27	1, 4, 1, 2, 6	14	2.8	77	1, 3, 3, 1, 5	13	2.6
28	3, 1, 2, 1, 5	12	2.4	78	4, 1, 5, 5, 3	18	3.6
29	1, 5, 5, 4, 5	20	4.0	79	4, 5, 6, 5, 4	24	4.8
30	4, 5, 3, 5, 2	19	3.8	80	1, 5, 3, 4, 2	15	3.0
31	4, 1, 6, 1, 1	13	2.6	81	4, 3, 4, 6, 3	20	4.0
32	3, 6, 4, 1, 2	16	3.2	82	5, 4, 2, 1, 6	18	3.6
33	3, 5, 5, 2, 2	17	3.4	83	1, 3, 2, 2, 5	13	2.6
34	1, 1, 5, 6, 3	16	3.2	84	5, 4, 1, 4, 6	20	4.0
35	2, 6, 1, 6, 2	17	3.4	85	2, 4, 2, 5, 5	18	3.6
36	2, 4, 3, 1, 3	13	2.6	86	1, 6, 3, 1, 6	17	3.4
37	1, 5, 1, 5, 2	14	2.8	87	2, 2, 4, 3, 2	13	2.6
38	6, 6, 5, 3, 3	23	4.6	88	4, 4, 5, 4, 4	21	4.2
39	3, 3, 5, 2, 1	14	2.8	89	2, 5, 4, 3, 4	18	3.6
40	2, 6, 6, 6, 5	25	5.0	90	5, 1, 6, 4, 3	19	3.8
41	5, 5, 2, 3, 4	19	3.8	91	5, 2, 5, 6, 3	21	4.2
42	6, 4, 1, 6, 2	19	3.8	92	6, 4, 1, 2, 1	14	2.8
43	2, 5, 3, 1, 4	15	3.0	93	6, 3, 1, 5, 2	17	3.4
44	4, 2, 3, 2, 1	12	2.4	94	1, 3, 6, 4, 2	16	3.2
45	4, 4, 5, 4, 4	21	4.2	95	6, 1, 4, 2, 2	15	3.0
46	5, 4, 5, 5, 4	23	4.6	96	1, 1, 2, 3, 1	8	1.6
47	6, 6, 6, 2, 1	21	4.2	97	6, 2, 5, 1, 6	20	4.0
48	2, 1, 5, 5, 4	17	3.4	98	3, 1, 1, 4, 1	10	2.0
49	6, 4, 3, 1, 5	19	3.8	99	5, 2, 1, 6, 1	15	3.0
50	4, 4, 4, 4, 4	20	4.0	100	2, 4, 3, 4, 6	19	3.8

measurements as well as the sample mean, $\bar{y}$. For experimental purposes, repeat the sampling procedure one-hundred times or preferably an even larger number of times. The results for one-hundred samples are given in Table 7.1 along with the corresponding values of $\sum_{i=1}^{5} y_i$ and $\bar{y}$. Construct a frequency histogram for $\bar{y}$ (or $\sum_{i=1}^{5} y_i$) for the one-hundred samples and observe the resulting distribution in Figure 7.2. The reader will

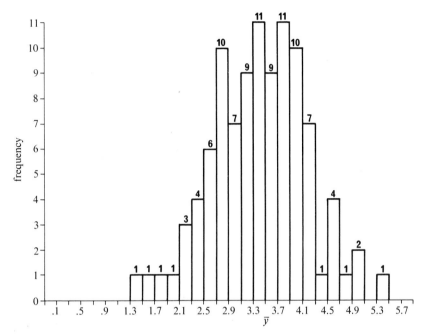

Figure 7.2. A Histogram of Sample Means for the
Die-Tossing Experiments in Section 7.2

observe an interesting result, namely that although the values of y in the population ($y = 1, 2, 3, 4, 5, 6$) are equiprobable and hence possess a probability distribution which is perfectly horizontal, the distribution of the sample means (or sums) chosen from the population possess a *mound-shaped* distribution. We will add one further comment without proof. If we should repeat the experiment outlined above for a larger sample size, say $n = 10$, we would find that the distribution of the sample means tends to become more nearly bell-shaped.

The reader will note that a proper evaluation of the form of the probability distribution of the sample means would require an infinitely large number of samples, or, at the very least, far more than the one-hundred samples contained in our experiment. Nevertheless, the one-hundred samples illustrate the basic idea involved in the Central Limit Theorem, which may be stated as follows.

The Central Limit Theorem: If random samples of n observations are drawn from a population with finite mean, μ, and standard deviation, σ, then, when n is large, the sample mean, $\bar{y}$, will be approximately normally distributed with mean equal to μ and standard deviation $\sigma/\sqrt{n}$. The approximation will become more and more accurate as n becomes large.

Note that the Central Limit Theorem could be restated to apply to the sum of the sample measurements, $\sum_{i=1}^{n} y_i$, which would also tend to possess a normal distribution, in repeated sampling, with mean equal to $n\mu$ and standard deviation $\sqrt{n}\,\sigma$, as n becomes large.

The reader will note that the mean and standard deviation of the distribution of sample means are definitely related to the mean and standard deviation of the sampled population as well as to the sample size, n. We will forego discussion of this point for the moment and consider the relevance of the Central Limit Theorem to our previous work.

The significance of the Central Limit Theorem is twofold. First, it explains why some measurements tend to possess, approximately, a normal distribution. We might imagine the height of a human as being composed of a number of elements, each random, associated with such things as the height of the mother, the height of the father, the activity of a particular gland, the environment, and diet. If each of these effects tends to add to the others to yield the measurement of height, then height is the sum of a number of random variables and the Central Limit Theorem may become effective and yield a distribution of heights which is approximately normal. All of this is conjecture, of course, because we really do not know the true situation which exists. Nevertheless, the Central Limit Theorem, along with other theorems dealing with normally distributed random variables, provides an explanation of the rather common occurrence of normally distributed random variables in nature.

The second and most important contribution of the Central Limit Theorem is in statistical inference. Many estimators and decision makers that are used to make inferences about population parameters are sums or averages of the sample measurements. When this is true and when the sample size, n, is sufficiently large, we would expect the estimator or decision maker to possess a normal probability distribution in repeated sampling according to the Central Limit Theorem. We can then use the

Empirical Rule discussed in Chapter 3 to describe the behavior of the inference maker. This aspect of the Central Limit Theorem will be utilized in Section 7.4 as well as in later chapters dealing with statistical inference.

One disturbing feature of the Central Limit Theorem, and of most approximation procedures, is that we must have some idea as to how large the sample size, n, must be in order for the approximation to give useful results.   Unfortunately, there is no clearcut answer to this question as the appropriate value for n will depend upon the population probability distribution as well as the use we will make of the approximation. Although the preceding comment sidesteps the difficulty and suggests that we must rely solely upon experience, we may take comfort in the results of the die-tossing experiment discussed previously in this section.   Note that the distribution of $\bar{y}$, in repeated sampling, based upon a sample of only $n = 5$ measurements, tends to be approximately bell-shaped.   Generally speaking, the Central Limit Theorem functions very well, even for small samples, but this is not always true.   We will observe an exception to this rule in Section 7.4.   The appropriate sample size, n, will be given for specific applications of the Central Limit Theorem as they are encountered in Section 7.4 and later in the text.

7.3 Random Samples

In previous sections we have referred to representative samples, sampling in a "random manner," and "random samples" without attempting an explicit definition of these phrases.   The reader will note that the Central Limit Theorem, as stated above, applies only when the sampling is conducted in a random manner.   What is a random sample and why, in general, is the method of sampling important to our objective, that is, statistical inference?   The latter question, being more basic, will be answered first.

Once again we refer the reader to the die-tossing example, Section 4.1, in which we wished to infer whether the die was or was not balanced.   We might also consider the decision-making procedures discussed in Chapter 6 in connection with lot acceptance sampling and the test of an hypothesis concerning the effectiveness of the cold vaccine.   In each case, a sample was drawn from the population of interest in order to make an inference (a decision in each of these examples) concerning a parameter of the population.

If, after sampling, we observe what we consider to be a highly improbable result (that is, an improbable sample, assuming the null hypothesis to be true), we reject the hypothesis.   If the sample is quite probable, assuming the null hypothesis to be true, we do not reject.   In other words, we must know the probability of the observed sample in order to arrive at a statistical inference.   Reiterating a statement made in Chapter 4, probability reasons from the population to the sample.   Statistics, on the other hand, reverses the procedure, using probability as a vehicle to make inferences about the population based upon information contained in a sample.   It should be reasonably clear that the sampling procedure will affect the probability of observing a particular sample and hence must be carefully considered.

Suppose that a sample of n measurements is drawn from a population consisting of N total measurements.   How many different samples of n measurements can be drawn from the population?   In effect, we ask how many different combinations of n measurements can be selected from the population.   This was shown in Chapter 4 to be

$$C_n^N = \frac{N!}{n!\,(N-n)!}.$$

If the sampling is conducted in such a way that each of the C_n^N samples has an equal probability of being selected, the sampling is said to be *random* and the result is said to be a *random sample*.

Perfect random sampling is difficult to achieve in practice.   If the population is not too large, we might place each of the N numbers on a poker chip, mix the total, and select a sample of n chips.   The numbers on the poker chips would specify the measurements to appear in the sample.   Other techniques are available when the population is large.

In many situations, the population is conceptual, as in an observation made during a laboratory experiment.   Here the population is envisioned to be the infinitely large number of measurements obtained when the experiment is repeated over and over again.   If we wish a sample of $n = 10$ measurements from this population, we repeat the experiment ten times and hope that the results represent, to a reasonable degree of approximation, a random sample.

While the primary purpose of this discussion was to clarify the meaning of a random sample, we would like to mention that some sampling techniques are partly systematic and partly random.   For instance, if we wish to determine the voting preference of the nation in a presidential election, we would not likely choose a random sample from the population of voters.   Just due to pure chance, all of the voters appearing in the sample might be drawn from a single city, say, San Francisco, which might not be at all representative of the population.   We would prefer a random selection of voters from smaller political districts, perhaps states, allotting a specified number to each state.   The information from the randomly selected sub-samples drawn from the respective states would be combined to form a prediction concerning the entire population of voters in the country. The purpose of *systematic sampling*, as in *the design of experiments* in general, is to obtain a maximum of information for a fixed sample size. This, we recall, was one of the three elements of a statistical problem discussed in Chapter I.

7.4   The Normal Approximation to the Binomial Distribution

In the preceding chapter we considered several applications of the binomial probability distribution, all of which required that we calculate the probability that y, the number of successes in n trials, would fall in a given region. For the most part we restricted our attention to examples where n was small because of the tedious calculations necessary in the computations of $p(y)$. Let us now consider the problem of calculating $p(y)$, or the probability that y will fall in a given region, when n is large, say $n = 1000$. A direct calculation of $p(y)$ for large values of n is not an impossibility but it does provide a formidable task which we would prefer to avoid. Fortunately, the Central Limit Theorem provides a solution to this dilemma since we may view y, the number of successes in n trials, as a sum which satisfies the conditions of the Central Limit Theorem. Each trial results in either 0 or 1 success with probability q and p, respectively. Therefore each of the n trials may be regarded as an independent observation drawn from a simpler binomial experiment consisting of one trial, and y, the total number of successes in n trials, is the sum of these n independent observations. Then, if n is sufficiently large, the binomial variable, y, will be approximately normally distributed with mean and variance (obtained in Chapter 6) np and npq, respectively. *We may then use areas under a fitted normal curve to approximate the binomial probabilities.*

For instance, consider a binomial probability distribution for y when $n = 10$ and $p = 1/2$. Then $\mu = np = 10(1/2) = 5$ and $\sigma = \sqrt{npq} = \sqrt{2.5} = 1.58$. Figure 7.3 shows the corresponding binomial probability distribution and the approximating normal curve on the same graph. A visual comparison of the figures would suggest that the approximation is reasonably good, even though a small sample, $n = 10$, was necessary for this graphic illustration.

The probability that $y = 2$, 3, or 4 is exactly equal to the area of the three rectangles lying over $y = 2$, 3, and 4. We may approximate this probability with the area under the normal curve from $y = 1.5$ to $y = 4.5$ which is shaded in Figure 7.3. The areas under the normal curve have been calculated and appear in Table 3, Appendix II, the use of which will be discussed in Section 7.5.

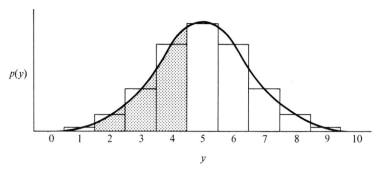

$p(y)$

*Figure 7.3.   A Comparison of a Binomial Probability
Distribution and the Approximating Normal
Distribution, $n = 10$, $p = 1/2$*

Although the normal probability distribution provides a reasonably good approximation to the binomial probability distribution, Figure 7.3, this will not always be the case.   When n is small and p is near 0 or 1, the binomial probability distribution will be non-symmetrical, that is, its mean will be located near 0 or n.   For example, when p is near zero, most values of y will be small, producing a distribution which is concentrated near $y = 0$ and which tails gradually toward n.   Certainly, when this is true, the normal distribution, symmetrical and bell-shaped, will provide a poor approximation to the binomial probability distribution.   How, then, can we tell whether n and p are such that the binomial distribution will be symmetrical?

Recalling the Empirical Rule, Chapter 3, approximately 95% of the measurements associated with a normal distribution will lie within two standard deviations of the mean and almost all will lie within three.   We would suspect that the binomial probability distribution would be nearly symmetrical if the distribution were able to spread out a distance equal to two standard deviations on either side of the mean and this is, in fact, the case.   Hence, to determine when the normal approximation will be adequate, calculate $\mu = np$ and $\sigma = \sqrt{npq}$.   If the interval $\mu \pm 2\sigma$ lies within the binomial bounds, 0 and n, the approximation will be reasonably good. Note that this criterion is satisfied for the example, Figure 7.3.

7.5   Tabulated Areas of the Normal Probability Distribution

The reader will note that the equation for the normal probability distribution, Section 7.1, is dependent upon the numerical values of μ and σ and that by supplying various values for these parameters, we could generate an infinitely large number of bell-shaped normal distributions. A separate table of areas for each of these curves is obviously impractical, rather we would like one table of areas applicable to all. The easiest way to do this is to work with areas lying within a specified number of standard deviations of the mean as was done in the case of the Empirical Rule. For instance, we know that approximately .68 of the area will lie within one standard deviation of the mean, .95 within two, and almost all within three. What fraction of the total area will lie within .7 standard deviations, for instance? This question, as well as others, will be answered by Table 3, Appendix II.

Inasmuch as the normal curve is symmetrical about the mean, we may simplify our table of areas by listing the areas between the mean, μ, and a specified number, z, of standard deviations to the right of μ. The distance from the mean to a given value of y is $(y - \mu)$. Expressing this distance in units of standard deviation, σ, we obtain

$$z = \frac{y - \mu}{\sigma}.$$

Note that there is a one-to-one correspondence between z and y and, particularly, that $z = 0$ when $y = \mu$. The probability distribution for z is often called the *standardized normal distribution* because its mean is equal to zero and its standard deviation is equal to one. It is shown below in Figure 7.4. The area under the normal curve between the mean, $z = 0$, and a specified value of z, say z_0, is recorded in Table 3, Appendix II, and is shown as the shaded area in Figure 7.4.

Since the normal distribution is symmetrical and the total area under the curve is equal to one, half of the area will lie to the right of the mean and half to the left. Areas to the left of the mean can be calculated by using the corresponding, and equal, area to the right of the mean.

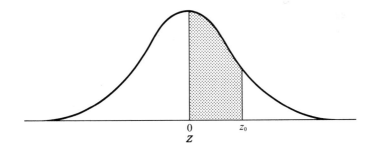

Figure 7.4. The Standardized Normal Distribution

Referring to Table 3, Appendix II, we note that z, correct to the nearest tenth, is recorded in the left-hand column. The second decimal place for z, corresponding to hundredths, is given across the top row. Thus the area between the mean and $z = .7$ standard deviations to the right, read in the second column of the table opposite $z = .7$, is found to equal .2580. Similarly, the area between the mean and $z = 1.0$ is .3413. The area lying within one standard deviation on either side of the mean would be two times the quantity .3413, or .6826. The area lying within two standard deviations of the mean, correct to four decimal places, is $2(.4772) = .9544$. These numbers provide the approximate values, 68% and 95%, used in the Empirical Rule, Chapter 3. We conclude this section with some examples.

Example 7.1: Find the value of z, say z_0, such that exactly (to four decimal places) .95 of the area is within $\pm z_0$ standard deviation of the mean.

Solution: Half of the total area, .95, will lie to the left of the mean and half to the right because the normal distribution is symmetrical. Thus we seek the value, z_0, corresponding to an area equal to .475. The area .475 falls in the row corresponding to $z = 1.9$ and the .06 column. Hence $z_0 = 1.96$. Note that this is very close to the approximate value, $z = 2$, used in the Empirical Rule.

Example 7.2: Find the area between $z = -.5$ and $z = 1.0$ as shown in Figure 7.5.

Solution: The area required is equal to the sum of A_1 and A_2 shown in Figure 7.5. From Table 3, Appendix II, we read $A_2 = .3413$. The

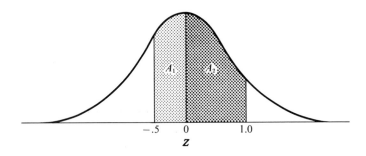

Figure 7.5. Area under the Normal Curve in Example 7.2

area, A_1, would equal the corresponding area between $z = 0$ and $z = .5$, or $A_1 = .1915$.   Thus the total area is

$$A = A_1 + A_2$$
$$= .1915 + .3413$$
$$= .5328.$$

Example 7.3: Let y be a normally distributed random variable with mean equal to 10 and standard deviation equal to 2.   Find the probability that y will lie between 11 and 13.6.

Solution: As a first step, we must calculate the values of z corresponding to $y_1 = 11$ and $y_2 = 13.6$.   Thus,

$$z_1 = \frac{y_1 - \mu}{\sigma} = \frac{11 - 10}{2} = .5,$$

$$z_2 = \frac{y_2 - \mu}{\sigma} = \frac{13.6 - 10}{2} = 1.80.$$

The probability desired, P, is therefore the area lying between z_1 and z_2 as shown in Figure 7.6.   The areas between $z = 0$ and z_1, $A_1 = .1915$, and

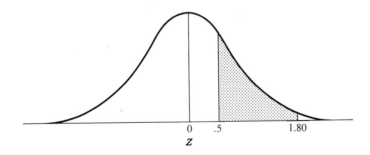

Figure 7.6.   Area under the Normal Curve in Example 7.3

$z = 0$ and z_2, $A_2 = .4641$, are easily obtained from Table 3.   The probability, P, is equal to the difference between A_1 and A_2; that is,

$$P = A_2 - A_1$$
$$= .4641 - .1915 = .2726.$$

Example 7.4: Refer to the binomial experiment illustrated in Figure 7.3, Section 7.4, where $n = 10$, $p = .5$. Calculate the probability that $y = 2, 3,$ or 4 correct to four decimal places using Table 1, Appendix II. Then calculate the corresponding normal approximation to this probability.

Solution: The exact probability, P_1, can be calculated using Table I (b). Thus

$$P_1 = \sum_{y=2}^{4} p(y) = \sum_{y=0}^{4} p(y) - \sum_{y=0}^{1} p(y)$$

$$= .377 - .011$$

$$= .366.$$

The normal approximation, as noted in Section 7.4, would require the area lying between $y_1 = 1.5$ and $y_2 = 4.5$, where $\mu = 5$ and $\sigma = 1.58$. The corresponding values of z are

$$z_1 = \frac{y_1 - \mu}{\sigma} = \frac{1.5 - 5}{1.58} = -2.22,$$

$$z_2 = \frac{y_2 - \mu}{\sigma} = \frac{4.5 - 5}{1.58} = -.32.$$

The probability, P_2, is shown in Figure 7.7. The area between $z = 0$ and $z = 2.22$ is $A_1 = .4868$. Likewise, the area between $z = 0$ and $z = .32$ is $A_2 = .1255$. It is obvious from Figure 7.7 that

$$P_2 = A_1 - A_2$$

$$= .4868 - .1255 = .3613.$$

Note that the normal approximation is quite close to the binomial probability obtained from Table 1.

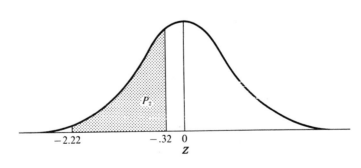

Figure 7.7. Area under the Normal Curve in Example 7.4

7.6   Examples of the Normal Approximation to the Binomial Distribution

Example 7.5: The reliability of an electrical fuse is the probability that a fuse, chosen at random from production, will function under the conditions for which it has been designed.   A random sample of 1000 fuses was tested and $y = 27$ defectives were observed. Calculate the probability of observing 27 or more defectives, assuming that the fuse reliability is .98.

Solution: The probability of observing a defective when a single fuse is tested is $p = .02$, given that the fuse reliability is .98.   Then,

$$\mu = np = 1000(.02) = 20,$$

$$\sigma = \sqrt{npq} = \sqrt{1000(.02)(.98)} = 4.43.$$

The probability of 27 or more defective fuses, given $n = 1000$, is

$$P = P(y \geq 27),$$

$$P = P(27) + P(28) + P(29) + \ldots + P(999) + P(1000).$$

The normal approximation to P would be the area under the normal curve to the right of $y = 26.5$.   (Note that we must use $y = 26.5$ rather than $y = 27$ so as to include the entire probability rectangle associated with $y = 27$.)   The z value corresponding to $y = 26.5$ is

$$z = \frac{y - \mu}{\sigma} = \frac{26.5 - 20}{4.43} = \frac{6.5}{4.43} = 1.47$$

and the area between $z = 0$ and $z = 1.47$ is equal to .4292, as shown in Figure 7.8.   Since the total area to the right of the mean is equal to .5,

$$P = .5 - .4292$$
$$= .0708.$$

Example 7.6: A new serum was tested to determine its effectiveness in preventing the common cold.   One-hundred people were injected with the serum and observed for a period of one year.   Sixty-eight survived the winter without a cold.   Suppose that according to prior information it is known that the probability of surviving the winter without a cold is equal to .5 when the serum is not used.   On the basis of the results of the above experiment, what conclusions would you make regarding the effectiveness of the serum?

Solution: Translating the question into an hypothesis concerning the parameter of the binomial population, we wish to test the null hypothesis that p, the probability of survival on a single trial, is equal to .5.   Assume that the content of the serum is such that it could not increase the susceptibility to colds.   Then the alternative to the null hypothesis would reject the null hypothesis when y, the number of survivors, is large.

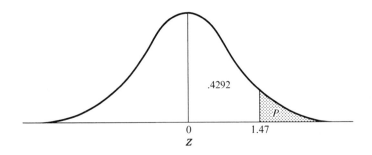

.4292

0
z

1.47

P

Figure 7.8.   Normal Approximation to the Binomial in Example 7.5

Since the normal approximation to the binomial will be adequate for this example, we would interpret a large and improbable value of y to be one which lies several standard deviations away from the hypothesized mean, $\mu = np = 100(.5) = 50$.

Noting that

$$\sigma = \sqrt{npq} = \sqrt{(100)(.5)(.5)} = 5,$$

we may arrive at a conclusion without bothering to locate a specific rejection region.   The observed value of y, 68, lies more than 3σ away from the hypothesized mean, $\mu = 50$.   Specifically, y lies

$$z = \frac{y - \mu}{\sigma} = \frac{68 - 50}{5} = 3.6$$

standard deviations away from the hypothesized mean.   This result is so improbable, assuming the serum ineffective, that we would reject the null hypothesis and conclude that the probability of surviving a winter without a cold is greater than $p = .5$ when the serum is used.   (The reader will observe that the area above $z = 3.6$ is so small that it is not included in Table 3.)

Rejecting the null hypothesis raises additional questions.   How effective is the serum and is it sufficiently effective, from an economic point of view, to warrant commercial production?   The former question leads to an estimation problem, a topic discussed in Chapter 8, while the latter, involving a business decision, would utilize the results of our experiment as well as a study of consumer demand, sales and production costs, etc. to achieve an answer useful to the drug company.

Example 7.7: The probability of a type I error, α, and location of the rejection region for a statistical test of an hypothesis are usually specified before the data are collected.   Suppose that we wish to test the null hypothesis, $p = .5$, in a situation identical to the cold serum problem in Example 7.6.   Find the appropriate rejection region for the test if we wish α to be approximately equal to .05.   (See Figure 7.9.)

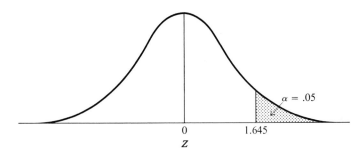

Figure 7.9. Location of the Rejection Region in Example 7.7

Solution: We have previously stated in Example 7.6 that y, the number of survivors, would be used as a test statistic and that the rejection region would be located in the upper tail of the probability distribution for y. Desiring α approximately equal to .05, we seek a value of y, say y_α, such that

$$P(y \geq y_\alpha) \approx .05.$$

(Note: The symbol $\approx$ means "approximately equal to".)   This can be determined by first finding the corresponding z_α which gives the number of standard deviations between the mean, $\mu = 50$, and y_α.   Since the total area to the right of $z = 0$ is .5, the area between $z = 0$ and z_α will equal .45. Checking Table 3, we find that $z = 1.64$ corresponds to an area equal to .4495 and $z = 1.65$ to an area of .4504.   A linear interpolation between these values would give

$$z_\alpha = 1.645.$$

Recalling the relation between z and y,

$$z_\alpha = \frac{y_\alpha - \mu}{\sigma}$$

or

$$1.645 = \frac{y_\alpha - 50}{5}.$$

Solving for y_α, we obtain

$$y_\alpha = 58.225.$$

Obviously, we cannot observe $y = 58.225$ survivors and hence must choose 58 or 59 as the point where the rejection region commences.

Suppose that we decide to reject when y is greater than or equal to 59. Then the actual probability of the type I error, α, for the test is

$$P(y \geq 59) = \alpha,$$

which can be approximated by using the area under the normal curve above $y = 58.5$, a problem similar to that encountered in Example 7.5. The z-value corresponding to $y = 58.5$ is

$$z = \frac{y - \mu}{\sigma} = \frac{58.5 - 50}{5} = 1.7,$$

and the tabulated area between $z = 0$ to $z = 1.7$ is .4554:

$$\alpha = .5 - .4554$$

$$= .0446.$$

While the method described above provides a more accurate value for α, there is very little practical difference between an α of .0446 and one equal to .05. When n is large, time and effort may be saved by using z as a test statistic rather than y. This method was employed in Example 7.6. We would then reject the null hypothesis when z is greater than or equal to 1.645.

Example 7.8: A cigarette manufacturer believed that approximately 10% of all smokers favored his product, brand A. To test this belief, 2500 smokers were selected at random from the population of cigarette smokers and questioned concerning their cigarette brand preference. A total of $y = 218$ expressed a preference for brand A. Do these data provide sufficient evidence to contradict the hypothesis that 10% of all smokers favor brand A? Conduct a statistical test using an α equal to .05.

Solution: We wish to test the null hypothesis that p, the probability that a single smoker prefers brand A, is equal to .1 against the alternative that p is greater than or less than .1.   The rejection region corresponding to an $\alpha = .05$ would be located as shown in Figure 7.10.   We would reject

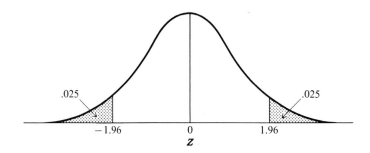

.025   .025

-1.96 0   1.96

z

*Figure 7.10.   Location of the Rejection Region in
Example 7.8*

the null hypothesis when $z > 1.96$ or $z < -1.96$.   In other words, we would reject when y lies more than approximately two standard deviations away from its hypothesized mean.   Note that half of α is placed in one tail of the distribution and half in the other because we wish to reject the null hypothesis when p is *either* larger or smaller than $p = .1$.   This is called a two-tailed statistical test in contrast to the one-tailed test discussed in Examples 7.6 and 7.7 when the alternative to the null hypothesis was only that p was larger than the hypothesized value.

   Assuming the null hypothesis to be true, the mean and standard deviation for y are

$$\mu = np = (2500)(.1) = 250,$$

$$\sigma = \sqrt{npq} = \sqrt{(2500)(.1)(.9)} = 15.$$

Then z value corresponding to the observed $y = 218$ is

$$z = \frac{y - \mu}{\sigma} = \frac{218 - 250}{15} = \frac{-32}{15} = -2.1.$$

Noting that z falls in the rejection region, we would reject the null hypothesis and conclude that less than 10% of all smokers prefer brand A.

   What is the probability that we have made an incorrect decision? The answer, of course, is either 1 or 0, depending upon whether our decision was correct or incorrect in this specific case.   However, we know that if this statistical test were employed over and over again, the probability of rejecting the null hypothesis when it is true is only $\alpha = .05$.   Hence we are reasonably certain that we have made the correct decision.

7.7   Summary

Many continuous random variables observed in nature possess a probability distribution which is bell-shaped and which may be approximated by the normal probability distribution discussed in Section 7.1.   The common occurrence of normally distributed random variables may be partly explained by the Central Limit Theorem, which states that, under rather general conditions, the sum or the mean of a random sample of n measurements drawn from a population will be approximately normally distributed in repeated sampling when n is large.

As a case in point, the number of successes, y, associated with a binomial experiment may be regarded as a sum of n sample measurements which will possess, approximately, a normal probability distribution when n, the total number of trials, is large.   This application of the Central Limit Theorem provides a method for calculating, with reasonable accuracy, the probabilities of the binomial probability distribution by using corresponding areas under the normal probability distribution.   While other applications of the Central Limit Theorem and the normal distribution will be encountered in succeeding chapters, we particularly note that the Central Limit Theorem provides justification for the use of the Empirical Rule, Chapter 3.   Furthermore, we observe that the contents of this chapter provide an extension and refinement of the thought embodied in the Empirical Rule.

EXERCISES

1. A sample of $n = 4$ supermarkets is to be selected from a total of nine in a small community.   Give the number of different samples which might be selected.   If the sampling is random, what is the probability that a given sample will be selected?

2. Looking at the histogram of Figure 7.2, guess the value of its mean and standard deviation.   (Hint: The Empirical Rule states that approximately 95% of the measurements associated with a mound-shaped distribution will lie within two standard deviations of the mean.)

3. Let y equal the number of dots observed when a single die is tossed. The mean value of y, Example 5.4, and standard deviation (Exercise 8, Chapter 5) were found to equal $\mu = 3.5$ and $\sigma = 1.71$, respectively. Suppose that the sampling experiment, Section 7.2, were repeated over and over again for an infinitely large number of times, each sample consisting of $n = 5$ measurements. Find the mean and standard deviation for this distribution of sample means. (Hint: See the Central Limit Theorem.) Compare this solution with the solution to Exercise 2, above.

4. Using Table 3, calculate the area under the normal curve between
   (a) $z = 0$ and $z = 1.2$,
   (b) $z = 0$ and $z = -.9$.

5. Repeat Exercise 4 for
   (a) $z = 0$ and $z = 1.6$,
   (b) $z = 0$ and $z = .75$.

6. Repeat Exercise 4 for
   (a) $z = 0$ and $z = 1.46$,
   (b) $z = 0$ and $z = -.42$.

7. Repeat Exercise 4 for
   (a) $z = 0$ and $z = -1.44$,
   (b) $z = 0$ and $z = 2.01$.

8. Repeat Exercise 4 for
   (a) $z = .3$ and $z = 1.56$,
   (b) $z = .2$ and $z = -.2$.

9. Repeat Exercise 4 for
   (a) $z = 1.21$ and $z = 1.75$,
   (b) $z = -1.3$ and $z = 1.74$.

10. Find the probability that z is greater than $-.75$.

11. Find the probability that z is less than 1.35.

12. Find a z_0 such that $P[z > z_0] = .5$.

13. Find a z_0 such that $P[z < z_0] = .8643$.

14. Find the probability that z lies between $z = 0.6$ and $z = 1.67$.

15. Find a z_0 such that $P[z < z_0] = .05$.

16. Find a z_0 such that $P[-z_0 < z < z_0] = .90$.

17. Find a z_0 such that $P[-z_0 < z < z_0] = .99$.

18. Let y be a normally distributed random variable with mean equal to 7 and standard deviation equal to 1.5. If a value of y is chosen at random from the population, find the probability that y falls between $y = 8$ and $y = 9$.

19. The grade-point averages of a large population of college students are approximately normally distributed with mean equal to 2.4 and standard deviation equal to .8. What fraction of the students will possess a grade point average in excess of 3.0?

20. Refer to Exercise 19. If students possessing a grade-point average equal to or less than 1.9 are dropped from college, what percentage of the students will be dropped?

21. The length of life of a type of an automatic washer is approximately normally distributed with mean and standard deviation equal to 3.1 and 1.2 years, respectively. If this type of washer is guaranteed for one year, what fraction of original sales will require replacement?

22. The average length of time required for a college achievement test was found to equal 70 minutes with a standard deviation of 12 minutes. When should the test be terminated if we wish to allow sufficient time for 90% of the students to complete the test? (Assume that the time required to complete the test is normally distributed.)

23. Consider a binomial experiment with $n = 25$, $p = .4$. Calculate $P[8 \leq y \leq 11]$ using
    (a) the binomial probabilities, Table 1, Appendix II,
    (b) the normal approximation to the binomial.

24. Consider a binomial experiment with $n = 25$, $p = .2$. Calculate $P[y \leq 4]$ using
    (a) Table 1, Appendex II,
    (b) the normal approximation to the binomial.

25. A machine operation produces bearings whose diameters are normally distributed with mean and standard deviation equal to .498 and .002, respectively. If specifications require that the bearing diameter equal .500 inch plus or minus .004 inch, what fraction of the production will be unacceptable?

26. A salesman has found that, on the average, the probability of a sale on a single contact is equal to .3. If the salesman contacts 50 customers, what is the probability that at least 10 will buy? (Assume that y, the number of sales, follows a binomial probability distribution.)

27. Voters in a certain city were sampled concerning their voting preference in a primary election. Suppose that candidate A could win if he could poll 40% of the vote. If 920 out of a sample of 2500 voters favored A, does this contradict the hypothesis that A will win?

28. One-thousand flash bulbs were selected from a large production lot and tested. Sixty-three were found to be defective. Does the sample present sufficient evidence to indicate that more than 5% of the bulbs in the lot are defective?

29. A soft drink machine can be regulated so that it discharges an average of μ ounces per cup.   If the ounces of fill are normally distributed with standard deviation equal to .3 ounce, give the setting for μ so that eight-ounce cups will overflow only 1% of the time.

30. A statistical test is to be conducted to test the hypothesis that p, the parameter of a binomial population, is equal to .1.   If the sample size is $n = 400$ and we wish α to be approximately equal to .05 (two-tailed test), locate the rejection region if the test statistic is (a) z, (b) y.

31. Calculate β for the test in Exercise 30 if p really is equal to .15.

32. A newly designed portable radio was styled on the assumption that 50% of all purchasers are female.   If a random sample of 400 purchasers is selected, what is the probability that the number of female purchasers in the sample will be greater than 175?

33. Refer to Exercise 32.   Suppose we wish to test the hypothesis that 50% of all purchasers are female against the alternative that this percentage is less than 50.   To do this, we shall select a random sample of 400 purchasers and reject the hypothesis if the number of female purchasers in the sample is less than or equal to 175.
    (a) Find α for this test.
    (b) Find β if the true fraction of female purchasers is .4.

34. A manufacturing plant utilizes 3000 electric light bulbs that have a length of life which is normally distributed with mean and standard deviation equal to 500 and 50 hours, respectively.   In order to minimize the number of bulbs which burn out during operating hours, all of the bulbs are replaced after a given period of operation.   How often should the bulbs be replaced if we wish no more than 1% of the bulbs to burn out between replacement periods?

35. An advertising agency has stated that 20% of all television viewers watch a particular program.   In a random sample of 1000 viewers, $y = 184$ viewers were watching the program.   Do these data present sufficient evidence to contradict the advertiser's claim?

36. The admissions office of a small college is asked to accept deposits from a number of qualified prospective freshmen so that with probability about .95 the size of the freshman class will be less than or equal to 120.   Consider that the applicants comprise a random sample from a population of applicants 80% of whom would actually enter the freshman class if accepted.
    (a) How many deposits should the admissions counselor accept?
    (b) If applicants in the number determined in part (a) are accepted, what is the probability that the freshman class size will be less than 105?

REFERENCES

Alder, H. L., and E. B. Roessler, *Introduction to Probability and Statistics.* San Francisco: W. H. Freeman and Company, 1960.   Chapter 7.

Hoel, P. G., *Elementary Statistics.* New York: John Wiley & Sons, Inc., 1960.   Chapter 4.

Mack, S. F., *Elementary Statistics.* New York: Holt, Rinehart and Winston, Inc., 1960.   Chapter 5.

8

STATISTICAL
INFERENCE

8.1 Introduction

Inference, specifically decision making and prediction, is centuries old and plays a very important role in our individual lives. Each of us is faced with daily personal decisions and situations which require predictions concerning the future. The government is concerned with predicting the flow of gold to Europe. The broker wishes knowledge concerning the behavior of the stock market. The metallurgist seeks to use the results of an experiment to infer whether or not a new type of steel is more resistant to temperature changes than another. The housewife wishes to know whether detergent A is more effective than detergent B in her washing machine. Hopefully, these inferences are based upon relevant bits of available factual information which we would call observations or data.

In many practical situations the relevant information is abundant, seemingly inconsistent, and, in many respects, overwhelming. As a result, our carefully considered decision or prediction is often little better than an outright guess. The reader need only refer to the "Market Views" section of the *Wall Street Journal* to observe the diversity of expert opinion concerning future stock market behavior. Similarly, a visual analysis of data by scientists and engineers will often yield conflicting opinions regarding conclusions to be drawn from an experiment. While many individuals tend to feel that their own built-in inference-making equipment is quite good, experience would suggest that most people are incapable of utilizing large amounts of data, mentally weighing each bit of relevant information, and arriving at a good inference. (The reader may test his individual inference-making equipment using the exercises in Chapters 8 and 9. Scan the data and make an inference before using the appropriate statistical procedure. Compare the results.) Certainly, a study of inference-making systems is desirable, and this is the objective of the mathematical statistician. Although we have purposely touched upon some of the notions involved in statistical inference in preceding chapters, it will be beneficial to collect our ideas at this point as we attempt an elementary presentation of some of the basic ideas involved in statistical inference.

The objective of statistics is to make inferences about a population based upon information contained in a sample. Inasmuch as populations are characterized by numerical descriptive measures called *parameters*, statistical inference is concerned with making inferences about population parameters. Typical population parameters are the mean, the standard deviation, the area under the probability distribution above or below some value of the random variable, or the area between two values of the variable. Indeed, the practical problems mentioned in the first paragraph of this section can be restated in the framework of a population with a specified parameter of interest.

Methods for making inferences about parameters fall into one of two categories. We may make *decisions* concerning the value of the parameter, as exemplified by the lot acceptance sampling and test of an hypothesis described in Chapter 6. Or, we may *estimate* or predict the value of the parameter. While some statisticians view estimation as a decision making problem, it will be convenient for us to retain the two categories and, particularly, to concentrate on estimation and tests of hypotheses.

A statement of the objective and types of statistical inference would be incomplete without reference to a measure of goodness of inferential procedures. We may define numerous objective methods for making inferences in addition to our own individual procedures based upon intuition. Certainly a measure of goodness must be defined so that one procedure may be compared with another. More than that, we would like to state the goodness of a particular inference in a given physical situation. Thus, to say we predict that the price of a stock will be $80 next Monday would be insufficient and would stimulate few of us to take action to buy or sell.   Indeed, we ask whether the estimate is correct to within plus or minus one dollar, two dollars, or ten dollars.   Statistical inference in a practical situation contains two elements: (1) the inference and (2) a measure of its goodness.

Before concluding this introductory discussion of inference, it would be well to dispose of a question which frequently disturbs the beginner. Which method of inference should be used, that is, should the parameter be estimated or should we test an hypothesis concerning its value?   The answer to this equestion is dictated by the practical question which has been posed and very often is determined by personal preference.   Some people like to test theories concerning parameters while others prefer to express their inference as an estimate.   We will find that there are actually two methods of estimation, the choice of which, once again, is a matter of personal preference.   Inasmuch as both estimation and tests of hypotheses are frequently used in scientific literature, we would be remiss in excluding one or the other from our discussion.

8.2   Types of Estimators

Estimation procedures may be divided into two types, point estimation and interval estimation.   Suppose that we wish to estimate the grade-point average of a particular student at Bucknell University.   The estimate might be given as a single number, for instance, 2.9, or we might estimate that the grade-point average would fall in an interval, for instance, 2.7 to 3.2.   The first type of estimate is called a *point estimate* because the single number, representing the estimate, may be associated with a point on a line.   The second type, involving two points and defining an interval on a line, is called an *interval estimate*.   We will consider each of these methods of estimation in turn.

A point estimation procedure utilizes information in a sample to arrive at a single number or point which estimates the parameter of interest.   The actual estimation is accomplished by an *estimator*.   An estimator is a rule which tells us how to calculate the estimate based upon information in the sample and is generally expressed as a formula. For example, the sample mean,

$$\bar{y} = \frac{\sum\limits_{i=1}^{n} y_i}{n},$$

is an estimator of the population mean, μ, and explains exactly how the actual numerical value of the estimate may be obtained once the sample values, $y_1, y_2, \ldots, y_n$, are known. On the other hand, an interval estimator uses the data in the sample to calculate *two* points which are intended to enclose the true value of the parameter estimated.

An investigation of the reasoning used in calculating the goodness of a point estimator is facilitated by considering an analogy. Point estimation is similar, in many respects, to firing a revolver at a target. The estimator, generating estimates, is analogous to the revolver, a particular estimate to the bullet, and the parameter of interest to the bull's-eye. Drawing a sample from the population and estimating the value of the parameter is equivalent to firing a single shot at the target.

Suppose that a man fires a single shot at a target and that the shot pierces the bull's-eye. Do we conclude that he is an excellent shot? Obviously, the answer is no because not one of us would consent to hold the target while a second shot was fired. On the other hand, if one-million shots in succession hit the bull's-eye, we might acquire sufficient confidence in the marksman to hold the target for the next shot, if the compensation were adequate. The point which we wish to make is certainly clear. We cannot evaluate the goodness of an estimation procedure on the basis of a single estimate; rather, we must observe the results when the estimation procedure is used over and over again, many many times—we then observe how closely the shots are distributed about the bull's-eye. In fact, since the estimates are numbers, we would evaluate the goodness of the estimator by constructing a frequency distribution of the estimates obtained in repeated sampling and note how closely the distribution centers about the parameter of interest.

This point is aptly illustrated by considering the results of the die-tossing experiment, Section 7.2, where one-hundred samples of $n = 5$ measurements were drawn from the die-tossing population which possessed a mean and standard deviation equal to $\mu = 3.5$ and $\sigma = 1.71$, respectively. The distribution of the one-hundred sample means, each representing an estimate, is given in Figure 7.2. A glance at the distribution tells us that the estimates tend to pile up about the mean, $\mu = 3.5$, and also gives an indication as to the error of estimation which might be expected. While the distribution, Figure 7.2, is informative, we would like to have the distribution of estimates based upon an infinitely large number of samples, thus generating the *probability distribution* for the estimator. Fortunately, this task is not too difficult. Mathematical methods are available for deriving the probability distribution of estimators, but these techniques are beyond the scope of this course. A second and very powerful method utilizes a high speed electronic computer to draw the extremely large number of samples required, calculate the corresponding estimates, and record the results in the form of a frequency distribution.

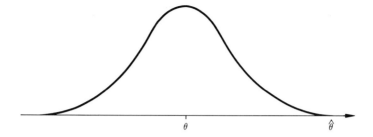

Figure 8.1.   A Distribution of Estimates

Suppose, then, that we wish to estimate some population parameter, which, for convenience, we will call θ.   The estimator of θ will be indicated by the symbol $\hat{\theta}$, where the "hat" indicates that we are estimating the parameter immediately beneath.   Now, with the revolver-firing example in mind, we see that the desirable properties of a good estimator are quite obvious.   We would like the distribution of estimates to center about the parameter estimated as shown in Figure 8.1 and, in addition, we would like the spread of the distribution to be as small as possible.   In other words, we would like the mean or expected value of the distribution of estimates to equal the parameter estimated.

Estimators which satisfy this property, that is

$$E(\hat{\theta}) = \theta,$$

are said to be *unbiased*.   Otherwise, they are said to be biased.   The frequency distributions for an unbiased estimator and a biased estimator are shown in Figures 8.2(a) and (b).

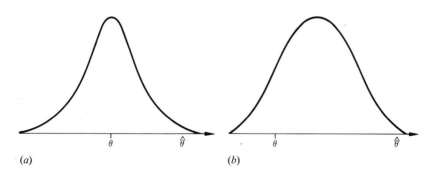

(a)   (b)

Figure 8.2.   Distributions for Unbiased and Biased Estimators

Also, we desire the variance or standard deviation for the estimator—that is, the distribution of estimates—to be a minimum. Thus the distribution of estimates in Figure 8.3(a) is preferable to that shown in Figure 8.3(b).

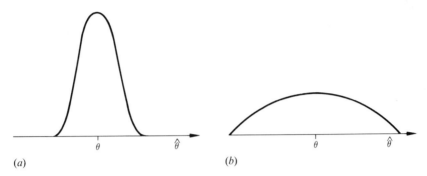

(a)   (b)

Figure 8.3.   A Comparison of Estimator Variability

The goodness of an interval estimator is analyzed in much the same manner as is a point estimator.   Samples of the same size are repeatedly drawn from the population and the interval estimate is calculated on each occasion.   This process will generate a large number of intervals rather than points.   A good interval estimate would successfully enclose the true value of the parameter a large fraction of the time.   This fraction is called the *confidence coefficient* for the estimator while the estimator itself is often called a *confidence interval.*

The selection of a " best " estimator—the proper formula to use in calculating the estimates—involves the comparison of various methods of estimation.   This is the task of the theoretical statistician and is beyond the scope of this text.   Throughout the remainder of this chapter and succeeding chapters, populations and parameters of interest will be defined and the appropriate estimator indicated along with its expected value and standard deviation.

8.3 Point Estimation of a Population Mean

Practical problems very often lead to the estimation of a population mean, μ.   We are concerned with the average achievement of college students in a particular university, in the average strength of a new type of steel, in the average number of deaths per capita in a given social class, and in the average demands for a new product.   Conveniently, the estimation of μ serves as a very practical application of statistical inference as well as an excellent illustration of the principles of estimation discussed in Section 8.2.   Many estimators are available for estimating the population mean, μ, including the sample median, the average between the largest and smallest measurements in the sample, and the sample mean, $\bar{y}$.   Each would generate a probability distribution in repeated sampling and, depending upon the population and practical problem involved, would possess certain advantages and disadvantages.   Although the sample median and the average of the sample extremes are easier to calculate, the sample mean, $\bar{y}$, is usually superior in that, for some populations, its variance is a minimum and, furthermore, regardless of the population, it is always unbiased.

Three facts emerge from a study of the probability distribution of $\bar{y}$ in repeated random sampling of n measurements from a population with mean equal to μ and variance equal to σ^2.   Regardless of the probability distribution of the population,

(1) the expected value of $\bar{y}$ is equal to μ, the population mean.
(2) the standard deviation of $\bar{y}$ is equal to

$$\sigma_{\bar{y}} = \frac{\sigma}{\sqrt{n}} \sqrt{\frac{N-n}{N-1}},$$

where N is equal to the number of measurements in the population.   In the following discussion we will assume that N is large relative to the sample size, n, and hence that $\sqrt{\frac{N-n}{N-1}}$ is approximately equal to 1.   Then,

$$\sigma_{\bar{y}} = \frac{\sigma}{\sqrt{n}}.$$

(3) When n is large, $\bar{y}$ will be approximately normally distributed according to the Central Limit Theorem (assuming that μ and σ are finite numbers.)

Thus $\bar{y}$ is an unbiased estimator of μ with a standard deviation which is proportional to the population standard deviation, σ, and inversely proportional to the square root of the sample size, n.   While we give no proof of these results, we suggest that they are intuitively reasonable. Certainly, the more variable the population data, measured by σ, the more variable will be $\bar{y}$.   On the other hand, more information will be available for estimating μ as n becomes large.   Hence the estimates should fall closer to μ, and $\sigma_{\bar{y}}$ should decrease.

In addition to knowledge of the mean and standard deviation of the probability distribution for $\bar{y}$, the Central Limit Theorem provides information on its form. That is, when the sample size, n, is large, the distribution of $\bar{y}$ will be approximately normal. This distribution is shown in Figure 8.4.

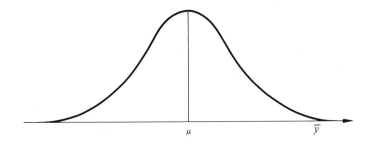

Figure 8.4.   Distribution of $\bar{y}$ for Large n

With the above results in mind, suppose we draw a single sample of $n = 5$ measurements from the die-tossing population described in Section 7.2 and calculate the sample mean, $\bar{y}$. How good will be this estimate of μ; that is, how far will it deviate from the mean, $\mu = 3.5$? While we cannot state that $\bar{y}$ will *definitely* lie within a specified distance of μ, Tchebysheff's Theorem states that if we were to draw many samples from the population, at least three-fourths of the estimates would lie within $2\sigma_{\bar{y}}$ of mean of the distribution of $\bar{y}$'s, that is, μ. We have noted previously (Section 8.2) that $\sigma = 1.71$. Therefore,

$$2\sigma_{\bar{y}} = 2\sigma/\sqrt{n} = \frac{2(1.71)}{\sqrt{5}} = \frac{2(1.71)}{2.24} = 1.53.$$

Better than that, we would expect the distribution of sample means to be approximately normally distributed according to the Central Limit Theorem, in which case approximately 95% of the estimates would lie within $2\sigma_{\bar{y}}$ or 1.53 of μ. A glance at Figure 7.2 will confirm this supposition.

The quantity $2\sigma_{\bar{y}}$ is an approximate bound on the error of estimation. We take this to imply that at least three-fourths of the estimates, and most likely 95%, will deviate from the mean less than $2\sigma_{\bar{y}}$. While the use of two standard deviations rather than three is not sacred, two would seem a reasonable choice for most practical problems.

Consider the following example of point estimation.

Example 8.1: Suppose that we wish to estimate the average daily yield of a chemical manufactured in a chemical plant. The daily yield, recorded for $n = 50$ days, produced a mean and standard deviation equal to

$$\bar{y} = 871 \text{ tons,}$$
$$s = 21 \text{ tons.}$$

Estimate the average daily yield, μ.

Solution: The estimate of the daily yield is then $\bar{y} = 871$ tons. The bound on the error of estimation is

$$2\sigma_{\bar{y}} = 2\sigma/\sqrt{n} = 2\sigma/\sqrt{50}.$$

Although σ is unknown, we may approximate its value by using s, the estimator of σ. Thus the bound on the error of estimation is approximately

$$2s/\sqrt{n} = \frac{2(21)}{\sqrt{50}} = \frac{42}{7.07} = 5.94.$$

We would feel fairly confident that our estimate of 871 tons is within 5.94 tons of the true average yield.

Example 8.1 deserves further comment in regard to two points. The erroneous use of 2σ as a bound on the error of estimation rather than $2\sigma_{\bar{y}}$ is common to beginners. Certainly, if we wish to discuss the distribution of $\bar{y}$, we must use its standard deviation, $\sigma_{\bar{y}}$, to describe its variability. Care must be taken not to confuse the descriptive measures of one distribution with another.

A second point of interest concerns the use of s to approximate σ. This approximation will be reasonably good when n is large, say 30 or greater. If the sample size is small, two techniques are available. Sometimes experience or data obtained from previous experiments will provide a good estimate of σ. When this is not available, we may resort to a small sample procedure described in Chapter 9. The choice of $n = 30$ as the division between "large" and "small" samples is arbitrary. The reasoning for its selection will become apparent in Chapter 9.

8.4   Interval Estimation of a Population Mean

The interval estimator, or *confidence interval*, for a population mean may be easily obtained from the results of Section 8.3. It is possible that $\bar{y}$ might lie either above or below the population mean, although we would not expect it to deviate more than approximately $2\sigma_{\bar{y}}$ from μ. Hence, if we choose $(\bar{y} - 2\sigma_{\bar{y}})$ as the lower point of the interval, called the *lower confidence limit* or LCL, and $(\bar{y} + 2\sigma_{\bar{y}})$ as the upper point, or *upper confidence limit*, UCL, the interval most probably will enclose the true population mean, μ.   In fact, if n is large and the distribution of $\bar{y}$ is approximately normal, we would expect approximately 95% of the intervals obtained in repeated sampling to enclose the population mean, μ.   Two possible distributions, each with means located a distance $2\sigma_{\bar{y}}$ from $\bar{y}$, are shown in Figure 8.5, the corresponding confidence limits being indicated by broken lines.

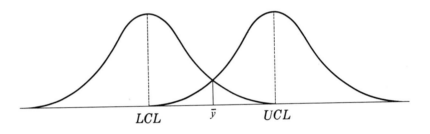

Figure 8.5.   Confidence Limits for μ

The confidence interval described is called a *large sample* confidence interval (or confidence limits) because n must be large enough for the Central Limit Theorem to be effective and hence for the distribution of $\bar{y}$ to be approximately normal.   Inasmuch as σ is usually unknown, the sample standard deviation must be used to estimate σ.   As a rule of thumb, this confidence interval would be appropriate when $n = 30$ or more.

The confidence coefficient, .95, corresponds to $\pm 2\sigma_{\bar{y}}$, or, more exactly, $1.96\sigma_{\bar{y}}$.   Recalling that .90 of the measurements in a normal distribution will fall within $z = 1.645$ standard deviations of the mean (Table 3, Appendix II), we could construct 90% confidence intervals by using

$$\text{LCL} = \bar{y} - 1.645\sigma_{\bar{y}} = \bar{y} - 1.645\sigma/\sqrt{n},$$

and

$$\text{UCL} = \bar{y} + 1.645\sigma_{\bar{y}} = \bar{y} + 1.645\sigma/\sqrt{n}.$$

In general, we may construct confidence intervals corresponding to any desired confidence coefficient, say $(1 - \alpha)$, using

$$\bar{y} \pm z_{\alpha/2}\sigma/\sqrt{n}.$$

We will define the quantity $z_{\alpha/2}$ to be the value in the z-table such that the area to the right of $z_{\alpha/2}$ is equal to $\alpha/2$ (see Figure 8.6); that is,

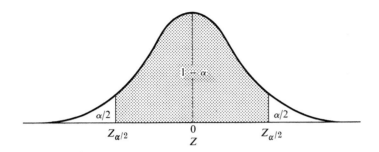

Figure 8.6.   Location of $z_{\alpha/2}$

$P[z > z_{\alpha/2}] = \alpha/2$. Thus, a confidence coefficient equal to .95 would imply $\alpha = .05$ and $z_{.025} = 1.96$. The value of z employed for a 90% confidence interval would be $z_{.05} = 1.645$.

Example 8.2: Find a 90% confidence interval for the population mean of Example 8.1.   Recall that $\bar{y} = 871$ tons and $s = 21$ tons.

Solution: The 90% confidence limits would be

$$\bar{y} \pm 1.645\sigma/\sqrt{n}.$$

Using s to estimate σ, we obtain

$$871 \pm (1.645)\frac{(21)}{\sqrt{50}},$$

or

$$871 \pm 4.89.$$

Therefore, we estimate that the average daily yield, μ, lies in the interval 866.11 to 875.89 tons. The confidence coefficient, .90, implies that in repeated sampling, 90% of the confidence intervals would enclose μ.

Note that the width of the confidence interval increases as the confidence coefficient increases, a result which is in agreement with our intuition.   Certainly if we wish to be more confident that the interval will enclose μ, we would increase the width of the interval.   Confidence limits corresponding to some of the commonly used confidence coefficients are tabulated in Table 8.1.

Table 8.1.   Confidence Limits for μ

CONFIDENCE COEFFICIENT	$z_{\alpha/2}$	LCL	UCL
.90	1.645	$\bar{y} - 1.645\sigma/\sqrt{n}$	$\bar{y} + 1.645\sigma/\sqrt{n}$
.95	1.96	$\bar{y} - 1.96\sigma/\sqrt{n}$	$\bar{y} + 1.96\sigma/\sqrt{n}$
.99	2.58	$\bar{y} - 2.58\sigma/\sqrt{n}$	$\bar{y} + 2.58\sigma/\sqrt{n}$

The choice of the confidence coefficient to be used in a given situation is made by the experimenter and will depend upon the degree of confidence that he wishes to place in his estimate.   As we have pointed out, the larger the confidence coefficient, the wider the interval.   As a result of this freedom of choice, it has become the custom of many experimenters to use a .95 confidence coefficient although there is no logical foundation for its popularity.

The frequent use of the .95 confidence coefficient introduces a question asked by many beginners.   Should one use $z = 1.96$ or $z = 2$ in the confidence interval?   The answer is that it does not really make much difference which value is used.   The value $z = 1.96$ is more exact for a .95 confidence coefficient but the error introduced by using $z = 2$ will be very small.   The use of $z = 2$ simplifies the calculations, particularly when the computing is done manually.   We will agree to use two standard deviations when placing bounds on the error of a point estimator but will use $z = 1.96$ when constructing a confidence interval, simply to remind the reader that this is the z-value obtained from the table of areas under the normal curve.

The reader will note the fine distinction between point estimators and interval estimators.   Note also that when we place bounds on the error of a point estimate, for all practical purposes, we construct an interval estimate.   Furthermore, the point estimate falls in the middle of the interval estimate when a population mean is being estimated.   While this close relationship will exist for most of the parameters estimated in this text, a word of defense of our separation of point and interval estimation is in order.   For instance, it is not obvious that the best point estimator will fall in the middle of the best interval estimator—in many cases it does not.

Furthermore, it is not a foregone conclusion that the best interval estimator will even be a function of the best point estimator. Although these problems are of a theoretical nature, they are important and worth mentioning. From a practical point of view, the two methods are closely related and the choice between the point and the interval estimator in an actual problem depends upon the preference of the experimenter.

8.5   Estimation from Large Samples

Estimation of a population mean, Sections 8.3 and 8.4, sets the stage for the other estimation problems to be discussed in this chapter. A thread of unity runs through all, which, once it is observed, will simplify the learning process for the beginner. The following conditions will be satisfied for all estimation problems discussed in this chapter. Each point estimator of a parameter, say θ, will be unbiased. That is, the mean of the distribution of estimates obtained in repeated sampling will equal the parameter estimated. The standard deviation of the estimator will be given so that we may place a two-standard deviation, $2\sigma_\theta$, bound on the error of estimation. In each case, the point estimator will be approximately normally distributed by the Central Limit Theorem when n is large, and the probability that the error will be less than the bound $2\sigma_\theta$, will be approximately .95.

The corresponding interval estimators will assume that the sample is large enough for the Central Limit Theorem to produce normality in the distribution of the point estimator of θ as well as to provide a good estimate of any other unknown (for example, σ). Then the confidence intervals for any confidence coefficient, $1 - \alpha$, will equal

$$\hat{\theta} \pm z_{\alpha/2}\sigma_\theta .$$

8.6   Estimating the Difference between Two Means

A problem of equal importance to the estimation of population means is the comparison of two population means. For instance, we might wish to compare the effectiveness of two teaching methods. Students would be randomly divided into two groups, the first subjected to method 1 and the second to method 2. We would then make inferences concerning the difference in average student achievement as measured by some testing procedure.

Or, we might wish to compare the average yield in a chemical plant using raw materials furnished by two suppliers, A and B. Samples of daily yield, one for each of the two raw materials, would be recorded and used to make inferences concerning the difference in mean yield.

Each of these examples postulates two populations, the first with means and variance μ_1 and σ_1^2, and the second with mean and variance μ_2 and σ_2^2. A random sample of n_1 measurements is drawn from population I and n_2 from population II, where the samples are assumed to have been drawn independently of one another. Finally, the estimates of the population parameters, $\bar{y}_1$, s_1^2, $\bar{y}_2$, and s_2^2, are calculated from the sample data.

The point estimator of the difference between the population means, $(\mu_1 - \mu_2)$, is $(\bar{y}_1 - \bar{y}_2)$, the difference between the sample means. If repeated pairs of samples of n_1 and n_2 measurements are drawn from the two populations and the estimate, $(\bar{y}_1 - \bar{y}_2)$, calculated for each pair, a distribution of estimates will result. The mean and standard deviation of the estimator, $(\bar{y}_1 - \bar{y}_2)$, will be

$$E(\bar{y}_1 - \bar{y}_2) = \mu_1 - \mu_2,$$

$$\sigma_{(\bar{y}_1 - \bar{y}_2)} = \sqrt{\frac{\sigma_1^2}{n_1} + \frac{\sigma_2^2}{n_2}}.$$

Furthermore, as pointed out in Section 8.5, when n_1 and n_2 are large, say 30 or more, the estimates will be approximately normally distributed in repeated sampling.

Although the formula for the standard deviation of $(\bar{y}_1 - \bar{y}_2)$ may appear to be complicated, a result derived in mathematical statistics will assist in its memorization. Certainly the variability of a difference between two independent random variables would seem, intuitively, to be greater than the variability of either of the two variables, since one may be extremely large at the same time that the other is extremely small. Hence each contributes a portion of its variability to the variability of the difference. This intuitive explanation is supported by a theorem in mathematical statistics which states that the variance of either the sum or the difference of two independent random variables is equal to the sum of their respective variances. That is,

$$\sigma_{(y+y)}^2 = \sigma_y^2 + \sigma_y^2,$$

and

$$\sigma_{(y-y)}^2 = \sigma_y^2 + \sigma_y^2.$$

Therefore,

$$\sigma_{(\bar{y}_1 - \bar{y}_2)}^2 = \sigma_{\bar{y}_1}^2 + \sigma_{\bar{y}_2}^2 = \frac{\sigma_1^2}{n_1} + \frac{\sigma_2^2}{n_2},$$

and the standard deviation is

$$\sigma_{(\bar{y}_1 - \bar{y}_2)} = \sqrt{\frac{\sigma_1^2}{n_1} + \frac{\sigma_2^2}{n_2}}.$$

We will have occasion to use this result again in Section 8.8.
The bound on the error of the point estimate is

$$2\sqrt{\frac{\sigma_1^2}{n_1} + \frac{\sigma_2^2}{n_2}}.$$

The sample variances, s_1^2 and s_2^2, may be used to estimate σ_1^2 and σ_2^2 when these parameters are unknown. This approximation will be reasonably good when n_1 and n_2 are each equal to 30 or more.

Example 8.3: A comparison of the wearing quality of two types of automobile tires was obtained by road testing samples of $n_1 = n_2 = 100$ tires for each type. The number of miles until wear-out was recorded, where wear-out was defined as a specific amount of tire wear. The test results were as follows:

$$\bar{y}_1 = 26,400 \text{ miles}, \qquad \bar{y}_2 = 25,100 \text{ miles};$$
$$s_1^2 = 1,440,000, \qquad s_2^2 = 1,960,000.$$

Estimate the difference in mean time to wear-out and place bounds on the error of estimation.

Solution: The point estimate of $(\mu_1 - \mu_2)$ is

$$(\bar{y}_1 - \bar{y}_2) = 26,400 - 25,100 = 1300 \text{ miles.}$$

Thus,

$$\sigma_{(\bar{y}_1 - \bar{y}_2)} = \sqrt{\frac{\sigma_1^2}{n_1} + \frac{\sigma_2^2}{n_2}}$$

$$\approx \sqrt{\frac{s_1^2}{n_1} + \frac{s_2^2}{n_2}} = \sqrt{\frac{1,440,000}{100} + \frac{1,960,000}{100}}$$

$$= \sqrt{34,000} = 184 \text{ miles.}$$

We would expect the error of estimation to be less than $2\sigma_{(\bar{y}_1 - \bar{y}_2)}$ or 368 miles. Therefore, it would appear that tire type 1 is superior to type 2 in wearing quality when subjected to the road test.

A confidence interval for $(\mu_1 - \mu_2)$ with confidence coefficient $(1 - \alpha)$ can be obtained by using

$$(\bar{y}_1 - \bar{y}_2) \pm z_{\alpha/2}\sqrt{\frac{\sigma_1^2}{n_1} + \frac{\sigma_2^2}{n_2}}.$$

As a rule of thumb, we will require both n_1 and n_2 to be equal to 30 or more in order that s_1^2 and s_2^2 provide good estimates of their respective population variances.

Example 8.4: Place a confidence interval on the difference in mean time to wear-out for the problem described in Example 8.3. Use a confidence coefficient of .99.

Solution: The confidence interval will be

$$(\bar{y}_1 - \bar{y}_2) \pm 2.58\sqrt{\frac{\sigma_1^2}{n_1} + \frac{\sigma_2^2}{n_2}}.$$

Using the results of Example 8.3, we find that the confidence interval is

$$1300 \pm 2.58(184).$$

Therefore, LCL = 825, UCL = 1775, and the difference in mean time to wear-out is estimated to lie between these two points. Note that the confidence interval is wider than the $\pm 2\sigma_{(\bar{y}_1 - \bar{y}_2)}$ used in Example 8.3 because we have chosen a larger confidence coefficient.

8.7 Estimating the Parameter of a Binomial Population

The best point estimator of the binomial parameter, p, is also the estimator that would be chosen intuitively. That is, the estimator, $\hat{p}$, would equal

$$\hat{p} = \frac{y}{n},$$

the total number of successes divided by the total number of trials. By "best" we mean that $\hat{p}$ is unbiased and possesses a minimum variance compared with other possible estimators.

We recall that, according to the Central Limit Theorem, y is approximately normally distributed when n is large. Inasmuch as n is a constant, we would suspect that $\hat{p}$ is also normally distributed when n is large, and this is indeed true. Furthermore, the expected value and standard deviation of $\hat{p}$ can be shown to equal

$$E(\hat{p}) = p,$$

$$\sigma_{\hat{p}} = \sqrt{\frac{pq}{n}}.$$

Bounds on the error of a point estimate will be

$$2\sqrt{\frac{pq}{n}},$$

and the $(1 - \alpha)$ confidence interval, appropriate for large n, is

$$\hat{p} \pm z_{\alpha/2}\sqrt{\frac{\hat{p}\hat{q}}{n}}.$$

The sample size will be considered large when we can assume that $\hat{p}$ is approximately normally distributed. These conditions were discussed in Section 7.4.

The only difficulty encountered in our procedure will be in calculating $\sigma_{\hat{p}}$, which involves p (and $q = 1 - p$), which is unknown. The reader will note that we have substituted $\hat{p}$ for the parameter p in the standard deviation, $\sqrt{pq/n}$. When n is large, little error will be introduced by this substitution. As a matter of fact, the standard deviation changes only slightly as p changes. This can be observed in Table 8.2, where $\sqrt{pq}$ is recorded for several values of p. Note that $\sqrt{pq}$ changes very little as p changes, especially when p is near .5.

Table 8.2.   Some Calculated Values of $\sqrt{pq}$

p	$\sqrt{pq}$
.5	.50
.4	.49
.3	.46
.2	.40
.1	.30

Example 8.5: A random sample of $n = 100$ voters in a community produced $y = 59$ voters in favor of candidate A. Estimate the fraction of the voting population favoring A and place a bound on the error of estimation.

Solution: The point estimate is

$$\hat{p} = \frac{y}{n} = \frac{59}{100} = .59,$$

and the bound on the error of estimation is

$$2\sigma_{\hat{p}} = 2\sqrt{\frac{pq}{n}} \approx 2\sqrt{\frac{(.59)(.41)}{100}} = .096.$$

A 95% confidence interval for p would be

$$\hat{p} \pm 1.96\sqrt{\frac{pq}{n}}$$

or

$$.59 \pm 1.96(.048).$$

Thus we would estimate that p lies in the interval .496 to .684 with confidence coefficient .95.

8.8   Estimating the Difference between Two Binomial Parameters

The fourth and final estimation problem considered in this chapter is the estimation of the difference between the parameters of two binomial populations. Assume that the two populations I and II possess parameters p_1 and p_2, respectively. Independent random samples consisting of n_1 and n_2 trials are drawn from the population and the estimates $\hat{p}_1$ and $\hat{p}_2$ are calculated.

The point estimator of $(p_1 - p_2)$, $(\hat{p}_1 - \hat{p}_2)$, is an unbiased estimator—that is,

$$E(\hat{p}_1 - \hat{p}_2) = (p_1 - p_2),$$

with standard deviation

$$\sigma_{(\hat{p}_1 - \hat{p}_2)} = \sqrt{\frac{p_1 q_1}{n_1} + \frac{p_2 q_2}{n_2}}.$$

Note that in accordance with the last paragraph of Section 8.5 the variance of $(\hat{p}_1 - \hat{p}_2)$ is equal to the sum of the variances of $\hat{p}_1$ and $\hat{p}_2$. Therefore, the bound on the error of estimation is

$$2\sqrt{\frac{p_1 q_1}{n_1} + \frac{p_2 q_2}{n_2}},$$

where the estimates, $\hat{p}_1$ and $\hat{p}_2$, may be substituted for p_1 and p_2.

The $(1 - \alpha)$ confidence interval, appropriate when n_1 and n_2 are large, is

$$(\hat{p}_1 - \hat{p}_2) \pm z_{\alpha/2}\sqrt{\frac{p_1 q_1}{n_1} + \frac{p_2 q_2}{n_2}},$$

Example 8.6: A manufacturer of fly sprays wished to compare two new concoctions, I and II. Two rooms of equal size, each containing 1000 flies, were employed in the experiment, one treated with fly spray I and the other treated with an equal amount of fly spray II. A total of 825 and 760 flies succumbed to sprays I and II, respectively. Estimate the difference in the rate of kill for the two sprays when used in the test environment.

Solution: The point estimate of $(p_1 - p_2)$ is

$$(\hat{p}_1 - \hat{p}_2) = .825 - .760 = .065.$$

The bound on the error of estimation is

$$2\sqrt{\frac{p_1 q_1}{n_1} + \frac{p_2 q_2}{n_2}} \approx 2\sqrt{\frac{(.825)(.175)}{1000} + \frac{(.76)(.24)}{1000}}$$

$$= .036.$$

The corresponding confidence interval, using confidence coefficient .95, is

$$(\hat{p}_1 - \hat{p}_2) \pm 1.96\sqrt{\frac{p_1 q_1}{n_1} + \frac{p_2 q_2}{n_2}}.$$

The resulting confidence interval is

$$.065 \pm .036.$$

Hence we estimate that the difference between the rates of kill, $(p_1 - p_2)$, will fall in the interval .029 to .101. We are fairly confident of this estimate because we know that if our sampling procedure were repeated over and over again, each time generating an interval estimate, approximately 95% of the estimates would enclose the quantity $(p_1 - p_2)$.

8.9 Choosing the Sample Size

The design of an experiment is essentially a plan for purchasing a quantity of information which, like any other commodity, may be acquired at varying prices depending upon the manner in which the data are obtained. Some measurements contain a large amount of information concerning the parameter of interest while others may contain little or none. Since the sole product of research is information, it behooves us to make its purchase at minimum cost.

The sampling procedure, or experimental design as it is usually called, affects the quantity of information per measurement. This, along with the sample size, n, controls the total amount of relevant information in a sample. With few exceptions we will be concerned with the simplest sampling situation, namely random sampling from a relatively large population, and will devote our attention to the selection of the sample size, n.

The researcher makes little progress in planning an experiment before encountering the problem of selecting the sample size. Indeed, perhaps one of the most frequent questions asked of the statistician is, "How many measurements should be included in the sample?" Unfortunately, the statistician cannot answer this question without knowing how much information the experimenter wishes to buy. Certainly, the total amount of information in the sample will affect the measure of goodness of the method of inference and must be specified by the experimenter. Referring specifically to estimation, we would like to know how accurate the experimenter wishes his estimate to be. This may be stated by specifying a bound on the error of estimation.

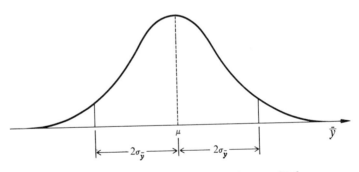

Figure 8.7. The Approximate Distribution of $\bar{y}$ for Large Samples

For instance, suppose that we wish to estimate the average daily yield of a chemical, μ (Example 8.1), and we wish the error of estimation to be less than 4 tons with a probability of .95. Since approximately 95% of the sample means will lie within $2\sigma_{\bar{y}}$ of μ in repeated sampling, we are asking that $2\sigma_{\bar{y}}$ equal 4 tons (see Figure 8.7). Then,

$$2\sigma_{\bar{y}} = 4$$

or

$$2\sigma/\sqrt{n} = 4.$$

Solving for n, we obtain

$$n = \frac{\sigma^2}{4}.$$

The reader will quickly note that we cannot obtain a numerical value for n unless the population standard deviation, σ, is known. And, certainly, this is exactly what we would expect because the variability of $\bar{y}$ depends upon the variability of the population from which the sample was drawn.

Lacking an exact value for σ, we would use the best approximation available, such as an estimate, s, obtained from a previous sample or knowledge of the range in which the measurements will fall. Since the range is approximately equal to 4σ (the Empirical Rule), one-fourth of the range will provide an approximate value for σ. For our example we would use the results of Example 8.1, which provided a reasonably accurate estimate of σ equal to $s = 21$. Then

$$n = \frac{\sigma^2}{4} \approx \frac{(21)^2}{4} = 110.25$$

or

$$n = 111.$$

Using a sample size $n = 111$, we would be reasonably certain (with probability approximately equal to .95) that our estimate will lie within $2\sigma_{\bar{y}} = 4$ tons of the true average daily yield.

Actually we would expect the error of estimation to be much less than 4 tons. According to the Empirical Rule, the probability is approximately equal to .68 that the error of estimation would be less than $\sigma_{\bar{y}} = 2$ tons. The reader will note that the probabilities .95 and .68 used in these statements will be inexact owing to the fact that s was substituted for σ. While this method of choosing the sample size is approximate for a specified desired accuracy of estimation, it is the best available and is certainly better than selecting the sample size on the basis of our intuition.

The method of choosing the sample size for all of the large sample estimation procedures discussed in preceding sections is identical to that described above. The experimenter must specify a desired bound on the error of estimation and an associated confidence level, $1 - \alpha$. For example, if the parameter is θ and the desired bound is B, we would equate

$$z_{\alpha/2}\sigma_\theta = B,$$

where $z_{\alpha/2}$ is the z value defined in Section 8.4; that is,

$$P(z > z_{\alpha/2}) = \alpha/2.$$

We will illustrate with examples.

Example 8.7: The reaction of an individual to a stimulus in a psychological experiment may take one of two forms, A or B. If an experimenter wishes to estimate the probability, p, that a person will react in favor of A, how many people must be included in the experiment? Assume that he will be satisfied if the error of estimation is less than .04 with probability equal to .90. Assume also that he expects p to lie somewhere in the neighborhood of .6.

Solution: Since the confidence coefficient is $1 - \alpha = .90$, α must equal .10 and $\alpha/2 = .05$. The z value corresponding to an area equal to .05 in the upper tail of the z distribution is $z_{\alpha/2} = 1.645$. We then require

$$1.645\sigma_{\hat{p}} = .04$$

or

$$1.645\sqrt{\frac{pq}{n}} = .04.$$

Since the variability of $\hat{p}$ is dependent upon p, which is unknown, we must use the guessed value of $p = .6$ provided by the experimenter as an approximation. Then

$$1.645\sqrt{\frac{(.6)(.4)}{n}} = .04$$

or

$$n = 406.$$

Example 8.8: An experimenter wishes to compare the effectiveness of two methods of training industrial employees to perform a certain assembly operation. A number of employees is to be divided into two equal groups, the first receiving training method 1 and the second training method 2. Each will perform the assembly operation, and the length of assembly time will be recorded. It is expected that the measurements for both groups will have a range of approximately eight minutes. If the estimate of the difference in mean time to assemble is desired correct to within one minute with probability equal to .95, how many workers must be included in each training group?

Solution: Equating $2\sigma_{(\bar{y}_1 - \bar{y}_2)}$ to one minute, we obtain

$$2\sqrt{\frac{\sigma_1^2}{n_1} + \frac{\sigma_2^2}{n_2}} = 1.$$

Or, since we desire n_1 to equal n_2, we may let $n_1 = n_2 = n$ and obtain the equation

$$2\sqrt{\frac{\sigma_1^2}{n} + \frac{\sigma_2^2}{n}} = 1.$$

As noted above, the variability of each method of assembly is approximately the same and hence $\sigma_1^2 = \sigma_2^2 = \sigma^2$. Since the range, equal to eight minutes, is approximately equal to 4σ, then

$$4\sigma = 8$$

and

$$\sigma = 2.$$

Substituting this value for σ_1 and σ_2 in the above equation, we obtain

$$2\sqrt{\frac{(2)^2}{n} + \frac{(2)^2}{n}} = 1.$$

Solving, we have $n = 32$. Thus each group should contain $n = 32$ members.

8.10   A Statistical Test of an Hypothesis

The basic reasoning employed in a statistical test of an hypothesis was outlined in Section 6.5 in connection with the test of the effectiveness of a cold vaccine. In this section we will attempt a condensation of the basic points involved and refer the reader to Section 6.5 for an intuitive presentation of the subject.

The objective of a statistical test is to test an hypothesis concerning the values of one or more population parameters. A statistical test involves four elements:

(1) null hypothesis,
(2) test statistic,
(3) rejection region,
(4) alternative hypothesis.

Note that the specification of these four elements defines a particular test and that changing one or more creates a new test.

The *null hypothesis*, indicated symbolically as H_0, states the hypothesis to be tested. Thus H_0 will specify hypothesized values for one or more population parameters. For example, we might wish to test the hypothesis that a population mean is equal to 50, or that two population means, say μ_1 and μ_2, are equal.

The decision to reject or accept the null hypothesis is based upon information contained in a sample drawn from the population of interest. The sample values are used to compute a single number, corresponding to a line, which operates as a *decision maker* and which is called the *test statistic*. The entire set of values which the test statistic may assume is divided into two sets or regions, one corresponding to the *rejection region* and the other to the *acceptance region*. If the test statistic computed from a particular sample assumes a value in the rejection region, the null hypothesis is rejected. If the test statistic falls in the acceptance region, the null hypothesis is accepted.

The decision procedure described above is subject to two types of errors which are prevalent in any two-choice decision problem. We may reject the null hypothesis when, in fact, it is true, or we may accept H_0 when it is false and some alternative hypothesis is true. These errors are called the type I and type II errors, respectively, for the statistical test. The two states for the null hypothesis, that is, true or false, along with the two decisions which the experimenter may make are indicated in the two-way table, Table 8.3. The occurrences of the type I and type II errors are indicated in the appropriate cells.

Table 8.3.   A Decision Table

	NULL HYPOTHESIS	
DECISION	TRUE	FALSE
Reject	Type I error	Correct decision
Accept	Correct decision	Type II error

The goodness of a statistical test of an hypothesis is measured by the probabilities of making a type I or a type II error, denoted by the symbols α and β, respectively. These probabilities, easily calculated for the elementary statistical tests presented in the Exercises for Chapter 6, illustrate the basic relationship between α, β, and the sample size, n. Since α is the probability that the test statistic will fall in the rejection region, assuming H_0 to be true, *an increase in the size of the rejection region will increase* α and, at the same time, decrease β for a fixed sample size. Reducing the size of the rejection region will decrease α and increase β. If the sample size, n, is increased, more information will be available upon which to base the decision and both α and β will decrease.

The probability of making a type II error, β, varies depending upon the true value of the population parameter. For instance, suppose that we wish to test the null hypothesis that the binomial parameter, p, is equal to $p_0 = .4$. (We will use a subscript 0 to indicate the parameter value specified in the null hypothesis, H_0.) Furthermore, suppose that H_0 is false and that p is really equal to some alternative value, say p_α. Which will be more easily detected, a $p_\alpha = .4001$ or a $p_\alpha = 1.0$? Certainly, if p is really equal to 1.0, every single trial will result in a success and the sample results will produce strong evidence to support a rejection of $H_0: p_0 = .4$. On the other hand, $p_\alpha = .4001$ lies so close to $p_0 = .4$ that it would be extremely difficult to detect without a very large sample. In other words, the probability of accepting H_0, β, will vary depending upon the difference between the true value of p and the hypothesized value, p_0. A graph of the probability of a type II error, β, as a function of the true value of the parameter is called the *operating characteristic curve* for the statistical test. The reader will note that the operating characteristic curves for the lot acceptance sampling plans, Chapter 6, were really graphs expressing β as a function of p.

Since the rejection region is specified and remains constant for a given test, α will also remain constant and, as a in lot acceptance sampling, the operating characteristic curve will describe the characteristics of the statistical test. An increase in the sample size, n, will decrease β and reduce its value for all alternative values of the parameter tested. Thus we will possess an operating characteristic curve corresponding to each sample size. This property of the operating characteristic curve was illustrated in the Exercises for Chapter 6.

Ideally, the experimenter will have in mind some values, α and β, which measure the risks of the respective errors he is willing to tolerate. He will also have in mind some deviation from the hypothesized value of the parameter, which he considers of *practical* importance and which he wishes to detect. The rejection region for the test will then be located in accordance with the specified value of α. Finally, he will choose the sample size necessary to achieve an acceptable value of β for the specified deviation that he wishes to detect. This could be done by consulting the operating characteristic curves, corresponding to various sample sizes, for the chosen test.

We will observe in the next section that the alternative hypothesis, denoted by the symbol, H_α, assists in the location of the rejection region.

8.11   A Large Sample Statistical Test

Large sample tests of hypotheses concerning the population parameters discussed in Section 8.3 to 8.9 are based upon a normally distributed test statistic and, for that reason, may be regarded as one and the same test. We will present the reasoning in a very general manner, referring to the parameter of interest as θ. Thus, we could imagine θ as representing μ, $(\mu_1 - \mu_2)$, p, or $(p_1 - p_2)$. The specific tests for each will be illustrated by examples.

Suppose that we wish to test an hypothesis concerning a parameter θ and that an unbiased point estimator, $\hat{\theta}$, is available and known to be normally distributed with standard deviation $\sigma_{\hat{\theta}}$. If the null hypothesis,

$$H_0: \quad \theta = \theta_0,$$

is true, then $\hat{\theta}$ will be normally distributed about θ_0 as shown in Figure 8.8.

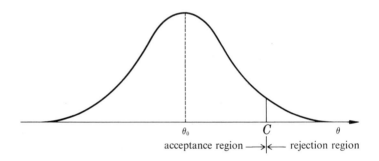

Figure 8.8.   Distribution of $\hat{\theta}$ When H_0 Is True

Suppose that, from a *practical* point of view, we are primarily concerned with the rejection of H_0 when θ is greater than θ_0. Then the alternative hypothesis would be $H_a: \theta > \theta_0$ and we would reject the null hypothesis when $\hat{\theta}$ is too large. "Too large," of course, means too many standard deviations, $\sigma_{\hat{\theta}}$, away from θ_0. The rejection region for the test is shown in Figure 8.8. The value of $\hat{\theta}$, C, which separates the rejection and acceptance regions is called the *critical value* of the test statistic. The probability of rejecting, assuming the null hypothesis to be true, would equal the area under the normal curve lying above the rejection region. Thus if we desire $\alpha = .05$, we would reject when $\hat{\theta}$ is more than $1.645\sigma_{\hat{\theta}}$ to the right of θ_0. A test rejecting in one tail of the distribution of the test statistic is called a *one-tailed statistical test*.

If we wish to detect departures *either* greater than or less than θ_0, the alternative hypothesis would be

$$H_a: \quad \theta \neq \theta_0;$$

that is,

$$\theta > \theta_0$$

or

$$\theta < \theta_0.$$

The probability of a type I error, α, would be equally divided between the two tails of the normal distribution, resulting in a *two-tailed statistical test*.

The calculation of β for the one-tailed statistical test described above can be facilitated by considering Figure 8.9.

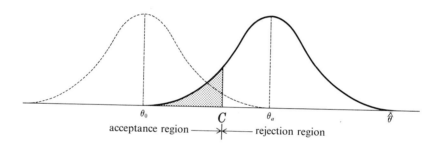

Figure 8.9. *Distribution of $\hat{\theta}$ When H_0 Is False and $\theta = \theta_a$*

When H_0 is false and $\theta = \theta_a$, the test statistic, $\hat{\theta}$, will normally distributed about a mean θ_a, rather than θ_0. The distribution of $\hat{\theta}$, assuming $\theta = \theta_a$, is shown by the solid line. The hypothesized distribution of $\hat{\theta}$, shown by broken lines, locates the rejection region and the critical value of $\hat{\theta}$, C. Since β is the probability of accepting H_0, given $\theta = \theta_a$, β would equal the area under the solid curve located above the *acceptance* region. This area, which is cross-hatched, could be easily calculated using the methods described in Chapter 7.

The reader will quickly note that all of the point estimators discussed in the preceding section satisfy the requirements of the test described above when the sample size, n, is large. That is, the sample size must be large enough so that the point estimator will be approximately normally distributed, by the Central Limit Theorem, and also must permit a reasonably good estimate of its standard deviation.   We may therefore test hypotheses concerning μ, p, $(\mu_1 - \mu_2)$, and $p_1 - p_2$.

The mechanics of testing are simplified by using

$$z = \frac{\hat{\theta} - \theta_0}{\sigma_\theta}$$

as a test statistic as noted in Example 7.8.   Note that z is simply the deviation of a normally distributed random variable, $\hat{\theta}$, from θ_0 expressed in units of σ_θ.   Thus for a two-tailed test with $\alpha = .05$ we would reject H_0 when $z > 1.96$ or $z < -1.96$.

As we have previously stated, the method of inference used in a given situation will often depend upon the preference of the experimenter. Some people wish to express an inference as an estimate; others prefer to test an hypothesis concerning the parameter of interest.   The following example will demonstrate the use of the z-test in testing an hypothesis concerning a population mean and, at the same time, will illustrate the close relationship between the statistical test and the large sample confidence intervals discussed in the preceding sections.

Example 8.9: Refer to Example 8.1, Section 8.3. Test the hypothesis that the average daily yield of the chemical is $\mu = 880$ tons per day against the alternative that μ is either greater or less than 880 tons per day.   The sample (Example 8.1), based upon $n = 50$ measurements, yielded $\bar{y} = 871$ and $s = 21$ tons.

Solution: The point estimate for μ is $\bar{y}$.   Therefore the test statistic is

$$z = \frac{\bar{y} - \mu_0}{\sigma_{\bar{y}}} = \frac{\bar{y} - \mu_0}{\sigma/\sqrt{n}}.$$

Using s to approximate σ, we obtain

$$z = \frac{871 - 880}{21/\sqrt{50}} = -3.03.$$

For $\alpha = .05$, the rejection region is $z > 1.96$ or $z < -1.96$.   Since the calculated value of z falls in the rejection region, we reject the hypothesis that $\mu = 880$ tons and conclude that it is less.   The probability of rejecting, assuming H_0 to be true, is only $\alpha = .05$.   Hence we are reasonably confident that our decision is correct.

The statistical test based upon a normally distributed test statistic, with given α, and the $(1 - \alpha)$ confidence interval, Section 8.5, are clearly related.   The interval $\bar{y} \pm 1.96\sigma/\sqrt{n}$, or approximately 871 ± 5.82, is constructed such that, in repeated sampling, $(1 - \alpha)$ of the intervals will enclose μ.   Noting that $\mu = 880$ does not fall in the interval, we would be inclined to reject $\mu = 880$ as a likely value and conclude that the mean daily yield was, indeed, less.

The following example will demonstrate the calculation of β for the statistical test, Example 8.9.

Example 8.10: Referring to Example 8.9, calculate the probability, β, of accepting H_0 when μ is actually equal to 870 tons.

Solution: The acceptance region for the test, Example 8.9, is located in the interval $\mu_0 \pm 1.96\sigma_{\bar{y}}$. Substituting numerical values, we obtain

$$880 \pm 1.96(21/\sqrt{50})$$

or

$$874.18 \text{ to } 885.82.$$

The probability of accepting H_0, given $\mu = 870$, is equal to the area under the frequency distribution for the test statistic, $\bar{y}$, above the interval 874.18 to 885.86. Since $\bar{y}$ will be normally distributed with mean equal to 870 and $\sigma_{\bar{y}} = 21/\sqrt{50} = 2.97$, β is equal to the area under the normal curve located to the right of 874.18 (see Figure 8.10).   Calculating the

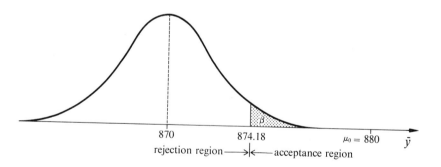

Figure 8.10.   Calculating β in Example 8.10

z-value corresponding to 874.18, we obtain

$$z = \frac{\bar{y} - \mu}{\sigma/\sqrt{n}} = \frac{874.18 - 870}{21/\sqrt{50}} = 1.41.$$

We see from Table 3, Appendix II, that the area between $z = 0$ and $z = 1.41$ is .4207. Therefore,

$$\beta = .5 - .4207 = .0793.$$

Thus the probability of accepting H_0, given that μ is really equal to 870, is .0793 or, approximately, eight chances in one-hundred.

Example 8.11: It is known that approximately one in ten smokers favor cigarette brand A. After a promotional campaign in a given sales region, a sample of 200 cigarette smokers were interviewed to determine the effectiveness of the campaign. The result of the survey showed that a total of 26 people expressed a preference for brand A. Do these data present sufficient evidence to indicate an increase in the acceptance of brand A in the region? (Note that, for all practical purposes, this problem is identical to the cold serum problem given in Example 7.6.)

Solution: It is assumed that the sample satisfies the requirements of a binomial experiment. The question posed may be answered by testing the hypothesis

$$H_0: \quad p = .10$$

against the alternative

$$H_a: \quad p > .10.$$

A one-tailed statistical test would be utilized because we are primarily concerned with detecting a value of p greater than .10. For this situation it can be shown that the probability of a type II error, β, is minimized by placing the entire rejection region in the upper tail of the distribution of the test statistic.

The point estimator of p is $\hat{p} = y/n$ and the test statistic would be

$$z = \frac{\hat{p} - p_0}{\sigma_{\hat{p}}} = \frac{\hat{p} - p_0}{\sqrt{p_0 q_0 / n}}.$$

Or, multiplying numerator and denominator by n, we obtain,

$$z = \frac{y - np_0}{\sqrt{np_0 q_0}},$$

which is the test statistic used in Example 7.8. Note that the two test statistics are equivalent.

Once again we require a value of p so that $\sigma_{\hat{p}} = \sqrt{pq/n}$, appearing in the denominator of z, may be calculated. Since we have hypothesized that $p = p_0$, it would seem reasonable to use p_0 as an approximation for p. Note that this differs from the estimation procedure where, lacking knowledge of p, we chose $\hat{p}$ as the best approximation. This apparent inconsistency will have a negligible effect on the inference, whether it is the result of a test or an estimation, when n is large.

Choosing $\alpha = .05$, we would reject H_0 when $z > 1.645$. Substituting the numerical values into the test statistic, we obtain

$$z = \frac{\hat{p} - p_0}{\sqrt{p_0 q_0/n}} = \frac{.13 - .10}{\sqrt{\dfrac{(.10)(.90)}{200}}} = 1.41.$$

The calculated value, $z = 1.41$, does not fall in the rejection region and hence *we do not reject* H_0.

Do we accept H_0? No, not until we have stated some alternative value of p which is larger than $p_0 = .10$ and which is considered to be of *practical* significance. The probability of a type II error, β, should be calculated for this alternative. If β is sufficiently small, we would accept H_0 and would do so with the risk of an erroneous decision fully known.

Examples 8.9 and 8.11 illustrate an important point. If the data present sufficient evidence to reject H_0, the probability of an erroneous conclusion, α, is known in advance because α is used in locating the rejection region. Since α is usually small, we are fairly certain that we have made a correct decision. On the other hand, if the data present insufficient evidence to reject H_0, the conclusions are not so obvious. Ideally, following the statistical test procedure outlined in Section 8.10, we would have specified a practically significant alternative, p_a, in advance and chosen n such that β would be small. Unfortunately, many experiments are not conducted in this ideal manner. Someone chooses a sample size and the experimenter or statistician is left to evaluate the evidence.

The calculation of β is not too difficult for the statistical test procedure outlined in this section but may be extremely difficult, if not beyond the capability of the beginner, in other test situations. A much simpler procedure for the beginner is *to not reject* H_0, rather than to accept it; then *estimate* using a confidence interval. The interval will give the experimenter a range of possible values for p.

Example 8.12: A university investigation, conducted to determine whether car ownership was detrimental to academic achievement, was based upon two random samples of 100 male students, each drawn from the student body. The grade-point average for the $n_1 = 100$ non-car owners possessed an average and variance equal to $\bar{y}_1 = 2.70$ and $s_1^2 = .36$ as opposed to a $\bar{y}_2 = 2.54$ and $s_2^2 = .40$ for the $n_2 = 100$ car owners. Do the data present sufficient evidence to indicate a difference in the mean achievement between car owners and non-car owners?

Solution: We wish to test the Null Hypothesis that the difference between two population means, $(\mu_1 - \mu_2)$, equals some specified value, say D_0. (For our example we would hypothesize that $D_0 = 0$.)

Recall that $(\bar{y}_1 - \bar{y}_2)$ is an unbiased point estimator of $(\mu_1 - \mu_2)$ which will be approximately normally distributed in repeated sampling when n_1 and n_2 are large. Furthermore, the standard deviation of $(\bar{y}_1 - \bar{y}_2)$ is

$$\sigma_{(\bar{y}_1 - \bar{y}_2)} = \sqrt{\frac{\sigma_1^2}{n_1} + \frac{\sigma_2^2}{n_2}}.$$

Then

$$z = \frac{(\bar{y}_1 - \bar{y}_2) - D_0}{\sqrt{\frac{\sigma_1^2}{n_1} + \frac{\sigma_2^2}{n_2}}}$$

will serve as a test statistic when σ_1^2 and σ_2^2 are known or when s_1^2 and s_2^2 provide a good approximation for σ_1^2 and σ_2^2 (that is, when n_1 and n_2 are larger than 30).

Thus, for our example,

$$H_0: \mu_1 - \mu_2 = D_0 = 0.$$

Substituting into the formula for the test statistic, we obtain

$$z = \frac{(\bar{y}_1 - \bar{y}_2) - D_0}{\sqrt{\frac{\sigma_1^2}{n_1} + \frac{\sigma_2^2}{n_2}}} = \frac{(2.70 - 2.54)}{\sqrt{\frac{.36}{100} + \frac{.40}{100}}} = 1.83$$

Using a two-tailed test with $\alpha = .05$, we would reject when $z > 1.96$ or $z < -1.96$. Since z does not fall in the rejection region, we do not reject the null hypothesis.

Note, however, that if we choose $\alpha = .10$, the rejection region would be $z > 1.645$ or $z < -1.645$ and the null hypothesis would be rejected.

The decision to reject or accept would, of course, depend upon the risk that we would be willing to tolerate. If we choose $\alpha = .05$, the null hypothesis would not be rejected, but we could not *accept* H_0 (that is, $\mu_1 = \mu_2$) without investigating the probability of a type II error. If α were chosen equal to .10, the null hypothesis would be rejected. With no other information given, we would be inclined to reject the null hypothesis that there is no difference in the average academic achievement of car owners versus non-car owners. The chance of rejecting H_0, assuming H_0 true, is only $\alpha = .10$ and hence we would be inclined to think that we have made a reasonably good decision.

Example 8.13: The records of a hospital show that 52 men in a sample of 1000 men versus 23 women in a sample of 1000 women were admitted because of heart disease. Do these data present sufficient evidence to indicate a higher rate of heart disease among men admitted to the hospital?

Solution: We will assume that the number of patients admitted for heart disease will follow approximately a binomial probability distribution for both men and women with parameters p_1 and p_2, respectively. Stated generally, we wish to test the hypothesis that a difference exists between p_1 and p_2, say $(p_1 - p_2) = D_0$. (For our example, we wish to test the hypothesis that $D_0 = 0$.) Recall that for large samples, the point estimator of $(p_1 - p_2)$, $(\hat{p}_1 - \hat{p}_2)$, is approximately normally distributed in repeated sampling with mean equal to $(p_1 - p_2)$ and standard deviation

$$\sigma_{(\hat{p}_1 - \hat{p}_2)} = \sqrt{\frac{p_1 q_1}{n_1} + \frac{p_2 q_2}{n_2}}.$$

Then,

$$z = \frac{(\hat{p}_1 - \hat{p}_2) - (p_1 - p_2)}{\sigma_{(\hat{p}_1 - \hat{p}_2)}}$$

would possess a standardized normal distribution in repeated sampling. Hence z could be employed as a test statistic to test

$$H_0 : (p_1 - p_2) = D_0$$

when suitable approximations are used for p_1 and p_2 which appear in $\sigma_{(\hat{p}_1 - \hat{p}_2)}$. Approximations are available for two cases.

Case I: If we hypothesize that p_1 equals p_2, that is,

$$H_0 : p_1 = p_2,$$

or

$$(p_1 - p_2) = 0,$$

then $p_1 = p_2 = p$ and the best estimate of p is obtained by *pooling* the data from both samples. Thus, if y_1 and y_2 are the numbers of successes obtained from the two samples, then

$$\hat{p} = \frac{y_1 + y_2}{n_1 + n_2}.$$

The test statistic would be

$$z = \frac{(\hat{p}_1 - \hat{p}_2) - 0}{\sqrt{\dfrac{\hat{p}\hat{q}}{n_1} + \dfrac{\hat{p}\hat{q}}{n_2}}}$$

or

$$z = \frac{\hat{p}_1 - \hat{p}_2}{\sqrt{\hat{p}\hat{q}\left(\dfrac{1}{n_1} + \dfrac{1}{n_2}\right)}}.$$

Case II: On the other hand, if we hypothesize that D_0 is *not equal* to zero, that is,

$$H_0 : (p_1 - p_2) = D_0,$$

where $D_0 \neq 0$, then the best estimates of p_1 and p_2 are $\hat{p}_1$ and $\hat{p}_2$, respectively. The test statistic would be

$$z = \frac{(\hat{p}_1 - \hat{p}_2) - D_0}{\sqrt{\dfrac{\hat{p}_1\hat{q}_1}{n_1} + \dfrac{\hat{p}_2\hat{q}_2}{n_2}}}.$$

For most practical problems involving the comparison of two binomial populations the experimenter will wish to test the null hypothesis that $(p_1 - p_2) = D_0 = 0$. Thus, for our example, we test

$$H_0 : (p_1 - p_2) = 0$$

against the alternative

$$H_a : (p_1 - p_2) \neq 0.$$

Note that a two-tailed statistical test will be employed because, if a difference exists, we wish to detect either a $p_1 > p_2$ or a $p_2 > p_1$. Choosing $\alpha = .05$, we will reject H_0 when $z > 1.96$ or $z < -1.96$.

The pooled estimate of p required for $\sigma_{(\hat{p}_1 - \hat{p}_2)}$ is

$$\hat{p} = \frac{y_1 + y_2}{n_1 + n_2} = \frac{52 + 23}{1000 + 1000} = .0375.$$

The test statistic is

$$z = \frac{\hat{p}_1 - \hat{p}_2}{\sqrt{\hat{p}\hat{q}\left(\dfrac{1}{n_1} + \dfrac{1}{n_2}\right)}} = \frac{.052 - .023}{\sqrt{(.0375)(.9625)\left(\dfrac{1}{1000} + \dfrac{1}{1000}\right)}}$$

or

$$z = 3.41.$$

Since the computed value of z falls in the rejection region, we reject the hypothesis that $p_1 = p_2$ and conclude that the data present sufficient evidence to indicate that the percentage of men entering the hospital because of heart disease is higher than that of women. Note that this does not imply the *incidence* of heart disease is higher in men. Perhaps fewer women enter the hospital when afflicted with the disease!

8.12   Some Comments on the Theory of Tests of Hypotheses

The theory of a statistical test of an hypothesis outlined in Section 8.10 is indeed a very clearcut procedure enabling the experimenter to either reject or accept the null hypothesis with measured risks, α and β. Unfortunately, the theoretical framework does not suffice for all practical situations.

The crux of the theory requires that we be able to specify a meaningful alternative hypothesis that permits the calculation of the probability of a type II error, β, for all alternative values of the parameter(s). This indeed can be done for many statistical tests, including the test discussed in Section 8.10, although the calculation of β for various alternatives and sample sizes may, in some cases, be a formidable task. On the other hand, it is extremely difficult, in some test situations, to clearly specify alternatives to H_0 which have *practical* significance. This may occur when we wish to test an hypothesis concerning the values of a *set* of parameters, a situation we will encounter in Chapter 11 in analyzing enumerative data.

The obstacle which we mention does not invalidate the use of statistical tests. Rather, it urges caution in drawing conclusions when insufficient evidence is available to reject the null hypothesis. It, together with the difficulty encountered in the calculation and tabulation for β for other than the simplest statistical tests, justifies skirting this issue in an introductory text. Hence, we will agree to adopt the procedure described in Example 8.10 when tabulated values of β (the operating characteristic curve) are unavailable for the test. When the test statistic falls in the acceptance region, we will "*not reject*" rather than "*accept*." Further conclusions may be made by calculating an interval estimate for the parameter or by consulting one of the several published statistical handbooks for tabulated values of β. We will not be too surprised to learn that these tabulations are inaccessible, if not completely unavailable, for some of the more complicated statistical tests.

The probability of making a type I error, α, is often called the *significance* level of the statistical test, a term which originated in the following way. The probability of the observed value of the test statistic, or some value even more contradictory to the null hypothesis, measures, in a sense, the weight of evidence favoring rejection. Thus some experimenters report test results as being *significant* (we would reject) at the 5% significance level but not at the 1% level. This means that we would reject H_0 if α were .05 but not if it were .01. This line of thought does not conflict with the procedure of choosing the test in advance of the data collection. Rather, it presents a convenient way of publishing the statistical results of a scientific investigation, permitting the reader to choose his own α and β as he pleases.

Finally, we might comment on the choice between a one- or two-tailed test for a given situation. We emphasize that this choice is dictated by the practical aspects of the problem and will depend upon the alternative value of the parameter, say θ, which the experimenter is trying to detect. Thus if we were to sustain a large financial loss if θ were greater than θ_0, but not if it were less, we would concentrate our attention on the detection of values of θ greater than θ_0. Hence, we would reject in the upper tail of the distribution for the test statistics previously discussed. On the other hand, if we are equally interested in detecting values of θ which are either less than or greater than θ_0, we would employ a two-tailed test.

8.13   Summary

The material presented in Chapter 8 was directed toward two objectives. First, we wanted to discuss the various methods of inference along with procedures for evaluating their goodness. Second, we wished to present a number of estimation procedures and statistical tests of hypotheses which, owing to the Central Limit Theorem, make use of the results of Chapter 7. The resulting techniques possess practical value and, at the same time, illustrate the principles involved in statistical inference.

Inferences concerning the parameter(s) of a population may be made by estimating or testing hypotheses concerning their value. A parameter may be estimated using either a point or an interval estimator with the confidence coefficient and width of the interval measuring the goodness of the procedure.

A statistical test of an hypothesis or theory concerning the population parameter(s), ideally, will result in its rejection or acceptance. Practically, we may be forced to view this decision in terms of rejection or non-rejection. The probabilities of making the two possible incorrect decisions, resulting in the type I and type II errors, measure the goodness of the decision procedure. While a test of an hypothesis may be best suited for some physical situations (for example, lot acceptance sampling), it would seem that estimation would be the eventual goal of many experimental investigations and hence would be desirable if one were permitted an option in his choice of a method of inference.

All of the confidence intervals and statistical tests described in this chapter were based upon the Central Limit Theorem and hence apply to large samples. When n is large, each of the respective estimators and test statistics will possess, for all practical purposes, a normal distribution in repeated sampling. This result, along with the properties of the normal distribution studied in Chapter 7, permits the construction of the confidence intervals and the calculation of α and β for the statistical tests.

EXERCISES

1. State the Central Limit Theorem. Of what value is the Central Limit Theorem in statistical inference?

2. The mean and standard deviations for the life of a random sample of one hundred light bulbs were calculated to be 1280 and 142 hours, respectively. Estimate the mean life of the population of light bulbs from which the sample was drawn and place bounds on the error of estimation.

3. Suppose that the population mean, Exercise 2, were really 1285 hours with $\sigma = 150$ hours. What is the probability that the mean of a random sample of $n = 100$ measurements would exceed 1300 hours?

4. A new type of photoflash bulb was tested to estimate the probability, p, that the new bulb would produce the required light output at the appropriate time. A sample of 1000 bulbs was tested and 920 were observed to function according to specifications. Estimate p and place bounds on the error of estimation.

5. Using a confidence coefficient equal to .90, place a confidence interval on the mean life of the light bulbs of Exercise 2.

6. Place a confidence interval on p of Exercise 4, using a confidence coefficient equal to .99.

7. A random sample of 400 radio tubes was tested and 40 tubes were found to be defective. With confidence coefficient equal to .90, estimate the interval within which the true fraction defective lies.

8. A hospital wished to estimate the average number of days required for treatment of patients between the ages of 25 and 34. A random sample of 500 hospital patients between these ages produced a mean and standard

deviation equal to 5.4 and 3.1 days, respectively. Estimate the mean length of stay for the population of patients from which the sample was drawn. Place bounds on the error of estimation.

9. An experiment was conducted to compare the depth of penetration for two different hydraulic mining nozzles. The rock structure and the length of drilling time were the same for both nozzles. With nozzle A the average penetration was 10.8 inches with a standard deviation of 1.2 inches for a sample of fifty holes. With nozzle B the average and standard deviation of the penetration measurements were 9.1 and 1.6 inches, respectively, for a sample of 80 holes. Estimate the difference in mean penetration rate and place bounds on the error of estimation.

10. Construct a confidence interval for the difference between the population means of Exercise 9, using a confidence coefficient equal to .90.

11. The percentage of D's and F's awarded to students by two college history professors was duly noted by the Dean. Professor A achieved a rate equal to 32% as opposed to 21% for Professor B, based upon 200 and 180 students, respectively. Estimate the difference in the percentage of D's and F's awarded by the professors. Place bounds on the error of estimation.

12. The mean of a sample of 43 measurements is 26.3 and the standard deviation is 1.9. Find the 98% confidence limits for the mean of the population.

13. A chemist has prepared a product designed to kill 60% of a particular type of insect. How large a sample should be used if he desires to be 95% confident that he is within .02 of the true fraction of insects killed?

14. Past experience shows that the standard deviation of the yearly income of textile workers in a certain state was $400. How large a sample of textile workers would one need to take if one wished to estimate the population mean to within $50.00, with a probability of .95 of being correct? Given that the mean of the sample in this problem is $4800, determine 95% confidence limits for the population mean.

15. How many voters must be included in a sample collected to estimate the fraction of the popular vote favorable to a presidential candidate in a national election if the estimate is desired correct to within .005? Assume that the true fraction will lie somewhere in the neighborhood of .5.

16. In a poll taken among college students, 300 of 500 fraternity men favored a certain proposition whereas 64 of 100 nonfraternity men favored it. Estimate the difference in the fractions favoring the proposition and place a bound upon the error of estimation.

17. Refer to Exercise 16. How many fraternity and nonfraternity students must be included in a poll if we wish to estimate the difference in the fractions correct to within .05? Assume that the groups will be of equal size and that $p = .6$ will suffice as an approximation to both fractions.

18. From each of two normal populations with identical means and with standard deviations of 6.40 and 7.20, independent random samples of 64 variates are drawn. Find the probability that the difference between the means of the samples exceeds 0.60 in absolute value.

19. If it is assumed that the heights of men are normally distributed with a standard deviation of 2.5 inches, how large a sample should be taken in order to be fairly sure (probability 0.95) that the sample mean does not differ from the true mean (population mean) by more than 0.50 in absolute value?

20. It is desired to use the same mean, $\bar{y}$, to estimate the mean of a normally distributed population with an error of less than .5 with probability .9. If it is known that the variance of the population is equal to 4, how large should the sample be in order to achieve the accuracy stated above?

21. It is desired to estimate the difference in grade-point average between two groups of college students accurate to within .2 grade point. If the standard deviation of the grade-point measurements is approximately equal to .6, how many students must be included in each group. (Assume that the groups will be of equal size.)

22. Define α and β for a statistical test of an hypothesis.

23. What is the level of significance of a statistical test of an hypothesis?

24. The daily wages in a particular industry are normally distributed with a mean of \$13.20 and a standard deviation of \$2.50. If a company in this industry employing 40 workers pays these workers on the average \$12.20, can this company be accused of paying inferior wages at the 1% level of significance?

25. Two sets of 50 elementary school children were taught to read by two different methods. At the conclusion of the instructional period, a reading test gave the results $\bar{y}_1 = 74$, $\bar{y}_2 = 71$, $s_1 = 9$, $s_2 = 10$. Test to see if there is evidence of a real difference between the two population means. (Use $\alpha = .10$.)

26. A manufacturer of automatic washers provides a particular model in one of three colors, A, B, or C. Of the first 1000 washers sold, it is noticed that 400 of the washers were of color A. Would you conclude that customers have a preference for color A? Justify your answer.

27. A manufacturer claimed that at least 20% of the public preferred his product. A sample of 100 persons is taken to check his claim. With an $\alpha = .05$, how small would the sample percentage need to be before the claim could be rightfully refuted? (Note that this would require a one-tailed test of an hypothesis.)

28. Refer to Exercise 27. Sixteen people in the sample of one hundred consumers expressed a preference for the manufacturer's product. Does this

present sufficient evidence to reject the manufacturer's claim?   Test at the 10% level of significance.

29. To test the effects of a new fertilizer on wheat production, a tract of land was divided into 60 squares of equal areas, all portions having similar qualities in respect to soil, exposure to sunlight, etc.   The new fertilizer was applied to 30 squares and the old fertilizer was applied to the remaining squares.   The mean number of bushels of wheat harvested per square of land using the new fertilizer was 18 bushels with a standard deviation of .6 bushels.   The corresponding mean and standard deviation for the squares using the old fertilizer were 17 and .5 bushels, respectively.   Using a significance level of .05, test the hypothesis that there is no difference between the fertilizers against the alternative that the new fertilizer is better than the old.

30. What conditions must be met in order that the z-test may be used to test an hypothesis concerning a population mean, μ?

31. A manufacturer claimed that at least 95% of the equipment which he supplied to a factory conformed to specifications.   An examination of a sample of 700 pieces of equipment revealed that 53 were faulty.   Test his claim at a significance level of .05.

32. Refer to Exercise 2.   Test the hypothesis that the average length of life of the light bulbs is equal to 1300 hours against the alternative that the mean is less.   Use $\alpha = .05$.

33. Refer to Exercise 9.   Do the data present sufficient evidence to indicate a difference in the mean depth of penetration obtained using the two nozzles?

34. Random samples of 200 bolts manufactured by machine A and 200 bolts manufactured by machine B showed 16 and 8 defective bolts, respectively. Do these data present sufficient evidence to suggest a difference in the performance of the machines?   Use a .05 level of significance.

35. In measuring reaction time a psychologist estimates that the standard deviation is .05 seconds.   How large a sample of measurements must he take in order to be 90% confident that the error of his estimate will not exceed .01 seconds?

36. The mean lifetime of a sample of 100 fluorescent bulbs produced by a company is computed to be 1570 hours with a standard deviation of 120 hours.   If μ is the mean lifetime of all the bulbs produced by the company, test the hypothesis $\mu = 1600$ hours against the alternative hypothesis $\mu < 1600$, using a level of significance of .05.

37. Suppose that the true fraction p in favor of the death penalty is the same for Democrats as it is for Republicans.   Independent random samples are selected, one consisting of 800 Republicans and the other of 800 Democrats.

Find the probability that the sample fraction of Republicans favoring the death penalty exceeds that of the Democrats by more than .03 if $p = .5$. What is this probability if $p = .1$?

38. Mr. Sands believes that the fraction p_1 of Republicans in favor of the death penalty is greater than the fraction p_2 of Democrats in favor of the death penalty. He acquired independent random samples of 200 Republicans and 200 Democrats respectively, and found 46 Republicans and 34 Democrats favoring the death penalty. Does this evidence provide statistical support at the .05 level of significance for Mr. Sand's belief?

39. Refer to Exercise 38. Mr. Sands should have put some thought into designing a test for which β is tolerably low when p_1 exceeds p_2 by an important amount. For example, show Mr. Sands how to find a common sample size n for a test with $\alpha = .05$ and $\beta \le .20$ when in fact p_1 exceeds p_2 by .1. Hint: The maximum value of $p(1 - p)$ is .25.

SUPPLEMENTARY EXERCISES

1. Refer to Exercise 27 and calculate the value of β for an alternative, $p_a = .15$.

2. Refer to Exercise 32. What is the probability of not rejecting the null hypothesis, $\mu_0 = 1300$ hours, if the true mean life is equal to 1290 hours?

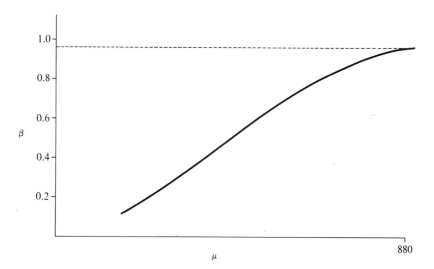

Figure 8.11

3. Refer to Exercise 7.   Suppose that ten samples of $n = 400$ radio tubes were tested and a confidence interval constructed for p for each of the ten samples. What is the probability that exactly one of the intervals will not enclose the true value of p?   At least one?

4. Refer to Example 8.10, Section 8.11.   Using the procedure described in Example 8.10, calculate β for several alternative values of μ.   (For example, $\mu = 873$, 875, and 877.)   Use the three computed values of β along with the value computed in Example 8.10 to construct an operating characteristic curve for the statistical test.   The resulting graph will be similar to that shown in Figure 8.11.

5. Repeat the procedure described in the preceding exercise for a sample size $n = 25$ (as opposed to $n = 50$ used in Sup. Exercise 4) and compare the two operating characteristic curves.

REFERENCES

Dixon, W. J., and F. J. Massey, Jr., *Introduction to Statistical Analysis.*   New York: McGraw-Hill Book Co., Inc., 1957.   Chapters 6 and 7.

Freund, J. E., *Mathematical Statistics.*   Englewood Cliffs, N. J.: Prentice-Hall, Inc., 1962.   Chapters 9, 10, and 11.

9

INFERENCE FROM
SMALL SAMPLES

9.1 Introduction

Large sample methods for making inferences concerning population means and the difference between two means were discussed with examples in Chapter 8. Frequently cost, available time, and other factors limit the size of the sample which may be acquired. When this occurs, the large sample procedures of Chapter 8 are inadequate and other tests and estimation procedures must be employed. In this chapter we will study several small sample inferential procedures which are closely related to the large sample methods presented in Chapter 8. Specifically, we will consider methods for estimating and testing hypotheses concerning population means, the difference between two means, a population variance and a comparison of two population variances. Small sample tests and confidence intervals for binomial parameters will be omitted from our discussion.

9.2 Student's t Distribution

We introduce our topic by considering the following problem. A very costly experiment has been conducted to evaluate a new process for producing synthetic diamonds. Six diamonds have been generated by the new process with recorded weights .46, .61, .52, .48, .57, and .54 karat.

A study of the process costs indicates that the average weight of the diamonds must be greater than .5 karat in order that the process be operated at a profitable level. Do the six diamond weight measurements present sufficient evidence to indicate that the average weight of the diamonds produced by the process is in excess of .5 karat?

The reader will recall that, according to the Central Limit Theorem,

$$z = \frac{\bar{y} - \mu}{\sigma/\sqrt{n}}$$

possesses approximately a normal distribution in repeated sampling when n is large. For $\alpha = .05$, we would employ a one-tailed statistical test and reject when $z > 1.645$. This, of course, assumes that σ is known or that a good estimate, s, is available and is based upon a reasonably large sample (we have suggested $n \geq 30$). Unfortunately, this latter requirement will not be satisfied for the $n = 6$ diamond weight measurements. How, then, may we test the hypothesis that $\mu = .5$ against the alternative that $\mu > .5$?

The problem which we pose is not new; rather it is one that received serious attention by statisticians and experimenters at the turn of the century. If a sample standard deviation, s, were substituted for σ in z, would the resulting quantity possess approximately a standardized normal distribution in repeated sampling? More specifically, would the rejection region $z > 1.645$ be appropriate, that is, would approximately 5% of the values of the test statistic, computed in repeated sampling, exceed 1.645? The answers to these questions, not unlike many of the problems encountered in the sciences, may be resolved by *experimentation*. That is, we could draw a small sample, say $n = 6$ measurements, and compute the value of the test statistic. Then we would repeat this process over and over again a very large number of times and construct a frequency distribution for the computed values of the test statistic. The general shape of the distribution and the location of the rejection region would then be evident.

The distribution of

$$t = \frac{\bar{y} - \mu}{s/\sqrt{n}}$$

for samples drawn from a *normally distributed population* was discovered by W. S. Gosset and published (1908) under the pen name of Student. He referred to the quantity under study as t and it has ever since been known as Student's t. We omit the complicated mathematical expression for the density function for t but describe some of its characteristics.

The distribution of the test statistic

$$t = \frac{\bar{y} - \mu}{s/\sqrt{n}}$$

in repeated sampling is, like z, mound-shaped and perfectly symmetrical about $t = 0$. Unlike z, it is much more variable, tailing rapidly out to the right and left, a phenomenon which may readily be explained. The variability of z in repeated sampling is due solely to $\bar{y}$; the other quantities appearing in z (n and σ) are non-random. On the other hand, the variability of t is contributed by *two* random quantities, namely $\bar{y}$ and s, which can be shown to be independent of one another. Thus when $\bar{y}$ is very large, s may be very small, and vice versa. As a result, t will be more variable than z in repeated sampling. Finally, as we might surmise, the variability of t decreases as n increases because the estimate of σ, s, will be based upon more and more information. When n is infinitely large, the t and z distributions will be identical. Thus Gosset discovered that the distribution of t depended upon the sample size, n.

The divisor of the sum of squares of deviations $(n - 1)$ that appears in the formula for s^2 is called the number of degrees of freedom associated with s^2. The origin of the term, "degrees of freedom," is linked to the statistical theory underlying the probability distribution of s^2. We will not pursue this point further except to note that one may say that the test statistic t is based upon a sample of n measurements or that it possesses $(n - 1)$ degrees of freedom.

The critical values of t which separate the rejection and acceptance regions for the statistical test are presented in Table 4, Appendix II. The tabulated value, t_α, records the value of t such that an area, α, lies to its right as shown in Figure 9.1. The sample size, n, is shown in the first column of the table, and the t_α, corresponding to various values of α, appear in the top row. Thus, if we wish to find the value of t, such that 5% of the area lies to its right, we would use the column marked $t_{.05}$. The critical value of t for our example, found in the $t_{.05}$ column opposite $n = 6$, is $t = 2.015$. Thus we would reject H_0: $\mu = .5$ when $t > 2.015$. Observe that we may use either the sample size, n, or the degrees of freedom, $d.f.$ (shown in the last column of Table 4), to locate the critical value of t.

Note that the critical value of t will always be larger than the corresponding critical value of z for a specified α. For example, where $\alpha = .05$, the critical value of t for $n = 2$ is $t = 6.314$, which is very large

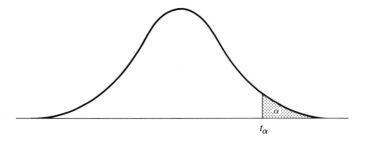

Figure 9.1.   Tabulated Values for Student's t

when compared with the corresponding $z = 1.645$.   Proceeding down the $t_{.05}$ column, we note that the critical value of t decreases, reflecting the effect of a larger sample size on the estimation of σ.   Finally, when n is infinitely large, the critical value of t will equal 1.645.

The reason for choosing $n = 30$ as the dividing line between large and small samples is apparent.   For $n = 30$, the critical value of $t_{.05} = 1.699$ is numerically quite close to $z_{.05} = 1.645$.   For a two-tailed test based upon $n = 30$ measurements and $\alpha = .05$, we would place .025 in each tail of the t distribution and reject $H_0: \mu = \mu_0$ when $t > 2.045$ or $t < -2.045$.   Note that this is very close to the $z_{.025} = 1.96$ employed in the z test.

It is important to note that the Student's t and corresponding tabulated critical values are based upon the assumption that the sampled population possesses a normal probability distribution.   This indeed is a very restrictive assumption because, in many sampling situations, the properties of the population will be completely unknown and may well be non-normal.   If this were to seriously affect the distribution of the t statistic, the application of the t test would be very limited.   Fortunately, this point is of little consequence as it can be shown that the distribution of the t statistic is relatively stable for populations which are non-normal but possess a mound-shaped probability distribution.   This property of the t statistic and the common occurrence of mound-shaped distributions of data in nature enhance the value of Student's t for use in statistical inference.

Secondly, we should note that $\bar{y}$ and s^2 must be independent (in a probabilistic sense) in order that the quantity,

$$\frac{\bar{y} - \mu}{s/\sqrt{n}}$$

possess a t distribution in repeated sampling. As mentioned previously this requirement will automatically be satisfied when the sample has been randomly drawn from a normal population.

Having discussed the origin of Student's t and the tabulated critical values, Table 4, Appendix II, we now return to the problem of making an inference about the mean diamond weight based upon our sample of $n = 6$ measurements. Prior to considering the solution, the reader may wish to test his built-in inference-making equipment by glancing at the six measurements and arriving at a conclusion concerning the significance of the data.

9.3   Small Sample Inferences Concerning a Population Mean

The statistical test of an hypothesis concerning a population mean may be stated as follows:

$$H_0: \mu = \mu_0.$$

$$\text{Test Statistic: } t = \frac{\bar{y} - \mu_0}{s/\sqrt{n}}.$$

Alternative Hypothesis, H_a: Specified by the experimenter depending upon the alternative values of μ which he wishes to detect.

Rejection Region: See the critical values of t, Table 4, Appendix II.

The mean and standard deviation for the six diamond weights are .53 and .0559, respectively, and the elements of the test as defined above are:

$$H_0: \mu = .5.$$

$$\text{Test Statistic: } t = \frac{\bar{y} - \mu_0}{s/\sqrt{n}} = \frac{.53 - .5}{.0559/\sqrt{6}} = 1.31.$$

$$H_a: \mu > .5.$$

Rejection Region: The rejection region for $\alpha = .05$ is $t > 2.015$.

Noting that the calculated value of the test statistic does not fall in the rejection region, we do not reject H_0. This implies that the data do not present sufficient evidence to indicate that the mean diamond weight exceeds .5 karat.

The calculation of the probability of a type II error, β, for the t test is very difficult and is beyond the scope of this text. Therefore, we will avoid this problem and obtain an interval estimate for μ, as noted in Section 8.12.

We recall that the large sample confidence interval for μ is

$$\bar{y} \pm z_{\alpha/2}\sigma/\sqrt{n},$$

where $z_{\alpha/2} = 1.96$ for a confidence coefficient equal to .95. This result assumes that σ is known and simply involves a measurement of $1.96\sigma_{\bar{y}}$ (or approximately $2\sigma_{\bar{y}}$) on either side of $\bar{y}$ in conformity with the Empirical Rule. When σ is unknown and must be estimated by a small sample standard deviation, s, the large sample confidence interval will not enclose μ 95% of the time in repeated sampling. While we omit the derivation, it seems fairly clear that the corresponding small sample confidence interval for μ will be

$$\bar{y} \pm t_{\alpha/2}s/\sqrt{n},$$

where $s/\sqrt{n}$ is the *estimated* standard deviation of $\bar{y}$.

For our example,

$$\bar{y} \pm t_{\alpha/2}s/\sqrt{n} = .53 \pm 2.571 \frac{(.0559)}{\sqrt{6}}$$

or

$$.53 \pm .059.$$

The interval estimate for μ is therefore .471 to .589 with confidence coefficient equal to .95. If the experimenter wishes to detect a small increase in mean diamond weight in excess of .5 karat, the width of the interval must be reduced by obtaining more diamond weight measurements. This will decrease both $1/\sqrt{n}$ and $t_{\alpha/2}$ and thereby decrease the width of the interval. Or, looking at it from the standpoint of a statistical test of an hypothesis, more information will be available upon which to base a decision and the probability of making a type II error will decrease.

Example 9.1: A manufacturer of gunpowder has developed a new powder which is designed to produce a muzzle velocity equal to 3000 feet per second. Eight shells are loaded with the charge and the muzzle velocities measured. The resulting velocities are shown in Table 9.1.

Table 9.1

MUZZLE VELOCITY, ft./sec.

3005	2995
2925	3005
2935	2935
2965	2905

Do the data present sufficient evidence to indicate that the average velocity differs from 3000 feet per second?

Solution: Testing the null hypothesis that $\mu = 3000$ feet per second against the alternative that μ is either greater than or less than 3000 feet per second will result in a two-tailed statistical test. Thus,

$$H_0: \mu = 3000,$$

$$H_a: \mu \neq 3000.$$

Using $\alpha = .05$ and placing .025 in each tail of the t distribution, we find that the critical value of t for $n = 8$ measurements (or seven degrees of freedom) is $t = 2.365$. Hence we will reject H_0 if $t > 2.365$ or $t < -2.365$. (Recall that the t distribution is symmetrical about $t = 0$.)

The sample mean and standard deviation for the recorded data are

$$\bar{y} = 2959 \quad \text{and} \quad s = 39.4.$$

Then

$$t = \frac{\bar{y} - \mu_0}{s/\sqrt{n}} = \frac{2959 - 3000}{39.4/\sqrt{8}} = -2.94.$$

Since the observed value of t falls in the rejection region, we will reject H_0 and conclude that the average velocity is less than 3000 feet per second. Furthermore, we will be reasonably confident that we have made the correct decision. Using our procedure, we should erroneously reject H_0 only $\alpha = .05$ of the time in repeated applications of the statistical test.

A confidence interval will provide additional information concerning μ. Calculating

$$\bar{y} \pm t_{\alpha/2} s/\sqrt{n},$$

we obtain

$$2959 \pm (2.365)\frac{39.4}{\sqrt{8}}$$

or

$$2959 \pm 33.$$

Thus we estimate the average muzzle velocity to lie in the interval 2926 to 2992 feet per second. A more accurate estimate can be obtained by increasing the sample size.

9.4 Small Sample Inferences Concerning the Difference between Two Means

The physical setting for the problem which we consider is identical to that discussed in Section 8.6. Independent random samples of n_1 and n_2 measurements, respectively, are drawn from two populations which possess means and variances μ_1, σ_1^2 and μ_2, σ_2^2. Our objective is to make inferences concerning the difference between the two population means, $\mu_1 - \mu_2$.

The following small sample methods for testing hypotheses and placing a confidence interval on the difference between two means are, like the case for a single mean, founded upon assumptions regarding the probability distributions of the sampled populations. Specifically, we will assume that both populations possess a normal probability distribution and, also, that the population variances, σ_1^2 and σ_2^2, are equal. In other words, we assume that the variability of the measurements in the two populations is the same and can be measured by a common variance which we will designate as σ^2, that is, $\sigma_1^2 = \sigma_2^2 = \sigma^2$.

The point estimator of $\mu_1 - \mu_2$, $(\bar{y}_1 - \bar{y}_2)$, the difference between the sample means, was discussed in Section 8.8 where it was observed to be unbiased and to possess a standard deviation,

$$\sigma_{(\bar{y}_1 - \bar{y}_2)} = \sqrt{\frac{\sigma_1^2}{n_1} + \frac{\sigma_2^2}{n_2}},$$

in repeated sampling. This result was used in placing bounds on the error of estimation, the construction of a large sample confidence interval, and the z test statistic,

$$z = \frac{(\bar{y}_1 - \bar{y}_2) - D_0}{\sqrt{\frac{\sigma_1^2}{n_1} + \frac{\sigma_2^2}{n_2}}},$$

for testing an hypothesis, $H_0: \mu_1 - \mu_2 = D_0$. Utilizing the assumption that $\sigma_1^2 = \sigma_2^2 = \sigma^2$, the z test statistic could be simplified as follows:

$$z = \frac{(\bar{y}_1 - \bar{y}_2) - D_0}{\sqrt{\frac{\sigma^2}{n_1} + \frac{\sigma^2}{n_2}}} = \frac{(\bar{y}_1 - \bar{y}_2) - D_0}{\sigma\sqrt{\frac{1}{n_1} + \frac{1}{n_2}}}.$$

For small sample tests of the hypothesis $H_0: \mu_1 - \mu_2 = D_0$, where D_0 is the hypothesized difference between the means, it would seem reasonable to use the test statistic

$$\frac{(\bar{y}_1 - \bar{y}_2) - D_0}{s\sqrt{\dfrac{1}{n_1} + \dfrac{1}{n_2}}};$$

that is, we would substitute a sample standard deviation s for σ. Surprisingly enough, this test statistic will possess a Student's t distribution in repeated sampling when the stated assumptions are satisfied, a fact which can be proved mathematically or verified by experimental sampling from two normal populations.

The estimate, s, to be used in the t statistic could be either s_1 or s_2, the standard deviations for the two samples, although the use of either would be wasteful since both estimate σ. Since we wish to obtain the best estimate available, it would seem reasonable to use an estimator that would pool the *information* from both samples. This estimator, utilizing the sums of squares of the deviations about the mean for both samples, is

$$s^2 = \frac{\displaystyle\sum_{i=1}^{n_1}(y_i - \bar{y}_1)^2 + \sum_{i=1}^{n_2}(y_i - \bar{y}_2)^2}{n_1 + n_2 - 2},$$

where

$$s_1^2 = \frac{\displaystyle\sum_{i=1}^{n_1}(y_i - \bar{y}_1)^2}{n_1 - 1}$$

and

$$s_2^2 = \frac{\displaystyle\sum_{i=1}^{n_2}(y_i - \bar{y}_2)^2}{n_2 - 1}.$$

Note that the pooled estimator may also be written as

$$s^2 = \frac{(n_1 - 1)s_1^2 + (n_2 - 1)s_2^2}{n_1 + n_2 - 2}.$$

As in the case for the single sample, the denominator in the formula for s^2, $(n_1 + n_2 - 2)$, is called the "number of degrees of freedom" associated with s^2. It can be proven either mathematically or experimentally that the expected value of the pooled estimator, s^2, is equal to σ^2 and hence s^2 is an unbiased estimator of the common population variance.

Finally, we note that the divisors of the sums of squares of deviations in s_1^2 and s_2^2, $(n_1 - 1)$ and $(n_2 - 1)$, respectively, are the numbers of degrees of freedom associated with these two independent estimators of σ^2. It is interesting to note that an estimator using the pooled information from both samples would possess $(n_1 - 1) + (n_2 - 1)$ or $(n_1 + n_2 - 2)$ degrees of freedom.

Summarizing, the small sample statistical test for the difference between two means is as follows.

$$H_0: \mu_1 - \mu_2 = D_0.$$

$$\text{Test Statistic}: t = \frac{(\bar{y}_1 - \bar{y}_2) - D_0}{s\sqrt{\dfrac{1}{n_1} + \dfrac{1}{n_2}}}.$$

The alternative hypothesis, H_a, and α would be specified by the experimenter and would be used to locate the critical value of t for the rejection region.

The critical value of t can be obtained from Table 4, Appendix II, with one slight adjustment to the procedure outlined in Section 9.2. Now that we are utilizing information from two samples to estimate σ^2, we can no longer use the first column indicating sample size, n, to locate the critical value for t. Rather, we will use the last column on the right, marked d.f., for degrees of freedom. Thus if $n_1 = 10$ and $n_2 = 12$, we would use the t value corresponding to $(n_1 + n_2 - 2) = 20$ degrees of freedom. The following example will serve as an illustration.

Example 9.2: An assembly operation in a manufacturing plant requires approximately a one-month training period for a new employee

Table 9.2

STANDARD PROCEDURE	NEW PROCEDURE
32	35
37	31
35	29
28	25
41	34
44	40
35	27
31	32
34	31

to reach maximum efficiency. A new method of training was suggested and a test was conducted to compare the new method with the standard procedure. Two groups of nine new employees were trained for a period of three weeks, one group using the new method and the other following standard training procedure. The length of time in minutes required for each employee to assemble the device was recorded at the end of the three-week period. These measurements appear in Table 9.2. Do the data present sufficient evidence to indicate that the mean time to assemble at the end of a three-week training period is less for the new training procedure?

Solution: Let μ_1 and μ_2 equal the mean time to assemble for the standard and the new assembly procedures, respectively. Also, assume that the variability in mean time to assemble is essentially a function of individual differences and that the variability for the two populations of measurements will be approximately equal.

The sample means and sums of squares of deviations are

$$\bar{y}_1 = 35.22,$$

$$\sum_{i=1}^{9} (y_i - \bar{y}_1)^2 = 195.56;$$

$$\bar{y}_2 = 31.56,$$

$$\sum_{i=1}^{9} (y_i - \bar{y}_2)^2 = 160.22.$$

Then the pooled estimate of the common variance is

$$s^2 = \frac{\sum_{i=1}^{9} (y_i - \bar{y}_1)^2 + \sum_{=1}^{9} (y_i - \bar{y}_2)^2}{n_1 + n_2 - 2}$$

$$= \frac{195.56 + 160.22}{9 + 9 - 2}$$

$$= 22.24,$$

and the standard deviation is $s = 4.71$.

The null hypothesis to be tested is

$$H_0: \mu_1 - \mu_2 = 0.$$

Suppose that we are concerned only with detecting whether the new method reduces the assembly time, and therefore that the alternative hypothesis is

$$H_a: \mu_1 - \mu_2 > 0.$$

This would imply that we should use a one-tailed statistical test and that the rejection region for the test will be located in the upper tail of the t distribution. Referring to Table 4, Appendix II, we note that the critical value of t for $\alpha = .05$ and $(n_1 + n_2 - 2) = 16$ degrees of freedom is 1.746. Therefore, we will reject when $t > 1.746$.

The calculated value of the test statistic is

$$t = \frac{(\bar{y}_1 - \bar{y}_2)}{s\sqrt{\dfrac{1}{n_1} + \dfrac{1}{n_2}}} = \frac{35.22 - 31.56}{4.71\sqrt{\dfrac{1}{9} + \dfrac{1}{9}}}$$

$$= 1.65.$$

Comparing this with the critical value, $t = 1.746$, we note that the calculated value does not fall in the rejection region. Therefore, we must conclude that there is insufficient evidence to indicate that the new method of training is superior at the .05 level of significance.

The small sample confidence interval for $(\mu_1 - \mu_2)$ is based upon the same assumptions as was the statistical test procedure. This confidence interval, with confidence coefficient $(1 - \alpha)$, is given by the formula

$$(\bar{y}_1 - \bar{y}_2) \pm t_{\alpha/2} s \sqrt{\frac{1}{n_1} + \frac{1}{n_2}}.$$

Note the similarity in the procedures for constructing the confidence intervals for a single mean, Section 9.2, and the difference between two means. In both cases, the interval is constructed by using the appropriate point estimator and then adding and subtracting an amount equal to $t_{\alpha/2}$ times the *estimated* standard deviation of the point estimator.

Example 9.3: Find an interval estimate for $(\mu_1 - \mu_2)$, Example 9.2, using a confidence coefficient equal to .95.

Solution: Substituting into the formula

$$(\bar{y}_1 - \bar{y}_2) \pm t_{\alpha/2} s \sqrt{\frac{1}{n_1} + \frac{1}{n_2}},$$

we find the interval estimate (or 95% confidence interval) to be

$$(35.22 - 31.56) \pm (2.120)(4.71)\sqrt{\frac{1}{9} + \frac{1}{9}}$$

or

$$3.66 \pm 4.68.$$

Thus, we estimate the difference in mean time to assemble, $\mu_1 - \mu_2$, to fall in the interval -1.02 to 8.34. Note that the interval width is considerable and that it would seem advisable to increase the size of the samples and re-estimate.

Before concluding our discussion it is necessary to comment on the two assumptions upon which our inferential procedures are based. Moderate departures from the assumption that the populations possess a normal probability distribution do not seriously affect the distribution of the test statistic and the confidence coefficient for the corresponding confidence interval. On the other hand, the population variances should be nearly equal in order that the aforementioned procedures be valid.

If there is reason to believe that the population variances are unequal, an adjustment must be made in the test procedure and the corresponding confidence interval. We omit a discussion of these techniques but refer the interested reader to texts by Li or Anderson and Bancroft (see page 221).

A procedure will be presented in Section 9.7 for testing an hypothesis concerning the equality of two population variances.

9.5   A Paired-Difference Test

A manufacturer wished to compare the wearing qualities of two different types of automobile tires, A and B. To make the comparison, a tire of type A and one of type B were randomly assigned and mounted on the rear wheels of each of five automobiles. The automobiles were then operated for a specified number of miles and the amount of wear was recorded for each tire. These measurements appear in Table 9.3.

Table 9.3

AUTOMOBILE	A	B
1	10.6	10.2
2	9.8	9.4
3	12.3	11.8
4	9.7	9.1
5	8.8	8.3
	$\bar{y}_1 = 10.24$	$\bar{y}_2 = 9.76$

Do the data present sufficient evidence to indicate a difference in the average wear for the two tire types?

Analyzing the data, we note that the difference between the two sample means is $(\bar{y}_1 - \bar{y}_2) = .48$, a rather small quantity, considering the variability of the data and the small number of measurements involved. At first glance it would seem that there is little evidence to indicate a difference between the population means, a conjecture which we may check by the method outlined in Section 9.3.

The pooled estimate of the common variance, σ^2, is

$$s^2 = \frac{\sum\limits_{i=1}^{n_1} (y_i - \bar{y}_1) + \sum\limits_{i=1}^{n_2} (y_i - \bar{y}_2)^2}{n_1 + n_2 - 2} = \frac{6.932 + 7.052}{5 + 5 - 2} = 1.748,$$

and

$$s = 1.32.$$

The calculated value of t used to test the hypothesis that $\mu_1 = \mu_2$ is

$$t = \frac{(\bar{y}_1 - \bar{y}_2)}{s\sqrt{\dfrac{1}{n} + \dfrac{1}{n}}} = \frac{10.24 - 9.76}{1.32\sqrt{\dfrac{1}{5} + \dfrac{1}{5}}} = .58,$$

a value that is not nearly large enough to reject the hypothesis that $\mu_1 = \mu_2$.

The corresponding 95% confidence interval is

$$(\bar{y}_1 - \bar{y}_2) \pm t_{\alpha/2} s \sqrt{\frac{1}{n_1} + \frac{1}{n_2}} = (10.24 - 9.76) \pm (2.306)(1.32)\sqrt{\frac{1}{5} + \frac{1}{5}}$$

or -1.45 to 2.41. Note that the interval is quite wide, considering the small difference between the sample means.

A second glance at the data reveals a marked inconsistency with this conclusion. We note that the wear measurement for the type A is larger than the corresponding value for type B for *each* of the five automobiles. These differences, recorded as $d = A - B$, are shown below.

AUTOMOBILE	$d = A - B$
1	.4
2	.4
3	.5
4	.6
5	.5

$$\bar{d} = .48$$

Suppose that we were to use y, the number of times that A is larger than B, as a test statistic, as was done in Exercise 21, Chapter 6. Then the probability that A would be larger than B on a given automobile, assuming no difference between the wearing quality of the tires, would be $p = 1/2$, and y would be a binomial random variable.

If we choose $y = 0$ and $y = 5$ as the rejection region for a two-tailed test, then $\alpha = P(0) + P(5) = 2(1/2)^5 = 1/16$. We would then *reject* $H_0: \mu_1 = \mu_2$ with a probability of a type I error equal to $\alpha = 1/16$. Certainly this is evidence to indicate that a difference exists in the mean wear of the two tire types.

The reader will note that we have employed two different statistical tests to test the same hypothesis. Is it not peculiar that the t test, which utilizes more information (the actual sample measurements) than the binomial test, fails to supply sufficient evidence for rejection of the hypothesis $\mu_1 = \mu_2$?

The explanation of this seeming inconsistency is quite simple. The t test described in Section 9.3 is *not* the proper statistical test to be used for our example. The statistical test procedure, Section 9.3, required that the two samples be *independent* and random. Certainly, the independence requirement was violated by the manner in which the experiment was conducted. The (pair of) measurements, an A and a B, for a particular automobile are definitely related. A glance at the data will show that the readings are of approximately the same magnitude for a particular automobile but vary from one automobile to another. This, of course, is exactly what we might expect. Tire wear, in a large part, is determined by driver habits, the balance of the wheels, and the road surface. Since each automobile had a different driver, we would expect a large amount of variability in the data from one automobile to another.

The familiarity we have gained with interval estimation has shown that the width of the large and small sample confidence intervals will depend upon the magnitude of the standard deviation of the point estimator of the parameter. The smaller its value, the better the estimate and the more likely that the test statistic will reject the null hypothesis if it is, in fact, false. Knowledge of this phenomenon was utilized in *designing* the tire wear experiment.

The experimenter would realize that the wear measurements would vary greatly from auto to auto and that this variability could not be separated from the data if the tires were assigned to the ten wheels in a *random* manner. (A random assignment of the tires would have implied that the data be analyzed according to the procedure of Section 9.3.) Instead, a comparison of the wear between the tire types A and B made on each automobile resulted in the five difference measurements. This design eliminates the effect of the car-to-car variability and yields more information on the mean difference in the wearing quality for the two tire types.

The proper analysis of the data would utilize the five difference measurements to test the hypothesis that the average difference is equal to zero, a statement which is equivalent to $H_0: \mu_1 = \mu_2$.

The reader may verify that the average and standard deviation of the five difference measurements are

$$\bar{d} = .48,$$

$$s_d = .0837.$$

Then,

$$H_0: \mu_d = 0$$

and

$$t = \frac{\bar{d} - 0}{s_d/\sqrt{n}} = \frac{.48}{.0837/\sqrt{5}} = 12.8.$$

The critical value of t for a two-tailed statistical test, $\alpha = .05$ and four degrees of freedom, is 2.776. Certainly, the observed value of $t = 12.8$ is extremely large and highly significant. Hence we would conclude that the average amount of wear for tire type B is less than that for type A.

A 95% confidence interval for the difference between the mean wear would be

$$\bar{d} \pm t_{\alpha/2}s_d/\sqrt{n} = .48 \pm (2.776)\frac{(.0837)}{\sqrt{5}}$$

or $.48 \pm .10$.

The statistical design of the tire experiment represents a simple example of a *randomized block design* and the resulting statistical test is often called a *paired difference* test. The reader will note that the pairing occurred when the experiment was planned and *not* after the data were collected. Comparisons of tire wear were made within relatively homogeneous blocks (automobiles) with the tire types *randomly* assigned to the two automobile wheels.

An indication of the gain in the amount of information obtained by blocking the tire experiment may be observed by comparing the calculated confidence interval for the unpaired (and incorrect) analysis with the interval obtained for the paired-difference analysis. The confidence interval for $(\mu_1 - \mu_2)$ that might have been calculated, had the tires been randomly assigned to the ten wheels (unpaired), is unknown but likely would have been of the same magnitude as the interval -1.45 to 2.41, calculated by analyzing the observed data in an unpaired manner. Pairing the tire types on the automobiles (blocking) and the resulting analysis of the differences produced the interval estimate .38 to .58. Note the difference in the width of the intervals indicating the very sizeable increase in information obtained by blocking in this experiment.

While blocking proved to be very beneficial in the tire experiment, this may not always be the case. We observe that the degrees of freedom available for estimating σ^2 are less for the paired than for the corresponding unpaired experiment. If there were actually no difference between the blocks, the reduction in the degrees of freedom would produce a moderate increase in the $t_{\alpha/2}$ employed in the confidence interval and hence increase the width of the interval. This, of course, did not occur in the tire experiment because the large reduction in the standard deviation of $\bar{d}$ more than compensated for the loss in degrees of freedom.

9.6   Inference Concerning a Population Variance

We have seen in the preceding sections that an estimate of the population variance, σ^2, is fundamental to procedures for making inferences about population means. Moreover, there are many practical situations where σ^2 is the primary objective of an experimental investigation, thus it assumes a position of far greater importance than that of the population mean.

Scientific measuring instruments must provide unbiased readings with a very small error of measurement. An aircraft altimeter that measured the correct altitude on the *average* would be of little value if the standard deviation of the error of measurement were 5000 feet. Indeed, bias in a measuring instrument can often be corrected but the precision of the instrument, measured by the standard deviation of the error of measurement, is usually a function of the design of the instrument itself and cannot be controlled.

Machined parts in a manufactured process must be produced with minimum variability in order to reduce out-of-size and hence defective products. And, in general, it is desirable to maintain a minimum variance in the measurements of the quality characteristics of an industrial product in order to achieve process control and therefore minimize the percentage of poor quality product.

The sample variance,

$$s^2 = \frac{\sum_{i=1}^{n} (y_i - \bar{y})^2}{n - 1},$$

is an unbiased estimator of the population variance, σ^2. Thus the distribution of sample variances generated by repeated sampling will have a probability distribution that commences at $s^2 = 0$ (since s^2 cannot be negative) with a mean equal to σ^2. Unlike the distribution of $\bar{y}$, the distribution of s^2 is non-symmetrical, the exact form being dependent upon the probability distribution of the population.

For the methodology that follows we will assume that the sample is drawn from a normal population and that s^2 is based upon a random sample of n measurements. Or, using the terminology of Section 9.2, we would say that s^2 possesses $(n-1)$ degrees of freedom.

The next and obvious step would be to consider the distribution of s^2 in repeated sampling from a specified normal distribution—one with a specific mean and variance—and to tabulate the critical values of s^2 for some of the commonly used tail areas. If this is done, we will find that the distribution of s^2 is independent of the population mean, μ, but possesses a distribution for each sample size and each value of σ^2. This task would be quite laborious but fortunately it may be simplified by *standardizing*, as was done by using z in the normal tables.

The quantity

$$\chi^2 = \frac{(n-1)s^2}{\sigma^2},$$

called a *chi-square variable* by statisticians, admirably suits our purposes. Its distribution in repeated sampling is called, as we might suspect, a *chi-square* probability distribution. The equation of the density function for the chi-square distribution is well known to statisticians who have tabulated critical values corresponding to various tail areas of the distribution. These values are presented in Table 5, Appendix II.

The shape of the chi-square distribution, like that of the t distribution, will vary with the sample size or, equivalently, with the degrees of freedom associated with s^2. Thus Table 5, Appendix II, is constructed in exactly the same manner as the t-table, with the degrees of freedom shown in the last column. The symbol χ_α^2 indicates that the tabulated χ^2 value is such that an area, α, lies to its right. Stated in probabilistic terms,

$$P(\chi^2 > \chi_\alpha^2) = \alpha.$$

Thus, 99% of the area under the χ^2 distribution would lie to the right of $\chi_{.99}^2$. We note that the extreme values of χ^2 must be tabulated for both the lower and upper tail of the distribution because it is non-symmetrical.

The reader may check his ability to use the table by verifying the following statements. The probability that χ^2, based upon $n = 16$

measurements, will exceed 24.996 is .05.   For a sample of $n = 6$ measurements, 95% of the area under the χ^2 distribution will lie to the right of
$\chi^2 = 1.145$.

The statistical test of a null hypothesis concerning a population
variance,

$$H_0: \sigma^2 = \sigma_0^2,$$

will employ the test statistic

$$\chi^2 = \frac{(n-1)s^2}{\sigma_0^2}.$$

If σ^2 is really greater than the hypothesized value, σ_0^2, then the test statistic
will be large and will likely fall toward the upper tail of the distribution.
If $\sigma^2 < \sigma_0^2$, the test statistic will tend to be small and will likely fall toward
the lower tail of the χ^2 distribution.   As in other statistical tests, we may
use either a one- or two-tailed statistical test, depending upon the alternative
hypothesis that we choose.   We will illustrate with an example.

Example 9.4: A cement manufacturer claimed that concrete prepared
from his product would possess a relatively stable compressive strength
and that the strength, measured in kilograms per square centimeter, would
lie within a range of 40 kilograms per square centimeter.   A sample of
$n = 10$ measurements produced a mean and variance equal to, respectively,

$$\bar{y} = 312,$$

$$s^2 = 195.$$

Do these data present sufficient evidence to reject the manufacturer's
claim?

Solution: As stated, the manufacturer claimed that the range of the
strength measurements would equal 40 kilograms per square centimeter.
We will suppose that he meant that the measurements would lie within
this range 95% of the time and, therefore, that the range would equal
approximately 4σ and that $\sigma = 10$.   We would then wish to test the null
hypothesis

$$H_0: \sigma^2 = (10)^2 = 100$$

against the alternative

$$H_a: \sigma^2 > 100.$$

The alternative hypothesis would require a one-tailed statistical test with the entire rejection region located in the upper tail of the χ^2 distribution. The critical value of χ^2 for $\alpha = .05$, $n = 10$, is $\chi^2 = 16.919$, which implies that we will reject H_0 if the test statistic exceeds this value.

Calculating, we obtain

$$\chi^2 = \frac{(n-1)s^2}{\sigma_0^2} = \frac{1755}{100} = 17.55.$$

Since the value of the test statistic falls in the rejection region, we conclude that the null hypothesis is false and that the range of concrete strength measurements will exceed the manufacturer's claim.

A confidence interval for σ^2 with a $(1 - \alpha)$ confidence coefficient can be shown to be

$$\frac{(n-1)s^2}{\chi_U^2} < \sigma^2 < \frac{(n-1)s^2}{\chi_L^2},$$

where χ_L^2 and χ_U^2 are the lower and upper χ^2 values which would locate one-half of α in each tail.

For example, a 90% confidence interval for σ^2, Example 9.4, would use

$$\chi_L^2 = \chi_{.95}^2 = 3.325,$$

$$\chi_U^2 = \chi_{.05}^2 = 16.919.$$

Then the interval estimate for σ^2 would be

$$\frac{(9)(195)}{16.919} < \sigma^2 < \frac{(9)(195)}{3.325}$$

or

$$103.73 < \sigma^2 < 527.82.$$

Example 9.5: An experimenter was convinced that his measuring equipment possessed a variability measured by a standard deviation, $\sigma = 2$. During an experiment he recorded the measurements 4.1, 5.2, 10.2. Do these data disagree with his assumption? Test the hypothesis, $H_0: \sigma = 2$ or $\sigma^2 = 4$, and place a 90% confidence interval on σ^2.

Solution: The calculated sample variance is $s^2 = 10.57$. If we wish to detect $\sigma^2 > 4$ as well as $\sigma^2 < 4$, we should employ a two-tailed test. Using $\alpha = .10$ and placing .05 in each tail, we will reject when $\chi^2 > 5.991$ or $\chi^2 < .103$.

The calculated value of the test statistic is

$$\chi^2 = \frac{(n-1)s^2}{\sigma_0} = \frac{(2)(10.57)}{4} = 5.29.$$

Since the test statistic does not fall in the rejection region, the data do not provide sufficient evidence to reject the null hypothesis, $H_0 : \sigma^2 = 4$.

The corresponding 90% confidence interval is

$$\frac{(n-1)s^2}{\chi_U^2} < \sigma^2 < \frac{(n-1)s^2}{\chi_L^2}.$$

The values of χ_L^2 and χ_U^2 are

$$\chi_L^2 = \chi_{.95}^2 = .103,$$

$$\chi_U^2 = \chi_{.05}^2 = 5.991.$$

Substituting these values into the formula for the interval estimate, we obtain

$$\frac{2(10.57)}{5.991} < \sigma^2 < \frac{2(10.57)}{.103}$$

or

$$3.53 < \sigma^2 < 205.24.$$

9.7 Comparing Two Population Variances

The need for statistical methods to compare two population variances is readily apparent from the discussion in Section 9.6. We may frequently wish to compare the precision of one measuring device with that of another, the stability of one manufacturing process with that of another, or even the variability in the grading procedure of one college professor with that of another.

Intuitively, we might compare two population variances, σ_1^2 and σ_2^2, using the ratio of the sample variances s_1^2/s_2^2. If s_1^2/s_2^2 is nearly equal to one, we would find little evidence to indicate that σ_1^2 and σ_2^2 are unequal. On the other hand, a very large or very small value for s_1^2/s_2^2 would provide evidence of a difference in the population variances.

How large or small must s_1^2/s_2^2 be in order that sufficient evidence exist to reject the null hypothesis,

$$H_0 : \sigma_1^2 = \sigma_2^2?$$

The answer to this question may readily be acquired by studying the distribution of s_1^2/s_2^2 in repeated sampling.

When independent random samples are drawn from two normal populations with equal variances, that is, $\sigma_1^2 = \sigma_2^2$, then s_1^2/s_2^2 possesses a probability distribution in repeated sampling that is known to statisticians as an F distribution. We need not concern ourselves with the equation of the density function for F except to state that, as we might surmise, it is reasonably complex. For our purposes it will suffice to accept the fact that the distribution is well known and that critical values have been tabulated. These appear in Tables 6 and 7, Appendix II.

The shape of the F distribution is nonsymmetrical and will depend upon the number of degrees of freedom associated with s_1^2 and s_2^2. We will represent these quantities as v_1 and v_2, respectively. This fact complicates the tabulation of critical values for the F distribution and necessitates the construction of a table for each value that we may choose for a tail area, α. Thus, Table 6 and Table 7 (Appendix II) present critical values corresponding to $\alpha = .05$ and $.01$, respectively.

For example, Table 6 records the value $F_{.05}$ such that the probability that F will exceed $F_{.05}$ is $.05$. Another way of saying this is that 5% of the area under the F distribution lies to the right of $F_{.05}$. The degrees of freedom for s_1^2, v_1, are indicated across the top of the table while the degrees of freedom for s_2^2, v_2, appear in the first column on the left.

Referring to Table 6, we note that $F_{.05}$ for sample sizes $n_1 = 7$ and $n_2 = 10$ (that is, $v_1 = 6$, $v_2 = 9$) is 3.37. Likewise, the critical value, $F_{.05}$, for sample sizes $n_1 = 9$ and $n_2 = 16$ ($v_1 = 8$, $v_2 = 15$) is 2.64.

In a similar manner, the critical values for a tail area, $\alpha = .01$, are presented in Table 7. Thus,

$$P(F > F_{.01}) = .01.$$

The statistical test of the null hypothesis,

$$H_0: \sigma_1^2 = \sigma_2^2,$$

utilizes the test statistic,

$$F = s_1^2/s_2^2.$$

When the alternative hypothesis implies a one-tailed test, that is,

$$H_a: \sigma_1^2 > \sigma_2^2,$$

we may use the tables directly. However, when the alternative hypothesis requires a two-tailed test,

$$H_a: \sigma_1^2 \neq \sigma_2^2,$$

we note that the rejection region will be divided between the lower and upper tail of the F distribution and that tables of critical values for the lower tail are conspicuously missing. The reason for their absence is not too difficult to explain.

We are at liberty to identify either of the two populations as population I. If the population with the larger sample variance is designated as population II, then $s_2^2 > s_1^2$ and we will be concerned with rejection in the lower tail of the F distribution. Since the identification of the populations was arbitrary, we may avoid this difficulty by designating the population with the larger sample variance as population I. In other words, always place the larger sample variance in the numerator of

$$F = s_1^2/s_2^2$$

and designate that population as I. Then, since the area in the right-hand tail will represent only $\alpha/2$, we double this value to obtain the correct value for the probability of a type I error, α. Hence, if we use Table 6 for a two-tailed test, the probability of a type I error will be $\alpha = .10$.

We will illustrate with examples.

Example 9.6: Two samples consisting of 10 and 8 measurements each were observed to possess sample variances equal to $s_1^2 = 7.14$ and $s_2^2 = 3.21$, respectively. Do the sample variances present sufficient evidence to indicate that the population variances are unequal?

Solution: Assume that the populations possess probability distributions that are reasonably mound-shaped and hence will satisfy, for all practical purposes, the assumption that the populations are normal.

We wish to test the null hypothesis,

$$H_0: \sigma_1^2 = \sigma_2^2,$$

against the alternative,

$$H_a: \sigma_1^2 \neq \sigma_2^2.$$

Using Table 6 and doubling the tail area, we will reject when $F > 3.68$ with $\alpha = .10$.

The calculated value of the test statistic is

$$F = \frac{s_1^2}{s_2^2} = \frac{7.14}{3.21} = 2.22.$$

Noting that the test statistic does not fall in the rejection region, we do not reject $H_0: \sigma_1^2 = \sigma_2^2$. Thus, there is insufficient evidence to indicate a difference in the population variances.

The $(1 - \alpha)$ confidence interval for the ratio between two population variances can be shown to equal

$$\frac{s_1^2}{s_2^2}\frac{1}{F_{v_1,v_2}} < \frac{\sigma_1^2}{\sigma_2^2} < \frac{s_1^2}{s_2^2}F_{v_2,v_1},$$

where F_{v_1,v_2} is the tabulated critical value of F corresponding to v_1 and v_2 degrees of freedom in the numerator and denominator of F, respectively. Similar to the two-tailed test, the α will be double the tabulated value. Thus F values extracted from Tables 6 and 7 will be appropriate for confidence coefficients equal to .90 and .98, respectively.

The 90% confidence interval for σ_1^2/σ_2^2, Example 9.6, is therefore

$$\frac{s_1^2}{s_2^2}\frac{1}{F_{v_1,v_2}} < \frac{\sigma_1^2}{\sigma_2^2} < \frac{s_1^2}{s_2^2}F_{v_2,v_1}.$$

Noting that

$$v_1 = (n_1 - 1) = 9 \quad \text{and} \quad v_2 = (n_2 - 1) = 7,$$

$$F_{v_1,v_2} = F_{9,7} = 3.68$$

and

$$F_{v_2,v_1} = F_{7,9} = 3.29.$$

Substituting these values along with the sample variances into the formula for the confidence interval, we obtain

$$\frac{7.14}{3.21}\frac{1}{3.68} < \frac{\sigma_1^2}{\sigma_2^2} < \frac{(7.14)(3.29)}{3.21}$$

or,

$$.60 < \frac{\sigma_1^2}{\sigma_2^2} < 7.32.$$

The calculated interval estimate, .60 to 7.32, is observed to include 1.0, the value hypothesized in H_0.

Example 9.7: The variability in the amount of impurities present in a batch of a chemical used for a particular process depends upon the length of time the process is in operation. A manufacturer using two production lines, #1 and #2, has made a slight adjustment to process #2, hoping to reduce the variability as well as the average amount of impurities in the chemical. Samples of $n_1 = 25$ and $n_2 = 25$ measurements from the two batches yield means and variances as follows:

$$\bar{y}_1 = 3.2,$$

$$s_1^2 = 1.04;$$

$$\bar{y}_2 = 3.0,$$

$$s_2^2 = .51.$$

Do the data present sufficient evidence to indicate that the process variability is less for process #2? Test the null hypothesis, $H_0: \sigma_1^2 = \sigma_2^2$.

Solution: Testing the null hypothesis,

$$H_0: \sigma_1^2 = \sigma_2^2,$$

against the alternative,

$$H_a: \sigma_1^2 > \sigma_2^2,$$

at an $\alpha = .05$ significance level, we will reject H_0 when F is greater than $F_{.05} = 1.98$, that is, we will employ a one-tailed statistical test.

We readily observe that the calculated value of the test statistic,

$$F = \frac{s_1^2}{s_2^2} = \frac{1.04}{.51} = 2.04,$$

falls in the rejection region, and hence we conclude that the variability of process #2 is less than that for process #1.

The 90% confidence interval for the ratio σ_1^2/σ_2^2 is

$$\frac{s_1^2}{s_2^2} \frac{1}{F_{v_1, v_2}} < \frac{\sigma_1^2}{\sigma_2^2} < \frac{s_1^2}{s_2^2} F_{v_2, v_1},$$

$$\frac{(1.04)}{(.51)(1.98)} < \frac{\sigma_1^2}{\sigma_2^2} < \frac{(1.04)(1.98)}{(.51)},$$

or

$$1.03 < \frac{\sigma_1^2}{\sigma_2^2} < 4.04.$$

9.8 Summary

It is important to note that the t, χ^2, and F statistics employed in the small sample statistical methods discussed in the preceding sections are based upon the assumption that the sampled populations possess a normal probability distribution. This requirement will be satisfied for many types of experimental measurements.

The reader will observe the very close relationship connecting Student's t and the z statistic and therefore the similarity of the methods for testing hypotheses and the construction of confidence intervals. The χ^2 and F statistics employed in making inferences concerning population variances do not, of course, follow this pattern but the reasoning employed in the construction of the statistical tests and confidence intervals is identical for all of the methods we have presented.

A summary of the confidence intervals and statistical tests described in Chapters 8 and 9 is presented in Appendix I.

EXERCISES

1. Why is the z test usually inappropriate as a test statistic when the sample size is small?

2. What assumptions are made when Student's t test is employed to test an hypothesis concerning a population mean?

3. A chemical process has produced, on the average, 800 tons of chemical per day. The daily yields for the past week are 785, 805, 790, 793, and 802 tons. Do these data indicate that the average yield is less than 800 tons and hence that something is wrong with the process? Test at the 5% level of significance.

4. Find a 90% confidence interval for the mean yield in Exercise 3.

5. Refer to Exercises 3 and 4. How large should the sample be in order that the width of the confidence interval be reduced to approximately five tons?

6. The mean and standard deviation for a sample of nineteen measurements were found to equal 24.7 and 1.8, respectively. Find a 98% confidence interval for the mean of the population.

7. A coin-operated soft-drink machine was designed to discharge, on the average, seven ounces of beverage per cup. To test the machine, ten cupfuls of beverage were drawn from the machine and measured. The mean and standard deviation of the ten measurements were 7.1 and .12 ounces, respectively. Do these data present sufficient evidence to indicate that the mean discharge differs from seven ounces? Test at the 10% level of significance.

8. Find a 90% confidence interval for the mean discharge in Exercise 7.

9. The main stem growth, measured for a sample of seventeen four-year-old red pine trees, produced a mean and standard deviation equal to 11.3 and 3.4 inches, respectively. Find a 90% confidence interval for the mean growth of a population of four-year-old red pine trees subjected to similar environmental conditions.

10. Due to the variability of trade-in allowance, the profit per new car sold by an automobile dealer varies from car to car. The profit per sale, tabulated for the past week, was:

PROFIT PER SALE (IN HUNDREDS OF DOLLARS)

2.1
3.0
1.2
6.2
4.5
5.1

Do these data present sufficient evidence to indicate that the average profit per sale is less than $480? Test at an $\alpha = .05$ level of significance.

11. Find a 90% confidence interval for the mean profit per sale in Exercise 10.

12. A manufacturer of television sets claimed that his product possessed an average defect-free life of three years. Three households in a community have purchased the sets and all three sets are observed to fail before three years, with failure times equal to 2.5, 1.9, and 2.9 years respectively. Do these data present sufficient evidence to contradict the manufacturer's claim? Test at an $\alpha = .05$ level of significance.

13. Calculate a 90% confidence interval for the mean life of the television sets in Exercise 12.

14. Refer to Exercises 12 and 13. Approximately how many observations would be required to estimate the mean life of the television sets correct to within two-tenths of a year with probability equal to .90?

15. What assumptions are made about the populations from which independent random samples are obtained when utilizing the t distribution in making small sample inferences concerning the difference in population means?

16. Two random samples, each containing eleven measurements, were drawn from normal populations possessing means μ_1 and μ_2, respectively, and a common variance, σ^2. The sample means and variances are shown below:

POPULATION I	POPULATION II
$\bar{y}_1 = 60.4$	$\bar{y}_2 = 65.3$
$s_1^2 = 31.40$	$s_2^2 = 44.82$

Do the data present sufficient evidence to indicate a difference between the population means? Test at the $\alpha = .10$ level of significance.

17. Find a 90% confidence interval for the difference between the population means in Exercise 16.

18. Two methods for teaching reading were applied to two randomly selected groups of elementary school children and compared on the basis of a reading comprehension test given at the end of the learning period. The sample means and variances computed from the test scores are shown below.

	METHOD 1	METHOD 2
Number of children in group	11	14
$\bar{y}$	64	69
s^2	52	71

Do the data present sufficient evidence to indicate a difference in the mean scores for the populations associated with the two teaching methods? Test at an $\alpha = .05$ level of significance.

19. Four sets of identical twins (pairs A, B, C, and D) were selected at random from a population of identical twins. One child was taken at random from each pair to form an "experimental group." These four children were sent to school. The other four children were kept at home as a control group. At the end of the school year the following IQ scores were obtained:

PAIR	EXPERIMENTAL GROUP	CONTROL GROUP
A	110	111
B	125	120
C	139	128
D	142	135

Does this evidence justify the conclusion that lack of school experience has a depressing effect on IQ scores? Use $\alpha = .10$.

20. A comparison of reaction times for two different stimuli in a psychological word-association experiment produced the following results when applied

to a random sample of sixteen people:

REACTION TIME (SECONDS)

STIMULUS 1	STIMULUS 2
1	4
3	2
2	3
1	3
2	1
1	2
3	3
2	3

Do the data present sufficient evidence to indicate a difference in mean reaction time for the two stimuli? Test at the $\alpha = .05$ level of significance.

21. Refer to Exercise 20. Suppose that the word-association experiment had been conducted using people as blocks and making a comparison of reaction time within each person; that is, each person would be subjected to both stimuli in a random order. The data for the experiment are shown below.

REACTION TIME (SECONDS)

PERSON	STIMULUS 1	STIMULUS 2
1	3	4
2	1	2
3	1	3
4	2	1
5	1	2
6	2	3
7	3	3
8	1	3

Do the data present sufficient evidence to indicate a difference in mean reaction time for the two stimuli? Test at the $\alpha = .05$ level of significance.

22. Obtain a 90% confidence interval for $(\mu_1 - \mu_2)$ in Exercise 20.

23. Obtain a 95% confidence interval for $(\mu_1 - \mu_2)$ in Exercise 21.

24. Analyse the data in Exercise 21 as though the experiment had been conducted in an unpaired manner. Calculate a 95% confidence interval for $(\mu_1 - \mu_2)$ and compare with the answer to Exercise 23. Does it appear that blocking increased the amount of information available in the experiment?

25. The following data give readings in foot-pounds of the impact strength on two kinds of packaging material. Determine whether there is evidence of a difference in mean strength between the two kinds of material. Test at the $\alpha = .10$ level of significance.

A	B
1.25	.89
1.16	1.01
1.33	.97
1.15	.95
1.23	.94
1.20	1.02
1.32	.98
1.28	1.06
1.21	.98
$\sum y = 11.13$	8.80
$\bar{y} = 1.237$	.978
$\sum y_i^2 = 13.7973$	8.6240

26. Would the amount of information extracted from the data in Exercise 25 be increased by pairing successive observations and analysing the differences? Calculate 90% confidence intervals for $(\mu_1 - \mu_2)$ for the two methods of analysis (unpaired and paired) and compare the widths of the intervals.

27. When should one employ a paired-difference analysis in making inferences concerning the difference between two means?

28. An experiment was conducted to compare the density of cakes prepared from two different cake mixes, A and B. Six cake pans received batter A and six received batter B. Expecting a variation in oven temperature, the experimenter placed an A and a B side by side at six different locations within the oven. The six paired observations are shown below.

DENSITY, OUNCES/CUBIC INCH

A	B
.135	.129
.102	.120
.098	.112
.141	.152
.131	.135
.144	.163

Do the data present sufficient evidence to indicate a difference in the average density for cakes prepared using the two types of batter? Test at the $\alpha = .05$ level of significance.

29. Place a 95% confidence interval on the difference between the average densities for the two mixes in Exercise 28.

30. Two plastics, each produced by a different process, were tested for ultimate strength. The measurements shown below represent breaking load in units of 1000 pounds-per-square inch.

PLASTIC 1	PLASTIC 2
15.3	21.2
18.7	22.4
22.3	18.3
17.6	19.3
19.1	17.1
14.8	27.7

Do the data present sufficient evidence to indicate a difference between the mean ultimate strengths for the two plastics?

31. Refer to Exercise 30. Find a 90% confidence interval for the difference between the means, $(\mu_1 - \mu_2)$.

32. Refer to Exercise 30. How many observations would be required to estimate $(\mu_1 - \mu_2)$ correct to within 500 pounds-per-square-inch with a probability of .90?

33. Refer to Exercise 3. Find a 90% confidence interval for σ^2, the variance of the population of daily yields.

34. A manufacturer of a machine to package soap powder claimed that his machine could load cartons at a given weight with a range of no more than two-fifths of an ounce. The mean and variance of a sample of eight three-pound boxes were found to equal 3.1 and .018, respectively. Test the hypothesis that the variance of the population of weight measurement is $\sigma^2 = .01$ against the alternative, $\sigma^2 > .01$. Use an $\alpha = .05$ level of significance.

35. Find a 90% confidence interval for σ^2 in Exercise 34.

36. Under what assumptions may the F-distribution be used in making inferences about the ratio of population variances?

37. A dairy is in the market for a new bottle-filling machine and is considering models A and B manufactured by Company A and Company B, respectively. If ruggedness, cost, and convenience are comparable in the two models, the deciding factor is the variability of fills (the model producing fills with the smaller variance being preferred). Let σ_1^2 and σ_2^2 be the fill variances for

models A and B, respectively, and consider various tests of the null hypothesis $H_0: \sigma_1^2 = \sigma_2^2$. Obtaining samples of fills from the two machines and utilizing the test statistic s_1^2/s_2^2, one would set up as rejection region an upper-tail area, lower-tail area, or two-tailed area of the F distribution depending on his point of view. Which type of rejection region would be most favored by the following persons:

(a) The manager of the dairy? Why?
(b) A salesman for Company A? Why?
(c) A salesman for Company B? Why?

38. The closing prices of two common stocks were recorded for a period of fifteen days. The means and variances are

$$\bar{y}_1^2 = 40.33, \qquad \bar{y}_2 = 42.54,$$

$$s_1^2 = 1.54, \qquad s_2^2 = 2.96.$$

Do these data present sufficient evidence to indicate a difference in variability of the two stocks for the populations associated with the two samples?

39. Place a 90% confidence interval on the ratio of the two population variances in Exercise 38.

40. Place a 98% confidence interval on the population variance in Exercise 6.

41. A precision instrument is guaranteed to read accurate to within 2 units. A sample of four instrument readings on the same object yielded the measurements 353, 351, 351, and 355. Test the null hypothesis that $\sigma = .7$ against the alternative, $\sigma > .7$. Conduct the test at the $\alpha = .05$ level of significance.

42. Find a 90% confidence interval for the population variance in Exercise 41.

43. The temperature of operation of two paint-drying ovens associated with two manufacturing production lines was recorded for twenty days. (Pairing was ignored.) The means and variances of the two samples are

$$\bar{y}_1 = 164, \qquad \bar{y}_2 = 168,$$

$$s_1^2 = 81, \qquad s_2^2 = 172.$$

Do the data present sufficient evidence to indicate a difference in temperature variability for the two ovens? Test the hypothesis that $\sigma_1^2 = \sigma_2^2$ at the $\alpha = .10$ level of significance.

44. Refer to Exercise 37. Wishing to demonstrate that the variability of fills is less for model A than for model B, a salesman for Company A acquired a sample of 30 fills from a machine of model A and a sample of 10 fills from a machine of model B. The sample variances were $s_1^2 = .027$ and $s_2^2 = .065$ respectively. Does this result provide statistical support at the .05 level of significance for the salesman's claim?

REFERENCES

Anderson, R. L., and T. A. Bancroft, *Statistical Theory in Research*.   New York: McGraw-Hill Book Co., Inc., 1952.   Chapter 7.

Li, J. C. R., *Introduction to Statistical Inference*.   Ann Arbor, Mich.: J. W. Edwards, Publisher, Inc., 1961.   Chapter 10.

10

LINEAR REGRESSION
AND CORRELATION

10.1 Introduction

An estimation problem of more than casual interest to high school seniors, freshmen entering college, their parents, and a university administration concerns the expected academic achievement of a particular student after he has enrolled in a university. For example, we might wish to estimate a student's grade-point average at the end of the freshman year *before* the student has been accepted or enrolled in the university. At first glance this would seem to be a difficult task.

The statistical approach to this problem is, in many respects, a formalization of the procedure we might follow intuitively. If data were available giving the high school academic grades, psychological and sociological information, as well as the grades attained at the end of the college freshmen year for a large number of students, we might categorize the students into groups possessing similar characteristics. Certainly, highly motivated students who have had a high rank in their high school class, have graduated from a high school with known superior academic standards, etc. should achieve, on the average, a high grade-point average at the end of the college freshmen year. On the other hand, students who lack proper motivation, who achieved only moderate success in high school, would not be expected, on the average, to do as well. Carrying this line of thought to the ultimate and idealistic extreme, we would expect the grade-point average of a student to be a *function* of the many variables that define the characteristics, psychological and physical, of the individual as well as those that define the environment, academic and social, to which he will be exposed. Ideally, we would like to possess a mathematical equation that would relate a student's grade-point average to all of these independent variables so that it could be used for prediction.

The reader will observe that the problem we have defined is of a very general nature. We are interested in some random variable, y, that is related to a number of independent variables, x_1, x_2, x_3, ... The variable, y, for our example, would be the student's grade-point average, and the independent variables might be

x_1 = rank in high school class,

x_2 = score on a mathematics achievement test,

x_3 = score on a verbal achievement test,

and so on. The ultimate objective would be to measure x_1, x_2, x_3, ... for a particular student, substitute these values into the prediction equation, and thereby predict the student's grade-point average. In order to accomplish this end, we must first locate the related variables x_1, x_2, x_3, ... and obtain a measure of the strength of their relationship to y. Then we must construct a good prediction equation that will express y as a function of the selected independent variables.

Practical examples of our prediction problem are very numerous in business, industry, and the sciences. The stockbroker wishes to predict stock market behavior as a function of a number of "key indices" which are observable and serve as the independent variables, x_1, x_2, x_3, ... The manager of a manufacturing plant would like to relate yield of a chemical to a number of process variables. He would then use the prediction equation to find the settings for the controllable process variables that would provide the maximum yield of the chemical. The personnel director of a corporation, like the admissions director of a university, wishes to test and measure individual characteristics so that he may hire the person best suited for a particular job. The biologist would like to relate body characteristics to the amount of various glandular secretions. The political scientist may wish to relate success in a political campaign to the characteristics of a candidate, his opposition, and various campaign issues and promotional techniques. Certainly, all of these prediction problems are, in many respects, one and the same.

In this chapter we will be primarily concerned with the *reasoning* involved in acquiring a prediction equation based upon one or more independent variables.   Thus we will restrict our attention to the simple problem of predicting *y* as a *linear* function of a *single* variable and observe that the solution for the multivariate problem, for example, predicting student grade-point average, will consist of a generalization of our technique.   The methodology for the multivariate predictor will be fairly complex, as will later be apparent to the reader, and is omitted from our discussion.

10.2   A Simple Linear Probabilistic Model

We will introduce our topic by considering the problem of predicting a student's final grade in a college freshman calculus course based upon his score on a mathematics achievement test administered prior to college entrance.   As noted in Section 10.1, we wish to determine whether the achievement test is really worthwhile—whether the achievement test score is related to a student's grade in calculus—and, in addition, we wish to obtain an equation which may be useful for prediction purposes.   The evidence, presented in Table 10.1. represents a sample of the achievement

Table 10.1.   Mathematics Achievement Test Scores and Final Calculus Grades for Ten College Freshmen

STUDENT	MATHEMATICS ACHIEVEMENT TEST SCORE	FINAL CALCULUS GRADE
1	39	65
2	43	78
3	21	52
4	64	82
5	57	92
6	47	89
7	28	73
8	75	98
9	34	56
10	52	75

test scores and calculus grades for ten college freshmen.   Hopefully, the ten students represent a random sample drawn from the population of freshmen who have already entered the university or will do so in the immediate future.

Our initial approach to the analysis of the data of Table 10.1 would be to plot the data as points on a graph, representing a student's calculus grade as y and the corresponding achievement test score as x.   The graph is shown in Figure 10.1   The reader will quickly observe that y appears to increase as x increases.   (Could this arrangement of the points occur due to chance even if x and y were unrelated?)

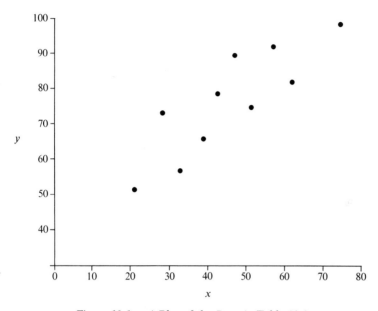

Figure 10.1.   A Plot of the Data in Table 10.1

One method of obtaining a prediction equation relating y to x would be to place a ruler on the graph and move it about until it seems to pass through the points and provide what we might regard as the "best fit" to the data.   Indeed, if we were to draw a line through the points, it would appear that our prediction problem were solved.   Certainly, we may now use the graph to predict a student's calculus grade as a function of his score on the mathematics achievement test.   Furthermore, we note that we have chosen a *mathematical model* expressing the supposed functional relation between y and x.

The student will recall several facts concerning the graphing of mathematical functions.   First, the mathematical equation of a straight line is

$$y = \beta_0 + \beta_1 x,$$

where β_0 is the y intercept and β_1 is the slope of the line. Second, the line which we may graph corresponding to any linear equation is unique. Each equation will correspond to only one line and vice versa. Thus, when we draw a line through the points, we have automatically chosen a mathematical equation

$$y = \beta_0 + \beta_1 x,$$

where β_0 and β_1 have unique numerical values.

The linear model, $y = \beta_0 + \beta_1 x$, is said to be a *deterministic* mathematical model because when a value of x is substituted into the equation the value of y is determined and no allowance is made for error. Fitting a straight line through a set of points by eye produces a deterministic model. Many other examples of deterministic mathematical models may be found by leafing through the pages of elementary chemistry, physics, or engineering textbooks.

Deterministic models are quite suitable for explaining physical phenomena and predicting when the error of prediction is negligible for practical purposes. Thus, Newton's Law, which expresses the relation between the force, F, imparted by a moving body with mass, m, and acceleration, a, given by the deterministic model,

$$F = ma,$$

predicts force with very little error for most practical applications. "Very little" is, of course, a relative concept. An error of .1 inch in forming an I-beam for a bridge is extremely small but would be impossibly large in the manufacture of parts for a wrist watch. Thus, in many physical situations the error of prediction cannot be ignored. Indeed, consistent with our stated philosophy, we would be hesitant to place much confidence in a prediction unaccompanied by a measure of its goodness. For this reason, a visual choice of a line to relate the calculus grade and achievement test score would be of limited utility.

In contrast to the deterministic model, we might employ a *probabilistic mathematical model* to explain some physical phenomenon. As we might suspect, probabilistic mathematical models contain one or more random elements with specified probability distributions. For our example we will relate the calculus score to the achievement test score by the equation

$$y = \beta_0 + \beta_1 x + \varepsilon,$$

where ε is assumed to be a random variable with expected value equal to zero and variance equal to σ^2. In addition, we will assume that any pair, ε_i and ε_j, corresponding to two observations, y_i and y_j, are independent. In other words, we assume that the *average* or expected value of y is linearly related to x and that observed values of y will deviate above and below this line by a random amount, ε. Furthermore, we have assumed that the distribution of errors about the line will be identically the same, regardless of the value of x, and that any pair of errors will be independent of one another. The assumed line, giving the expected value of y for a given value of x, is indicated in Figure 10.2. The probability distribution of the random error, ε, is shown for several values of x.

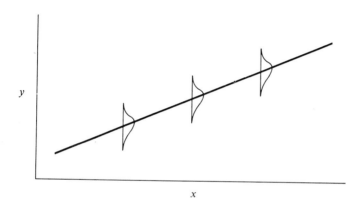

Figure 10.2.   A Linear Probabilistic Model

Let us now consider the problem of finding the prediction equation, or *regression line* as it is commonly known in statistics.

10.3   The Method of Least Squares

The statistical procedure for finding the "best fitting" straight line for a set of points would seem, in many respects, a formalization of the procedure employed when we fit a line by eye. For instance, when we visually fit a line to a set of data, we move the ruler until we think that we have minimized the *deviations* of the points from the prospective line. If we denote the predicted value of y obtained from the fitted line as $\hat{y}$, then the prediction equation will be

$$\hat{y} = \hat{\beta}_0 + \hat{\beta}_1 x,$$

where $\hat{\beta}_0$ and $\hat{\beta}_1$ represent estimates of the true β_0 and β_1. This line for the data of Table 10.1 is shown in Figure 10.3.   The vertical lines drawn from the prediction line to each point represent the deviations of the points from the predicted value of y.   Thus the deviation of the ith point is

$$y_i - \hat{y}_i ,$$

where

$$\hat{y}_i = \hat{\beta}_0 + \hat{\beta}_1 x_i .$$

Having decided that in some manner or other we will attempt to minimize the deviations of the points in choosing the best fitting line, we must now define what we mean by " best."   That is, we wish to define a

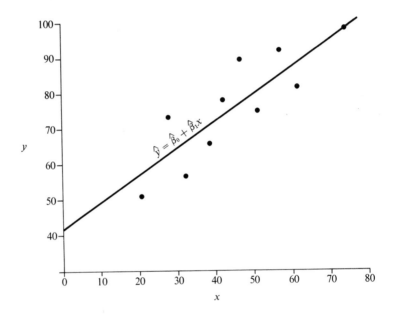

Figure 10.3.   The Linear Prediction Equation

criterion for " best fit " which will seem intuitively reasonable, which is objective, and which under certain conditions will give the best prediction of y for a given value of x.

We will employ a criterion of goodness that is known as the principle of least squares and which may be stated as follows.   Choose as the " best fitting " line that one which minimizes the sum of squares of the deviations of the observed values of y from those predicted.   Expressed mathematically, we wish to minimize

$$SSE = \sum_{i=1}^{n} (y_i - \hat{y}_i)^2.$$

The symbol SSE represents the sum of squares of deviations or, as commonly called, the sum of squares for error.

Substituting for $\hat{y}_i$ in SSE, we obtain

$$SSE = \sum_{i=1}^{n} [y_i - (\hat{\beta}_0 + \hat{\beta}_1 x_i)]^2.$$

The method for finding the numerical values of $\hat{\beta}_0$ and $\hat{\beta}_1$ that minimize SSE utilizes the differential calculus and hence is beyond the scope of this text. We simply state that it can be shown that $\hat{\beta}_0$ and $\hat{\beta}_1$ are the solutions to the following pair of simultaneous linear equations:

$$\hat{\beta}_1 = \frac{\sum_{i=1}^{n} (x_i - \bar{x})(y_i - \bar{y})}{\sum_{i=1}^{n} (x_i - \bar{x})^2} = \frac{n\sum_{i=1}^{n} x_i y_i - \left(\sum_{i=1}^{n} x_i\right)\left(\sum_{i=1}^{n} y_i\right)}{n\sum_{i=1}^{n} x_i^2 - \left(\sum_{i=1}^{n} x_i\right)^2}$$

and

$$\hat{\beta}_0 = \bar{y} - \hat{\beta}_1 \bar{x}.$$

These are known as the *least squares* equations.

Table 10.2 *Calculations for the Data, Table 10.1*

y_i	x_i	x_i^2	$x_i y_i$	y_i^2
65	39	1521	2535	4225
78	43	1849	3354	6084
52	21	441	1092	2704
82	64	4096	5248	6724
92	57	3249	5244	3464
89	47	2209	4183	7921
73	28	784	2044	5329
98	75	5625	7350	9604
56	34	1156	1904	3136
75	52	2704	3900	5625
Sum 760	460	23,634	36,854	59,816

The calculation of $\hat{\beta}_0$ and $\hat{\beta}_1$ for the data of Table 10.1 is simplified by the use of Table 10.2.

Substituting the appropriate sums from Table 10.2 into the least squares equations, we obtain

$$\hat{\beta}_1 = \frac{n \sum_{i=1}^{n} x_i y_i - \left(\sum_{i=1}^{n} x_i\right)\left(\sum_{i=1}^{n} y_i\right)}{n \sum_{i=1}^{n} x_i^2 - \left(\sum_{i=1}^{n} x_i\right)^2}$$

$$= \frac{10(36854) - (460)(760)}{10(23634) - (460)^2} = .76556 \cong .77$$

and

$$\hat{\beta}_0 = \bar{y} - \hat{\beta}_1 \bar{x} = 76 - (.76556)(46) = 40.78424$$

$$\cong 40.78.$$

Then, according to the principle of least squares, the best fitting straight line relating the calculus grade to the achievement test score is

$$\hat{y} = \hat{\beta}_0 + \hat{\beta}_1 x$$

or

$$\hat{y} = 40.78 + .77x.$$

The graph of this equation is shown in Figure 10.3.

We may now predict y for a given value of x by referring to Figure 10.3 or by substituting into the prediction equation. For example, if a student scored $x = 50$ on the achievement test, his predicted calculus grade would be

$$\hat{y} = \hat{\beta}_0 + \hat{\beta}_1 x = 40.78 + (.77)(50) = 79.28.$$

Our next and obvious step would be to place a bound upon our error of estimation. We will consider this and related problems in succeeding sections.

10.4 Calculating s^2, an Estimator of σ^2

The first step toward acquiring a bound on a prediction error requires that we estimate σ^2, the variance of the random error, ε. For this purpose it would seem reasonable to use SSE, the sum of squares of deviations (sum of squares for error) about the predicted line. Indeed, it can be shown that

$$\hat{\sigma}^2 = s^2 = \frac{SSE}{n - 2}$$

provides a good estimator for σ^2 which will be unbiased and be based upon $(n - 2)$ degrees of freedom.

The sum of squares of deviations, SSE, may be calculated directly by using the prediction equation to calculate $\hat{y}$ for each point, then calculating the deviations $(y_i - \hat{y}_i)$, and finally calculating

$$SSE = \sum_{i=1}^{n} (y_i - \hat{y}_i)^2.$$

This tends to be a very tedious procedure and is rather poor from a computational point of view because the numerous subtractions tend to introduce computational rounding errors. An easier and computationally better procedure is to use the formula

$$SSE = \sum_{i=1}^{n} (y_i - \bar{y})^2 - \frac{\hat{\beta}_1}{n} \left[n \sum_{i=1}^{n} x_i y_i - \left(\sum_{i=1}^{n} x_i \right) \left(\sum_{i=1}^{n} y_i \right) \right].$$

Observe that the quantity in the brackets is simply the numerator used in the calculation of $\hat{\beta}_1$ and hence has already been computed. Furthermore, note that it is desirable to retain a large number of digits (preferably all) in the calculations in order to avoid serious rounding errors in the final answer.

Substituting into this formula, we find that SSE for the data of Table 10.1 is

$$SSE = \sum_{i=1}^{n} (y_i - \bar{y})^2 - \frac{\hat{\beta}_1}{n} \left[n \sum_{i=1}^{n} x_i y_i - \left(\sum_{i=1}^{n} x_i \right) \left(\sum_{i=1}^{n} y_i \right) \right]$$

$$= 2056 - \frac{.76556}{10} [(10)(36854) - (460)(760)]$$

$$= 606.03.$$

Then,

$$s^2 = \frac{SSE}{n - 2} = \frac{606.03}{8} = 75.754.$$

10.5 Inferences Concerning the Slope of the Line β_1

The initial inference desired in studying the relationship between y and x concerns the *existence* of the relationship. That is, do the data present sufficient evidence to indicate that y and x are linearly related over the region of observation? Or, is it quite probable that the points would fall on the graph in a manner similar to that observed in Figure 10.1 when y and x are completely unrelated?

The practical question we pose concerns the value of β_1 which is the average change in y for a one-unit change in x. Stating that y and x are not linearly related is equivalent to saying that $\beta_1 = 0$. Thus, we would wish to test an hypothesis that $\beta_1 = 0$ against the alternative that $\beta_1 \neq 0$. As we might suspect, the estimator, $\hat{\beta}_1$, is extremely useful in constructing a test statistic to test this hypothesis. Therefore, we wish to examine the distribution of estimates, $\hat{\beta}_1$, that would be obtained when samples, each containing n points, are repeatedly drawn from the population of interest. If we assume that the random error, ε, is *normally* distributed, in addition to the previously stated assumptions, it can be shown that both $\hat{\beta}_0$ and $\hat{\beta}_1$ will be normally distributed in repeated sampling and that the expected value and variance of $\hat{\beta}_1$ will be

$$E(\hat{\beta}_1) = \beta_1,$$

$$\sigma_{\hat{\beta}_1}^2 = \sigma^2 \left/ \sum_{i=1}^{n} (x_i - \bar{x})^2 \right.$$

Thus, $\hat{\beta}_1$ is an unbiased estimator of β_1, we know its standard deviation, and hence we can construct a z statistic in the manner described in Section 8.11. Then

$$z = \frac{\hat{\beta}_1 - \beta_1}{\sigma_{\hat{\beta}_1}} = \frac{\hat{\beta}_1 - \beta_1}{\sigma \left/ \sqrt{\sum_{i=1}^{n} (x_i - \bar{x})^2} \right.}$$

would possess a standardized normal distribution in repeated sampling. Since the actual value of σ^2 is unknown, we would wish to obtain the estimated standard deviation of $\hat{\beta}_1$, which is $s \left/ \sqrt{\sum_{i=1}^{n} (x_1 - \bar{x})^2} \right.$. Substituting s for σ in z, we obtain, as in Chapter 9, a test statistic,

$$t = \frac{\hat{\beta}_1 - \beta_1}{s \left/ \sqrt{\sum_{i=1}^{n} (x_i - \bar{x})^2} \right.} = \frac{\hat{\beta}_1 - \beta_1}{s} \sqrt{\sum_{i=1}^{n} (x_i - \bar{x})^2},$$

which can be shown to follow a Student's t distribution in repeated sampling with $(n - 2)$ degrees of freedom. Note that the number of degrees of freedom associated with s^2 determines the number of degrees of freedom associated with t. Thus we observe that the test of an hypothesis that β_1 equals some particular numerical value, say β_{10}, is the familiar t test encountered in Chapter 9.

For example, suppose that we wish to test the null hypothesis

$$H_0: \beta_1 = 0$$

for the calculus grade achievement test score data in Table 10.1. The test statistic will be

$$t = \frac{\hat{\beta}_1 - 0}{s} \sqrt{\sum_{i=1}^{n} (x_i - \bar{x})^2},$$

and, if we choose $\alpha = .05$, we will reject H_0 when $t > 2.306$ or $t < -2.306$. The critical value of t is obtained from the t table using $(n - 2) = 8$ degrees of freedom. Substituting into the test statistic, we obtain

$$t = \frac{\hat{\beta}_1}{s} \sqrt{\sum_{i=1}^{n} (x_i - \bar{x})^2} = \frac{.76556}{8.71} \sqrt{2474}$$

or

$$t = 4.373.$$

Observing that the test statistic exceeds the critical value of t, we will reject the null hypothesis, $\beta_1 = 0$, and conclude that there is evidence to indicate that the calculus final grade is linearly related to the achievement test score.

Once we have decided that x and y are linearly related we would be interested in examining this relationship in detail. If x increases by one unit, what is the predicted change in y and how much confidence can be placed in the estimate? In other words, we require an estimate of the slope β_1. The reader will not be surprised to observe a continuity in the procedures of Chapters 9 and 10. That is, the $(1 - \alpha)$ confidence interval for β_1 can be shown to be

$$\hat{\beta}_1 \pm t_{\alpha/2} \left(\text{estimated } \sigma_{\hat{\beta}_1} \right)$$

or

$$\hat{\beta}_1 \pm \frac{t_{\alpha/2} s}{\sqrt{\sum_{i=1}^{n} (x_i - \bar{x})^2}}.$$

The 95% confidence interval for β_1 based upon the data of Table 10.1 is

$$\hat{\beta}_1 \pm \frac{t_{.025} s}{\sqrt{\sum_{i=1}^{n} (x_i - \bar{x})^2}}.$$

Substituting, we obtain,

$$.77 \pm \frac{(2.306)(8.70)}{\sqrt{2474}}$$

or

$$.77 \pm .40.$$

Several points concerning the interpretation of our results deserve particular attention. As we have noted, β_1 is the slope of the assumed line over the region of observation and indicates the *linear* change in y for a one-unit change in x. If we do not reject the null hypothesis, $\beta_1 = 0$, it *does not* mean that x and y are unrelated. In the first place, we must be concerned with the probability of committing a type II error, that is, accepting when H_0 is false. Secondly, it is possible that x and y might be *perfectly* related in some curvilinear but not in a linear manner. For example, Figure 10.4 depicts a curvilinear relationship between y and x over the domain of x, $a \leq x \leq f$. We note that a straight line would provide a good predictor of y if fitted over a small interval in the x domain, say $b \leq x \leq c$. The resulting line would be line #1. On the other hand,

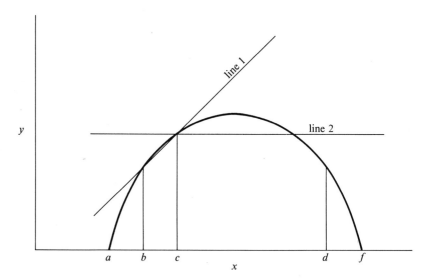

Figure 10.4.   A Curvilinear Relation

if we attempt to fit a line over the region $b \leq x \leq d$, β_1 will equal zero and the best fit to the data will be the horizontal line #2. This would occur even though *all* of the points fell perfectly on the curve and y and x possessed a functional relation as defined in Section 2. Thus we must take care in drawing conclusions if we do not find evidence to indicate that β_1 differs from zero. Perhaps we have chosen the wrong type of probabilistic model for the physical situation.

The reader will note that these comments contain a second implication. If the data provide values of x in an interval $b \leq x \leq c$, then the calculated prediction equation is appropriate only over this region.

Obviously, extrapolation in predicting y for values of x outside of the region, $b \leq x \leq c$, for the situation indicated in Figure 10.4 would result in a serious prediction error.

Finally, if the data present sufficient evidence to indicate that β_1 differs from zero, we do not conclude that the true relationship between y and x is linear. Undoubtedly, y is a function of a number of variables which demonstrate their existence to a greater or lesser degree in terms of the random error ε which appears in the model. This, of course, is why we have been obliged to use a probabilistic model in the first place. Large errors of prediction imply either curvatures in the true relation between y and x, the presence of other important variables which do not appear in the model, or, as most often is the case, both. All we can say is that we have evidence to indicate that y changes as x changes and that we may obtain a better prediction of y using x and the linear predictor than simply using $\bar{y}$ and ignoring x. Note that this *does not* imply a *causal* relationship between x and y. Some third variable may have caused the change in both x and y thus producing the relationship that we have observed.

10.6 Estimating the Expected Value of y for a Given Value of x

Let us assume that x and y are linearly related according to the probabilistic model defined in Section 10.2 and therefore that $E(y/x) = \beta_0 + \beta_1 x$ represents the expected value of y for a given value of x. Since the fitted line

$$\hat{y} = \hat{\beta}_0 + \hat{\beta}_1 x$$

attempts to estimate the true linear relation, that is, we estimate β_0 and β_1, then $\hat{y}$ would be used to estimate the *expected* value of y as well as a *particular* value of y for a given value of x. It would seem quite reasonable to assume that the error of estimation would differ for these two cases. In this situation we consider the estimation of the expected value of y for a given value of x.

The reader will observe that two lines are drawn in Figure 10.5. The first line represents the line of means for the true relationship,

$$E(y/x) = \beta_0 + \beta_1 x,$$

and the second is the fitted prediction equation,

$$\hat{y} = \hat{\beta}_0 + \hat{\beta}_1 x.$$

(Note that the symbol $E(y/x)$ means the expected value of y for a *given* value of x).

We readily observe that the error in predicting the expected value of y when $x = x_p$ will be the deviation between the two lines above the point x_p and that this error will increase as we move to the end points of the interval over which x has been measured.   It can be shown that the predicted value,

$$\hat{y} = \hat{\beta}_0 + \hat{\beta}_1 x,$$

is an unbiased estimator of $E(y/x)$, that is, $E(\hat{y}) = \beta_0 + \beta_1 x$, and that it will be normally distributed with variance,

$$\sigma_{\hat{y}}^2 = \sigma^2 \left[\frac{1}{n} + \frac{(x_p - \bar{x})^2}{\sum_{i=1}^{n} (x_i - \bar{x})^2} \right]$$

The corresponding estimated variance of $\hat{y}$ would use s^2 to replace σ^2 in the above expression.

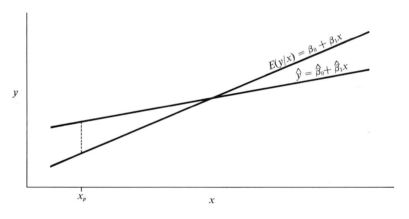

Figure 10.5.   The Expected and Predicted Values for y

The results outlined above may be used to test an hypothesis concerning the average or expected value of y for a given value of x, say x_p. This, of course, would also enable us to test an hypothesis concerning the y intercept, β_0, which is the special case where $x_p = 0$.   The null hypothesis would be

$$H_0: E(y/x = x_p) = E_0,$$

where E_0 is the hypothesized numerical value of $E(y)$ when $x = x_p$.

Once again, it can be shown that the quantity

$$t = \frac{\hat{y} - E_0}{\text{estimated } \sigma_{\hat{y}}}$$

$$= \frac{\hat{y} - E_0}{s\sqrt{\dfrac{1}{n} + \dfrac{(x_p - \bar{x})^2}{\displaystyle\sum_{i=1}^{n}(x_i - \bar{x})^2}}}.$$

follows a Student's t distribution in repeated sampling with $(n - 2)$ degrees of freedom. Thus the statistical test is conducted in exactly the same manner as the other t tests previously discussed.

The corresponding $(1 - \alpha)$ confidence interval for the expected value of y, given $x = x_p$, is

$$\pm t_{\alpha/2} s \sqrt{\frac{1}{n} + \frac{(x_p - \bar{x})^2}{\displaystyle\sum_{i=1}^{n}(x_i - \bar{x})^2}}.$$

For example, if we wish to estimate the average calculus grade for students whose achievement test score was $x_p = 50$, we would obtain

$$\hat{y} = \hat{\beta}_0 + \hat{\beta}_1 x,$$

or

$$\hat{y} = 40.78 + (.77)(50) = 79.28.$$

The 95% confidence interval would be

$$79.28 \pm (2.306)(8.70)\sqrt{\frac{1}{10} + \frac{(50 - 46)^2}{2474}}$$

or

$$79.28 \pm 6.54.$$

10.7   Predicting a Particular Value of y for a Given Value of x

Suppose that the prediction equation obtained for the ten measurements, Table 10.1, were used to predict the final calculus grade for a new student selected at random.

While the expected value of y for a particular value of x is of interest for our example, Table 10.1, we are primarily interested in *using* the prediction equation, $\hat{y} = \hat{\beta}_0 + \hat{\beta}_1 x$, based upon our observed data to predict the final calculus grade for some prospective student selected from the population of interest. If the student's achievement test score was x_p, we intuitively see that the error of prediction (the deviation between $\hat{y}$ and the actual grade, y, that the student will obtain) is composed of two elements. Since the student's grade will equal

$$y = \beta_0 + \beta_1 x_p + \varepsilon,$$

$(y - \hat{y})$ will equal the deviation between $\hat{y}$ and the expected value of y, described in Section 10.6, *plus* the random amount ε which represents the deviation of the student's grade from the expected value. Thus the variability in the error for predicting a single value of y will exceed the variability for predicting the expected value of y.

It can be shown that the variance of the error of predicting a particular value of y when $x = x_p$, that is $(y - \hat{y})$, is

$$\sigma^2 \left[1 + \frac{1}{n} + \frac{(x_p - \bar{x})^2}{\sum\limits_{i=1}^{n}(x_i - \bar{x})^2} \right]$$

When n is very large, the second and third terms under the radical will become small and the variance of the prediction error will approach σ^2. These results may be used to construct the following prediction interval for y, given $x = x_p$:

$$\hat{y} \pm t_{\alpha/2} s \sqrt{1 + \frac{1}{n} + \frac{(x_p - \bar{x})^2}{\sum\limits_{i=1}^{n}(x_i - \bar{x})^2}}.$$

For example, if a prospective student scored $x_p = 50$ on the achievement test, we would predict that his final calculus grade would be

$$79.28 \pm (2.306)(8.70)\sqrt{1 + \frac{1}{10} + \frac{(50 - 46)^2}{2474}}$$

or

$$79.28 \pm 21.10.$$

Note that in a practical situation we would likely possess the grades and achievement test scores for many more than the $n = 10$ students indicated in Table 10.1 and that this would reduce somewhat the width of the bound on the error of estimation.

10.8   A Coefficient of Correlation

It is sometimes desirable to obtain an indicator of the strength of the linear relationship between two variables, y and x, which will be independent of their respective scales of measurement. We will call this a measure of the *linear correlation* between y and x.

The measure of linear correlation commonly used in statistics is called the *coefficient of correlation* between y and x. This quantity, denoted by the symbol r, is computed as follows:

$$r = \frac{\sum\limits_{i=1}^{n}(x_i - \bar{x})(y_i - \bar{y})}{\sqrt{\sum\limits_{i=1}^{n}(x_i - \bar{x})^2 \sum\limits_{i=1}^{n}(y_i - \bar{y})^2}}$$

$$= \frac{n\sum\limits_{i=1}^{n} x_i y_i - \left(\sum\limits_{i=1}^{n} x_i\right)\left(\sum\limits_{i=1}^{n} y_i\right)}{\sqrt{\left[n\sum\limits_{i=1}^{n} x_i^2 - \left(\sum\limits_{i=1}^{n} x_i\right)^2\right]\left[n\sum\limits_{i=1}^{n} y_i^2 - \left(\sum\limits_{i=1}^{n} y_i\right)^2\right]}}$$

The second expression is easier to use computationally since many of these quantities will have been computed in the calculation of $\hat{\beta}_1$.

The coefficient of correlation for the calculus-grade achievement-test score data, Table 10.1, may be obtained by using the formula for r and the quantities

$$\left[n\sum\limits_{i=1}^{n} x_i y_i - \left(\sum\limits_{i=1}^{n} x_i\right)\left(\sum\limits_{i=1}^{n} y_i\right)\right] = 18940$$

and

$$\left[n\sum\limits_{i=1}^{n} x_i^2 - \left(\sum\limits_{i=1}^{n} x_i\right)^2\right] = 24740,$$

which were previously computed.

Then,

$$r = \frac{n\sum\limits_{i=1}^{n} x_i y_i - \left(\sum\limits_{i=1}^{n} x_i\right)\left(\sum\limits_{i=1}^{n} y_i\right)}{\sqrt{\left[n\sum\limits_{i=1}^{n} x_i^2 - \left(\sum\limits_{i=1}^{n} x_i\right)^2\right]\left[n\sum\limits_{i=1}^{n} y_i^2 - \left(\sum\limits_{i=1}^{n} y_i\right)^2\right]}}$$

$$= \frac{18940}{\sqrt{(24740)(20560)}}$$

$$= 0.84.$$

A study of the coefficient of correlation, r, yields rather interesting results and explains the reason for its selection as a measure of linear correlation. We note that the denominators used in calculating r and $\hat{\beta}_1$ will always be positive since they both involve sums of squares of numbers. Since the numerator used in calculating r is identical to the numerator of the formula for the slope, $\hat{\beta}_1$, the coefficient of correlation, r, will assume exactly the same sign as $\hat{\beta}_1$ and will equal zero when $\hat{\beta}_1 = 0$. Thus, $r = 0$ implies no linear correlation between y and x. A positive value for r will imply that the line slopes upward to the right; a negative value indicates that it slopes downward to the right.

The interpretation of non-zero values of r may be obtained by comparing the errors of prediction for the prediction equation

$$\hat{y} = \hat{\beta}_0 + \hat{\beta}_1 x$$

with the predictor of y, $\bar{y}$, that would be employed if x were ignored. Certainly, if x is of any value in predicting y, then SSE, the sum of squares of deviations of y about the linear model, should be less than the sum of squares about the predictor, $\bar{y}$, which would be

$$\sum_{i=1}^{n} (y_i - \bar{y})^2.$$

Indeed, we see that SSE can *never* be larger than

$$\sum_{i=1}^{n} (y_i - \bar{y})^2$$

because

$$SSE = \sum_{i=1}^{n} (y_i - \bar{y})^2 - \frac{\left[\sum_{i=1}^{n} (x_i - \bar{x})(y_i - \bar{y}) \right]^2}{\sum_{i=1}^{n} (x_i - \bar{x})^2}$$

is equal to $\sum_{i=1}^{n} (y_i - \bar{y})^2$ minus a positive quantity.

Furthermore, with the aid of a bit of algebraic manipulation, we may show that

$$r^2 = 1 - \frac{SSE}{\sum_{i=1}^{n} (y_i - \bar{y})^2}$$

$$= \frac{\sum_{i=1}^{n} (y_i - \bar{y})^2 - SSE}{\sum_{i=1}^{n} (y_i - \bar{y})^2}.$$

In other words, r^2 will lie in the interval

$$0 \le r^2 \le 1$$

and r will equal $+1$ or -1 only when all of the points fall exactly on the fitted line, that is, when SSE equals zero.   *Actually, we see that*

$$r^2 = \frac{\sum_{i=1}^{n} (y_i - \bar{y})^2 - SSE}{\sum_{i=1}^{n} (y_i - \bar{y})^2}$$

is equal to the ratio of the reduction in the sum of squares of deviations obtained by using the linear model to the total sum of squares of deviations about the sample mean, $\bar{y}$, which would be the predictor of y if x were ignored.   Thus r^2 would seem to give a more meaningful interpretation of the strength of the relation between y and x than would the correlation coefficient, r.

The reader will observe that the sample correlation coefficient, r, is an estimator of a population correlation coefficient, ρ, which would be obtained if the coefficient of correlation were calculated using all of the points in the population.   A discussion of a test of an hypothesis concerning the value of ρ is omitted as well as a bound on the error of estimation.   Ordinarily, we would be interested in testing the null hypothesis that $\rho = 0$ and, since this is equivalent to the hypothesis that $\beta_1 = 0$, we have already considered this problem.   If the evidence in the sample suggests that y and x are related, it would seem that we would redirect our attention to the objective of our search—the acquisition of a predictor for y—and would be more interested in the significance of β_1, and the interval estimates for a particular value of y, the $E(y/x)$ and β_1.

While r gives a rather nice measure of the goodness of fit of the least squares line to the fitted data, its use in making inferences concerning ρ would seem to be of dubious practical value in many situations.   It would seem unlikely that a phenomenon y, observed in the physical sciences, and especially the social sciences, would be a function of a single variable.   Thus the correlation coefficient between a student's predicted grade-point average and any one variable likely would be quite small and of questionable value.   A larger reduction in SSE could possibly be obtained by constructing a predictor of y based upon a set of variables $x_1, x_2, \ldots$.

One further reminder concerning the interpretation of r is worthwhile.   It is not uncommon for researchers in some fields to speak proudly of sample correlation coefficients, r, in the neighborhood of .5

(and, in some cases, as low as .1) as indicative of a "relation" between y and x. Certainly, even if these values were *accurate* estimates of ρ, only a very weak relation would be indicated. A value $r = .5$ would imply that the use of x in predicting y reduced the sum of squares of deviations about the prediction line by only $r^2 = .25$ or 25%. A correlation coefficient, $r = .1$, would imply only an $r^2 = .01$ or 1% reduction in the total sum of squares of deviations that could be explained by x.

If the linear coefficient of correlation between y and each of two variables, x_1 and x_2, were calculated to be .4 and .5, respectively, it does not follow that a predictor using both variables would account for a $[(.4)^2 + (.5)^2] = .41$ or a 41% reduction in the sum of squares of deviation. Actually, x_1 and x_2 might be highly correlated and therefore contribute the same information for the prediction of y.

Finally, we remind the reader that r is a measure of *linear* correlation and that x and y could be perfectly related by some curvilinear function when the observed value of r is equal to zero.

10.9   A Multivariate Predictor

A prediction equation based upon a number of variables, $x_1, x_2, \ldots, x_k$, could be obtained by the method of least squares in exactly the same manner as that employed for the simple linear model. For example, we might wish to fit the model

$$y = \beta_0 + \beta_1 x_1 + \beta_2 x_2 + \beta_3 x_3 + \varepsilon,$$

where y = student grade-point average at the end of the freshman year, x_1 = rank in high school class divided by the number in class, x_2 = score on a mathematics achievement test, x_3 = score on a verbal and written achievement test, to data on the achievement of freshman college students. (Note that we could add other variables as well as the squares, cubes, and cross products of x_1, x_2, and x_3.)

We would require a random sample of n freshmen selected from the population of interest and would record the values of y, x_1, x_2, and x_3 which, for each student, could be regarded as coordinates of a point in a four-dimensional space. Then, ideally, we would like to possess a multidimensional "ruler" (in our case, a plane) that we could visually move about among the n points until the deviations of the observed values of y from the predicted would in some sense be a minimum. Although we cannot graph points in four dimensions, the student readily recognizes that this device is provided by the method of least squares which, mathematically, performs the task for us.

The sum of squares of deviations of the observed value of y from the fitted model would be

$$SSE = \sum_{i=1}^{n} (y_i - \hat{y}_i)^2$$

$$= \sum_{i=1}^{n} [y_i - (\hat{\beta}_0 + \hat{\beta}_1 x_{1i} + \hat{\beta}_2 x_{2i} + \hat{\beta}_3 x_{3i})]^2,$$

where $\hat{y} = \hat{\beta}_0 + \hat{\beta}_1 x_1 + \hat{\beta}_2 x_2 + \hat{\beta}_3 x_3$ is the fitted model and $\hat{\beta}_0$, $\hat{\beta}_1$, $\hat{\beta}_2$, and $\hat{\beta}_3$ are estimates of the model parameters. We would then use the calculus to find the estimates, $\hat{\beta}_0$, $\hat{\beta}_1$, $\hat{\beta}_2$, and $\hat{\beta}_3$, that make SSE a minimum. The estimates, as for the simple linear model, would be obtained as the solution of a set of four simultaneous linear equations known as the least squares equations.

While the reasoning employed in obtaining the least squares multivariable predictor is identical to the procedure developed for the simple linear model, a description of the least squares equations, their solution and related methods of inference, becomes quite complex. These topics are omitted from this elementary discussion. Our primary objective in this chapter has been to indicate the generality and usefulness of the method of least squares as well as its role in prediction.

10.10 Summary

Although it was not stressed, the reader will observe that the prediction of a particular value of a random variable, y, was considered for the most elementary situation in Chapters 8 and 9. Thus, if we possessed no information concerning variables related to y, the sole information available for predicting y would be provided by its probability distribution. As we noted in Chapter 5, the probability that y would fall between two specific values, say y_1 and y_2, would equal the area under the probability distribution curve over the interval, $y_1 \leq y \leq y_2$. And, if we were to select randomly one member of the population, we would most likely choose μ, or some other measure of central tendency, as the most likely value of y to be observed. Thus we would wish to estimate μ and this of course was considered in Chapters 8 and 9.

Chapter 10 is concerned with the problem of predicting y when auxiliary information is available on other variables, say $x_1, x_2, x_3, \ldots$, which are related to y and hence assist in its prediction. Primarily, we have concentrated on the problem of predicting y as a linear function of a single variable, x, which provides the simplest extension of the prediction problem beyond that considered in Chapters 8 and 9.

EXERCISES

1. Graph the line corresponding to the equation $y = 2x + 1$ by locating points corresponding to $x = 0, 1,$ and 2.

2. Given the linear equation $2x + 3y + 6 = 0$,
   (a) give the y-intercept and slope for the line.
   (b) graph the line corresponding to the equation.

3. Follow the instructions given in Exercise 2 for the linear equation $2x - 3y - 5 = 0$.

4. Follow the instructions given in Exercise 2 for the linear equation $x/y = 1/2$.

5. Given five points whose coordinates are

y	0	0	1	1	3
x	-2	-1	0	1	2

   (a) find the least squares line for the data.
   (b) as a check on the calculations in (a), plot the five points and graph the line.

6. Given the following data for corresponding values of two variables, y and x,

y	2	1.5	1	2.5	2.5	4	5
x	-3	-2	-1	0	1	2	3

   follow the instructions of Exercise 5.

7. Calculate s^2 for the data in Exercise 5.

8. Calculate s^2 for the data in Exercise 6.

9. Do the data in Exercise 5 present sufficient evidence to indicate that y and x are linearly related? (Test the hypothesis that $\beta_1 = 0$, using $\alpha = .05$.)

10. Do the data in Exercise 6 present sufficient evidence to indicate that y and x are linearly related? (Test the hypothesis that $\beta_1 = 0$, using $\alpha = .05$.)

11. For what configurations of sample points will s^2 be zero?

12. For what parameter is s^2 an unbiased estimator? Explain how this parameter enters into the description of the probabilistic model $y = \beta_0 + \beta_1 x + \varepsilon$.

13. An experiment was conducted in a supermarket to observe the relation between the amount of display space allotted to a brand of coffee (brand A) and its weekly sales. The amount of space allotted to brand A was varied over three-, six-, and nine-square-feet displays in a random manner over twelve weeks while the space allotted to competing brands was maintained at a constant three square feet for each. The following data were observed:

WEEKLY SALES (DOLLARS)	y	526	421	581	630	412	560	434	443	590	570	346	672
SPACE ALLOTTED (SQUARE FEET)	x	6	3	6	9	3	9	6	3	9	6	3	9

(a) Find the least squares line appropriate for these data.
(b) Plot the points and graph the least squares line as a check on your calculations.
(c) Calculate s^2.

14. Do the data in Exercise 13 present sufficient evidence to indicate that sales for brand A are linearly related to display area when the display area varies between 3 and 9 square feet? (Test using $\alpha = .05$.) Would you expect the relation between y and x to be linear if x were varied over a wider range (say, $x = 1$ to $x = 30$)?

15. Find a 95% confidence interval for the slope of the line in Exercise 13.

16. Find a 90% confidence interval for the slope of the line in Exercise 5.

17. Find a 95% confidence interval for the slope of the line in Exercise 6.

18. Refer to Exercise 5. Obtain a 90% confidence interval for the expected value of y when $x = 1$.

19. Refer to Exercise 6. Obtain a 95% confidence interval for the expected value of y when $x = -1$.

20. Refer to Exercise 13. On the average, how much coffee (brand A) would you expect to sell if a six-square-foot display is employed? (Obtain a 95% confidence interval for the expected value of y, given x equals six square feet.) Assume that sales conditions and all other factors would be similar to those used in the experiment.

21. Refer to Exercise 13. If a three-square-foot display of brand A were employed for the thirteenth week, what value would you predict for that

week's sales? Construct an interval estimate of the predicted sales using a confidence coefficient equal to .90.

22. Refer to Exercise 6. Given that $x = 2$, find an interval estimate for a particular value of y. Use a confidence coefficient equal to .90.

23. How does the coefficient of correlation measure the strength of the linear relationship between two variables, y and x?

24. Describe the significance of the algebraic sign and the magnitude of r.

25. What value does r assume if all the sample points fall on the same straight line if
(a) the line has positive slope?
(b) the line has negative slope?

26. Calculate the coefficient of correlation, r, for the data in Exercise 5. What is the significance of this particular value of r?

27. Calculate the coefficient of correlation for the data in Exercise 6.

28. By what percentage was the sum of squares of deviations reduced by using the least squares predictor, $\hat{y} = \hat{\beta}_0 + \hat{\beta}_1 x$, rather than $\bar{y}$ as a predictor of y for the data in Exercise 6?

29. Calculate the coefficient of correlation for the data in Exercise 13. How much of a reduction in SSE was obtained by using the least squares predictor rather than $\bar{y}$ in predicting y for the data in Exercise 13?

30. An experiment was conducted to observe the effect of an increase in temperature on the potency of an antibiotic. Three one-ounce portions of the antibiotic were stored for equal lengths of time at each of the following temperatures: 30°, 50°, 70°, and 90°. The potency readings observed at the temperature of the experimental period were:

POTENCY READINGS	38, 43, 29	32, 26, 33	19, 27, 23	14, 19, 21
TEMPERATURE	30	50	70	90

(a) Find the least squares line appropriate for this data.
(b) Plot the points and graph the lines as a check on your calculations.
(c) Calculate s^2.

31. Refer to Exercise 30. Estimate the change in potency for a one-unit change in temperature. Use a 90% confidence interval.

32. Refer to Exercise 30. Estimate the mean potency corresponding to a temperature of 50 degrees. Use a 90% confidence interval.

33. Refer to Exercise 30.   Suppose that a batch of the antibiotic were stored at 50 degrees for the same length of time as the experimental period.   Predict the potency of the batch at the end of the storage period.   Use a 90% confidence interval.

34. Calculate the coefficient of correlation for the data in Exercise 30.   Interpret the results.

35. A psychological experiment was conducted to study the relationship between the length of time necessary for a human being to reach a decision and the number of alternatives presented.   The questions presented to the participants required a classification of an object into two or more classes, similar to the situation that one might encounter in grading potatoes.   Five individuals classified one item each for a two-class, two-decision situation. Five each were also allotted to three-class and four-class categories.   The length of time necessary to reach a decision is recorded for the fifteen participants.

LENGTH OF REACTION TIME (SECONDS)	1, 3, 3, 2, 4	2, 4, 3, 4, 5	5, 6, 5, 7, 4
NUMBER OF ALTERNATIVES	2	3	4

(a) Find the least squares line appropriate for this data.
(b) Plot the points and graph the line as a check on your calculations.
(c) Calculate s^2.

36. Do the data in Exercise 35 present sufficient evidence to indicate that the length of reaction time is linearly related to the number of alternatives? (Test at the $\alpha = .05$ level of significance.)

37. A comparison of twelve student grade-point averages at the end of the college freshman year with corresponding scores on an IQ test produced the following results:

G.P.A.	y	2.1	2.2	3.1	2.3	3.4	2.9	2.9	2.7	2.1	1.7	3.3	3.5
IQ SCORE	x	116	129	123	121	131	134	126	122	114	118	132	129

(a) Find the least squares prediction equation appropriate for the data.
(b) Graph the points and the least squares line as a check on your calculations.
(c) Calculate s^2.

38. Do the data in Exercise 37 present sufficient evidence to indicate that x is useful in predicting y? (Test using $\alpha = .05$.)

39. Calculate the coefficient of correlation for the data in Exercise 37.

40. Refer to Exercise 37. Obtain a 90% confidence interval for the expected grade-point average given an IQ score equal to 120.

41. Use the least squares equation in Exercise 37 to predict the grade-point average of a particular student whose IQ score is equal to 120. Use a 90% confidence interval.

42. Solutions $\hat{\beta}_0$ and $\hat{\beta}_1$ are expressed in Section 10.3. Show that the following is an algebraic identity:

$$\sum_{i=1}^{n} (y_i - b_0 - b_1 x_i)^2 = SSE + n(b_0 - \hat{\beta}_0)^2 + \sum_{i=1}^{n} (x_i - \bar{x})^2 (b_1 - \hat{\beta}_1)^2$$

43. If $y_i = b_0 + b_1 x_i$ is used to represent measurements y_i, the sum of squares of deviations of the actual y_i from their respective representations is $\sum_{i=1}^{n}(y_i - b_0 - b_1 x_i)^2$. From the identity of Exercise 42 argue that the best fitting line according to the criterion of least squares is obtained by taking $b_0 = \hat{\beta}_0$ and $b_1 = \hat{\beta}_1$.

REFERENCES

Anderson, R. L., and T. A. Bancroft, *Statistical Theory in Research*. New York: McGraw-Hill Book Co., Inc., 1952. Chapter 13.

Freund, J. E., *Mathematical Statistics*. Englewood Cliffs, N. J.: Prentice-Hall, Inc., 1962. Chapter 13.

Kendall, M. G., and A. Stuart, *The Advanced Theory of Statistics*, Vol. 2. New York: Hafner Publishing Co., 1961. Chapter 19.

Li, J. C. R., *Introduction to Statistical Inference*. Ann Arbor, Mich.: J. W. Edwards, Publisher, Inc., 1961. Chapter 16.

Mendenhall, W., *An Introduction to Linear Models and the Design and Analysis of Experiments*. Belmont, Calif.: Wadsworth Publishing Company, Inc., 1967. Chapters 6 and 7.

11

ANALYSIS OF
ENUMERATIVE DATA

11.1 A Description of the Experiment

Many experiments, particularly in the social sciences, result in enumerative (or count) data. For instance, the classification of people into five income brackets would result in an enumeration or count corresponding to each of the five income classes. Or, we might be interested in studying the reaction of a mouse to a particular stimulus in a psychological experiment. If a mouse will react in one of three ways when the stimulus is applied and if a large number of mice were subjected to the stimulus, the experiment would yield three counts indicating the number of mice falling in each of the reaction classes. Similarly, a traffic study might require a count and classification of the type of motor vehicles using a section of highway. An industrial process manufactures items which fall into one of three quality classes: acceptable, seconds, and rejects. A student of the arts might classify paintings in one of k categories according to style and period in order to study trends in style over time. We might wish to classify ideas in a philosophical study or style in the field of literature. The results of an advertising campaign would yield count data indicating a classification of consumer reaction. Indeed, many observations in the physical sciences are not amenable to measurement on a continuous scale and hence result in enumerative or classificatory data.

The illustrations in the preceding paragraph exhibit, to a reasonable degree of approximation, the following characteristics which define a *multinomial* experiment:

(1) The experiment consists of n identical trials.

(2) The outcome of each trial falls into one of k classes or cells.

(3) The probability that the outcome of a single trial will fall in a particular cell, say cell i, is p_i ($i = 1, 2, \ldots, k$), and remains the same from trial to trial. Note that

$$p_1 + p_2 + p_3 + \cdots + p_k = 1.$$

(4) The trials are independent.

(5) We are interested in $n_1, n_2, n_3, \ldots, n_k$, where $n_i(i = 1, 2, \ldots, k)$ is equal to the number of trials in which the outcome falls in cell i. Note that $n_1 + n_2 + n_3 + \ldots + n_k = n$.

The above experiment is analogous to tossing n balls at k boxes where each ball must fall in one of the boxes. The boxes are arranged such that the probability that a ball will fall in a box varies from box to box but remains the same for a particular box in repeated tosses. Finally, the balls are tossed in such a way that the trials are independent. At the conclusion of the experiment, we observe n_1 balls in the first box, n_2 in the second, and n_k in the kth. The total number of balls is equal to

$$\sum_{i=1}^{k} n_i = n.$$

The reader will note the similarity between the binomial and multinomial experiments and, in particular, that the binomial experiment represents the special case for the multinomial experiment when $k = 2$. The single parameter of the binomial experiment, p, is replaced by the k parameters, $p_1, p_2, \ldots, p_k$, of the multinomial. In this chapter, inferences concerning $p_1, p_2, \ldots, p_k$ will be expressed in terms of a statistical test of an hypothesis concerning their specific numerical values or their relationship, one to another.

If we were to proceed as in Chapter 6, we would derive the probability of the observed sample ($n_1, n_2, \ldots, n_k$) for use in calculating the probability of the type I and type II errors associated with a statistical test. Fortunately, we have been relieved of this chore by the British statistician, Karl Pearson, who proposed a very useful test statistic for testing hypotheses concerning $p_1, p_2, \ldots, p_k$, and gave its approximate probability distribution in repeated sampling.

11.2   The Chi-Square Test

Suppose that $n = 100$ balls were tossed at the cells and that we knew that p_1 was equal to .1. How many balls would be expected to fall in the first cell? Referring to Chapter 6 and utilizing knowledge of the binomial experiment, we would calculate

$$E(n_1) = np_1 = 100(.1) = 10.$$

In like manner, the expected number falling in the remaining cells may be calculated using the formula

$$E(n_i) = np_i, \qquad i = 1, 2, \ldots, k.$$

Now suppose that we hypothesize values for $p_1, p_2, \ldots, p_k$ and calculate the expected value for each cell. Certainly, if our hypothesis is true, the cell counts, n_i, should not deviate greatly from their expected values, np_i $(i = 1, 2, \ldots, k)$. Hence it would seem intuitively reasonable to use a test statistic involving the k deviations,

$$(n_i - np_i) \qquad i = 1, 2, \ldots, k.$$

In 1900, Karl Pearson proposed the following test statistic which is a function of the square of the deviations of the observed counts from their expected values, weighted by the reciprocal of their expected value:

$$X^2 = \sum_{i=1}^{k} \frac{[n_i - E(n_i)]^2}{E(n_i)}$$

$$= \sum_{i=1}^{k} \frac{[n_i - np_i]^2}{np_i}.$$

While the mathematical proof is beyond the scope of this text, it can be shown that when n is large, X^2 will possess, approximately, a chi-square probability distribution in repeated sampling. Experience has shown that the cell counts, n_i, should not be too small in order that the chi-square distribution provide an adequate approximation to the distribution of X^2. As a rule of thumb, we will require that all expected cell counts equal or exceed five, although Cochran (see References, page 267) has noted that this value can be as low as one for some situations.

The reader will recall the use of the chi-square probability distribution for testing an hypothesis concerning a population variance, σ^2, in Section 9.6. Particularly, we stated that the shape of the chi-square distribution would vary depending upon the number of degrees of freedom associated with s^2, and we discussed the use of Table 5, Appendix II, which presents the critical values of χ^2 corresponding to various right-hand tail areas of the distribution. Therefore we must know which χ^2 distribution to use —that is, the number of degrees of freedom—in approximating the distribution of X^2, and we must know whether to use a one-tailed or two-tailed test in locating the rejection region for the test. The latter problem may be solved directly. Since large deviations of the observed cell counts from those expected would tend to contradict the null hypothesis concerning the cell probabilities $p_1, p_2, \ldots, p_k$, we would reject the null hypothesis when X^2 is large and employ a one-tailed statistical test using the upper tail values of χ^2 to locate the rejection region.

The determination of the appropriate number of degrees of freedom to be employed for the test can be rather difficult and therefore will be *specified* for the physical applications described in the following sections. In addition, we will state the principle involved (and which is fundamental to the mathematical proof of the approximation) so that the reader may understand why the number of degrees of freedom changes with various applications. This states that the appropriate number of degrees of freedom will equal the number of cells, k, less one degree of freedom for each independent linear restriction placed upon the observed cell counts. For example, one linear restriction is *always* present because the sum of the cell counts must equal n, that is,

$$n_1 + n_2 + n_3 + \ldots + n_k = n.$$

Other restrictions will be introduced for some applications because of the necessity for estimating unknown parameters required in the calculation of the expected cell frequencies or because of the method in which the sample is collected. These will become apparent as we consider various practical examples.

11.3   A Test of an Hypothesis Concerning Specified Cell Probabilities

The simplest hypothesis concerning the cell probabilities would be one which specifies numerical values for each. For example, suppose that we were to consider a simple extension of the rat experiment discussed in Exercise 20, Chapter 6. One or more rats proceed down a ramp to one of three doors. We wish to test the hypothesis that the rats have no preference concerning the choice of a door and therefore that

$$H_0: \ p_1 = p_2 = p_3 = 1/3,$$

where p_i is the probability that a rat will choose door i, $i = 1$, 2, or 3.

Suppose that the rat was sent down the ramp $n = 90$ times and that the three observed cell frequencies were $n_1 = 23$, $n_2 = 36$, and $n_3 = 31$.

The expected cell frequency would be the same for each cell: $E(n_i) = np_i = 90(1/3) = 30$. The observed and expected cell frequencies are presented in Table 11.1. Noting the discrepancy between the observed and expected cell frequency, we would wonder whether the data present sufficient evidence to warrant rejection of the hypothesis of no preference.

Table 11.1. Observed and Expected Cell Counts
for the Rat Experiment

DOOR	1	2	3
Observed cell frequency	$n_1 = 23$	$n_2 = 36$	$n_3 = 31$
Expected cell frequency	(30)	(30)	(30)

The chi-square test statistic for our example will possess $(k - 1) = 2$ degrees of freedom since the only linear restriction on the cell frequencies is that

$$n_1 + n_2 + \ldots + n_k = n,$$

or, for our example,

$$n_1 + n_2 + n_3 = 90.$$

Therefore, if we choose $\alpha = .05$, we would reject the null hypothesis when $X^2 > 5.991$ (see Table 5, Appendix II).

Substituting into the formula for X^2, we obtain

$$X^2 = \sum_{i=1}^{k} \frac{[n_i - E(n_i)]^2}{E(n_i)} = \sum_{i=1}^{k} \frac{[n_i - np_i]^2}{np_i}$$

$$= \frac{(23 - 30)^2}{30} + \frac{(36 - 30)^2}{30} + \frac{(31 - 30)^2}{30}$$

$$= 2.87.$$

Since X^2 is less than the tabulated critical value of χ^2, the null hypothesis is not rejected and we conclude that the data do not present sufficient evidence to indicate that the rat has a preference for a particular door.

11.4   Contingency Tables

A problem frequently encountered in the analysis of count data concerns the independence of two methods of classification of observed events. For example, we might wish to classify defects found on furniture produced in a manufacturing plant, first, according to the type of defect and, second, according to the production shift. Ostensibly, we wish to investigate a contingency—a dependence between the two classifications. Do the proportions of various types of defects vary from shift to shift?

A total of $n = 309$ furniture defects was recorded and the defects were classified according to one of four types: A, B, C, or D. At the same time, each piece of furniture was identified according to the production shift in which it was manufactured. These counts are presented in Table 11.2, which is known as a *contingency table*. (Note: Numbers in parentheses are the expected cell frequencies.)

Table 11.2.   A Contingency Table

	TYPE OF DEFECT				
SHIFT	A	B	C	D	TOTAL
1	15 (22.51)	21 (20.99)	45 (38.94)	13 (11.56)	94
2	26 (22.99)	31 (21.44)	34 (39.77)	5 (11.81)	96
3	33 (28.50)	17 (26.57)	49 (49.29)	20 (14.63)	119
TOTALS	74	69	128	38	309

Let p_A equal the unconditional probability that a defect will be of type A. Similarly, define p_B, p_C, and p_D as the probabilities of observing the three other types of defects. Then these probabilities, which we will call the column probabilities of Table 11.2, will satisfy the requirement

$$p_A + p_B + p_C + p_D = 1.$$

In like manner, let $p_i(i = 1, 2,$ or $3)$ equal the row probability that a defect will have occurred on shift i, where

$$p_1 + p_2 + p_3 = 1.$$

Then, if the two classifications are independent of each other, a cell probability will equal the product of its respective row and column probabilities in accordance with the multiplicative law of probability. For example, the probability that a particular defect will occur on Shift 1 and be of type A is $(p_1)(p_A)$. Thus, we observe that the numerical values of the cell probabilities are unspecified in the problem under consideration. The null hypothesis specifies only that each cell probability will equal the product of its respective row and column probabilities and therefore imply independence of the two classifications.

The analysis of the data obtained from a contingency table differs from the problem discussed in Section 11.3 because we must *estimate* the row and column probabilities in order to estimate the expected cell frequencies.

If proper estimates of the cell probabilities are obtained, the estimated expected cell frequencies may be substituted for the $E(n_i)$ in X^2, and X^2 will continue to possess a distribution in repeated sampling that is approximated by the chi-square probability distribution. The proof of this statement as well as a discussion of the methods for obtaining the estimates are beyond the scope of this text. Fortunately the procedures for obtaining the estimates, known as the method of maximum likelihood and the method of minimum chi-square, yield estimates that are intuitively obvious for our relatively simple applications.

It can be shown that the maximum likelihood estimator of a column probability will equal the column total divided by $n = 309$. If we denote the total of column j as c_j, then

$$\hat{p}_A = \frac{c_1}{n} = \frac{74}{309},$$

$$\hat{p}_B = \frac{c_2}{n} = \frac{69}{309},$$

$$\hat{p}_C = \frac{c_3}{n} = \frac{128}{309},$$

$$\hat{p}_D = \frac{c_4}{n} = \frac{38}{309}.$$

Likewise, the row probabilities, p_1, p_2, and p_3 may be estimated using the row totals r_1, r_2, and r_3:

$$\hat{p}_1 = \frac{r_1}{n} = \frac{94}{309},$$

$$\hat{p}_2 = \frac{r_2}{n} = \frac{96}{309},$$

$$\hat{p}_3 = \frac{r_3}{n} = \frac{119}{309}.$$

Denote the observed frequency of the cell in row i and column j of the contingency table as n_{ij}. Then the estimated expected value of n_{11} will be

$$\hat{E}(n_{11}) = n[\hat{p}_1 \cdot \hat{p}_A] = n\left(\frac{r_1}{n}\right)\left(\frac{c_1}{n}\right)$$

$$= \frac{r_1 \cdot c_1}{n},$$

where $(\hat{p}_1 \cdot \hat{p}_A)$ is the estimated cell probability.   Likewise, we may find the estimated expected value for any other cell, say $\hat{E}(n_{23})$,

$$\hat{E}(n_{23}) = n[\hat{p}_2 \cdot \hat{p}_C] = n\left(\frac{r_2}{n}\right) \cdot \left(\frac{c_3}{n}\right)$$

$$= \frac{r_2 c_3}{n}.$$

In other words, we observe that the estimated expected value of the observed cell frequency, n_{ij}, for a contingency table is equal to the product of its respective row and column totals divided by the total frequency; that is,

$$\hat{E}(n_{ij}) = \frac{r_i c_j}{n}.$$

The estimated expected cell frequencies for our example are shown in parentheses in Table 11.2.

We may now use the expected and observed cell frequencies shown in Table 11.2 to calculate the value of the test statistic:

$$X^2 = \sum_{i=1}^{12} \frac{[n_i - \hat{E}(n_i)]^2}{\hat{E}(n_i)}$$

$$= \frac{(15 - 22.51)^2}{22.51} + \frac{(26 - 22.99)^2}{22.99} + \dots + \frac{(20 - 14.64)^2}{14.64}$$

$$= 19.17.$$

The only remaining obstacle involves the determination of the appropriate number of degrees of freedom associated with the test statistic. We will give this as a rule which we will attempt to justify.   *The degrees of freedom associated with a contingency table possessing r rows and c columns will always equal* $(r - 1)(c - 1)$.   Thus, for our example, we will compare X^2 with the critical value of χ^2 with $(r - 1)(c - 1) = (3 - 1)(4 - 1) = 6$ degrees of freedom.

The reader will recall that the number of degrees of freedom associated with the X^2 statistic will equal the number of cells (in this case, $k = rc$) less one degree of freedom for each independent linear restriction placed upon the observed cell frequencies.   The total number of cells for the data of Table 11.2 is $k = 12$.   From this we subtract one degree of freedom because the sum of the observed cell frequencies must equal n, that is

$$n_{11} + n_{12} + \dots + n_{34} = 309.$$

In addition, we used the cell frequencies to estimate three of the four column probabilities. Note that the estimate of the fourth column probability will be determined once we have estimated p_A, p_B, and p_C because

$$p_A + p_B + p_C + p_D = 1.$$

Thus we lose $(c - 1) = 3$ degrees of freedom for estimating the column probabilities.

Finally, we used the cell frequencies to estimate $(r - 1) = 2$ row probabilities and therefore we lose $(r - 1) = 2$ additional degrees of freedom. The total number of degrees of freedom remaining will be

$$d.f. = 12 - 1 - 3 - 2 = 6.$$

And, in general, we see that the total number of degrees of freedom associated with an $r \times c$ contingency table will be

$$d.f. = rc - 1 - (c - 1) - (r - 1)$$
$$= (r - 1)(c - 1).$$

Therefore, if we use $\alpha = .05$, we will reject the null hypothesis that the two classifications are independent if $X^2 > 12.592$. Since the value of the test statistic, $X^2 = 19.17$, exceeds the critical value of χ^2, we will reject the null hypothesis. The data present sufficient evidence to indicate that the proportion of the various types of defects varies from shift to shift. A study of the production operations for the three shifts would likely reveal the cause.

Example 11.1: A survey was conducted to evaluate the effectiveness of a new flu vaccine which had been administered in a small community. The vaccine was provided free of charge in a two-shot sequence over a period of two weeks to those wishing to avail themselves of it. Some people received the two-shot sequence, some appeared only for the first shot, and others received neither.

A survey of one thousand local inhabitants in the following Spring provided the information shown in Table 11.3. Do the data present

Table 11.3. Data Tabulation for Example 11.1

	NO VACCINE	ONE SHOT	TWO SHOTS	TOTALS
FLU	24 (14.4)	9 (5.0)	13 (26.6)	46
NO FLU	289 (298.6)	100 (104.0)	565 (551.4)	954
TOTALS	313	109	578	1000

sufficient evidence to indicate that the vaccine was successful in reducing the number of flu cases in the community?

Solution: The question stated above asks whether the data provide sufficient evidence to indicate a *dependence* between the vaccine classification and the occurrence or nonoccurrence of flu. We therefore analyze the data as a contingency table.

The estimated expected cell frequencies may be calculated using the appropriate row and column totals,

$$\hat{E}(n_{ij}) = \frac{r_i c_j}{n}.$$

Thus,

$$\hat{E}(n_{11}) = \frac{r_1 c_1}{n} = \frac{(46)(313)}{1000} = 14.4,$$

$$\hat{E}(n_{12}) = \frac{r_1 c_2}{n} = \frac{(46)(109)}{1000} = 5.0.$$

· · · · · · · ·

These values are shown in parentheses in Table 11.3.

The value of the test statistic, X^2, will now be computed and compared with the critical value of χ^2 possessing $(r-1)(c-1) = (1)(2) = 2$ degrees of freedom. Then, for $\alpha = .05$, we will reject the null hypothesis when $X^2 > 5.991$. Substituting into the formula for X^2, we obtain

$$X^2 = \frac{(24 - 14.4)^2}{14.4} + \frac{(289 - 298.6)^2}{298.6} + \ldots + \frac{(565 - 551.4)^2}{551.4}$$

$$= 17.35.$$

Observing that X^2 falls in the rejection region, we reject the null hypothesis of independence of the two classifications. A comparison of the percentage incidence of flu for each of the three categories would suggest that those receiving the two-shot sequence were less susceptible to the disease. Further analysis of the data could be obtained by deleting one of the three categories, the second column, for example, to compare the effect of the vaccine with that of no vaccine. This could be done by using either a 2 × 2 contingency table or treating the two categories as two binomial populations and using the methods of Section 8.8. Or, we might wish to analyze the data by comparing the results of the two-shot vaccine sequence with those of the combined no vaccine–one-shot group. That is, we would combine the first two columns of the 2 × 3 table into one.

11.5 $r \times c$ Tables with Fixed Row or Column Totals

In the previous section we have described the analysis of an $r \times c$ contingency table using examples which, for all practical purposes, fit the multinomial experiment described in Section 11.1.   While the methods of collecting data in many surveys may obviously adhere to the requirements of a multinomial experiment, other methods do not.   For example, we might not wish to sample randomly the population described in Example 11.1 because we might find that, owing to chance, one category is completely missing.   For example, people who have received no flu shots might fail to appear in the sample.   Thus we might decide beforehand to interview a specified number of people in each column category, thereby fixing the column totals in advance.   While these restrictions tend to disturb somewhat our visualization of the experiment in the multinomial context, they have no effect on the analysis of the data.   As long as we wish to test the hypothesis of independence of the two classifications and none of the row or column probabilities are specified in advance, we may analyze the data as an $r \times c$ contingency table.   It can be shown that the resulting X^2 will possess a probability distribution in repeated sampling that is approximated by a chi-square distribution with $(r-1)(c-1)$ degrees of freedom.

To illustrate, suppose that we wish to test an hypothesis concerning the equivalence of four binomial populations as indicated in the following example.

Example 11.2: A survey of voter sentiment was conducted in four mid-city political wards to compare the fraction of voters favoring candidate A.   Random samples of two hundred voters were polled in each of the four wards with results as shown in Table 11.4.

Table 11.4.   Data Tabulation for Example 11.2

	WARD				TOTALS
	1	2	3	4	
FAVOR A	76 (59)	53 (59)	59 (59)	48 (59)	236
DO NOT FAVOR A	124 (141)	147 (141)	141 (141)	152 (141)	564
TOTALS	200	200	200	200	800

Do the data present sufficient evidence to indicate that the fractions of voters favoring candidate A differ in the four wards?

Solution: The reader will observe that the test of an hypothesis concerning the equivalence of the parameters of the four binomial populations corresponding to the four wards is identical to an hypothesis implying independence of the row and column classifications. Thus, if we denote the fraction of voters favoring A as p and hypothesize that p is the same for all four wards, we imply that the first- and second-row probabilities are equal to p and $(1 - p)$, respectively. The probability that a member of the sample of $n = 800$ voters falls in a particular ward will equal one-quarter since this was fixed in advance. Then the cell probabilities for the table would be obtained by multiplication of the appropriate row and column probabilities under the null hypothesis and be equivalent to a test of independence of the two classifications.

The estimated expected cell frequencies, calculated using the row and column totals, appear in parentheses in Table 11.4. We see that

$$X^2 = \frac{\sum_{i=1}^{8} [n_i - \hat{E}(n_i)]^2}{\hat{E}(n_i)}$$

$$= \frac{(79 - 59)^2}{59} + \frac{(124 - 141)^2}{141} + \ldots + \frac{(152 - 141)^2}{141}$$

$$= 10.72.$$

The critical value of χ^2 for $\alpha = .05$ and $(r - 1)(c - 1) = (1)(3) = 3$ degrees of freedom is 7.815. Since X^2 exceeds this critical value, we reject the null hypothesis and conclude that the fraction of voters favoring candidate A is not the same for all four wards.

11.6 Other Applications

The applications of the chi-square test in analyzing enumerative data described in Sections 11.3, 11.4, and 11.5 represent only a few of the interesting classificatory problems which may be approximated by the multinomial experiment and for which our method of analysis is appropriate. By and large, these applications are complicated to a greater or lesser degree because the numerical values of the cell probabilities are unspecified and hence require the estimation of one or more population parameters. Then, as in Sections 11.4 and 11.5, we can estimate the cell probabilities. Although we omit the mechanics of the statistical tests, several additional applications of the chi-square test are worth mention as a matter of interest.

For example, suppose that we wish to test an hypothesis stating that a population possesses a normal probability distribution. The cells of a sample frequency histogram (for example, Figure 3.2) would correspond to the k cells of the multinomial experiment and the observed cell frequencies would be the number of measurements falling in each cell of the histogram. Given the hypothesized normal probability distribution for the population we could use the areas under the normal curve to calculate the theoretical cell probabilities and hence the expected cell frequencies. The difficulty arises when μ and σ are unspecified for the normal population and these parameters must be estimated in order to obtain the estimated cell probabilities. This difficulty, of course, can be surmounted.

The construction of a two-way table to investigate dependency between two classifications can be extended to three or more classifications. For example, if we wish to test the mutual independence of three classifications, we would employ a three-dimensional "table" or rectangular parallelepiped. The reasoning and methodology associated with the analysis of both the two- and three-way tables are identical although the analysis of the three-way table is a bit more complex.

A third and interesting application of our methodology would be its use in the investigation of the rate of change of a multinomial (or binomial) population as a function of time. For example, we might study the decision-making ability of a human (or any animal) as he is subjected to an educational program and tested over time. If, for instance, he is tested at prescribed intervals of time and the test is of the yes or no type yielding a number of correct answers, y, that would follow a binomial probability distribution, we would be interested in the behavior of the probability of a correct response, p, as a function of time. If the number of correct responses was recorded for c time periods, the data would fall in a $2 \times c$ table similar to that in Example 11.2 (Section 11.5). We would then be interested in testing the hypothesis that p is equal to a constant, that is, that no learning has occurred, and we would then proceed to more interesting hypotheses to determine whether the data present sufficient evidence to indicate a gradual (say, linear) change over time as opposed to an abrupt change at some point in time. The procedures we have described could be extended to decisions involving more than two alternatives.

The reader will observe that our learning example is common to business, to industry, and to many other fields, including the social sciences. For example, we might wish to study the rate of consumer acceptance of a new product for various types of advertising campaigns as a function of the length of time that the campaign has been in effect. Or, we might wish to study the trend in the lot fraction defective in a manufacturing process as a function of time. Both of these examples, as well as many others, require a study of the behavior of a binomial (or multinomial) process as a function of time.

The examples which we have just described are intended to suggest the relatively broad application of the chi-square analysis of enumerative data, a fact that should be born in mind by the experimenter concerned with this type of data.   The statistical test employing X^2 as a test statistic is often called a "goodness-of-fit." test.   Its application for some of these examples requires care in the determination of the appropriate estimates and the number of degrees of freedom for X^2, which, for some of these problems, may be rather complex.

11.7   Summary

The preceding material has been concerned with a test of an hypothesis regarding the cell probabilities associated with a multinomial experiment.   When the number of observations, n, is large, the test-statistic, X^2, can be shown to possess, approximately, a chi-square probability distribution in repeated sampling, the number of degrees of freedom being dependent upon the particular application.   In general, we assume that n is large and that the minimum expected cell frequency is equal to or is greater than five.

Several words of caution concerning the use of the X^2 statistic as a method of analyzing enumerative type data are appropriate.   The determination of the correct number of degrees of freedom associated with the X^2 statistic is very important in locating the rejection region.   If the number is incorrectly specified, erroneous conclusions might result.   Also, note that nonrejection of the null hypothesis does not imply that it should be accepted.   We would have difficulty in stating a meaningful alternative hypothesis for many practical applications and, therefore, would lack knowledge of the probability of making a type II error.   For example, we hypothesize that the two classifications of a contingency table are independent.   A specific alternative would have to specify some measure of dependence which may or may not possess practical significance to the experimenter.   Finally, if parameters are missing and the expected cell frequencies must be estimated, the estimators of missing parameters should be of a particular type in order that the test be valid.   In other words, the application of the chi-square test for other than the simple applications outlined in Sections 11.3, 11.4, and 11.5 will require experience beyond the scope of this introductory presentation of the subject.

EXERCISES

1. List the characteristics of a multinomial experiment.

2. A city expressway utilizing four lanes in each direction was studied to see whether drivers preferred to drive on the inside lanes. A total of one thousand automobiles were observed during the heavy early morning traffic and their respective lanes recorded. The results were as follows:

LANE	1	2	3	4
OBSERVED COUNT	294	276	238	192

Do the data present sufficient evidence to indicate that some lanes were preferred over others? (Test the hypothesis that $p_1 = p_2 = p_3 = p_4 = 1/4$ using $\alpha = .05$.)

3. A die was rolled six hundred times with the following results:

OBSERVED NUMBER	1	2	3	4	5	6
FREQUENCY	89	113	98	104	117	79

Do these data present sufficient evidence to indicate that the die is unbalanced? Test using $\alpha = .05$.

4. After inspecting the data in Exercise 3, one might wish to test the hypothesis that the probability of a "6" is 1/6 against the alternative that this probability is less than 1/6.
   (a) Carry out the above test using $\alpha = .05$.
   (b) What tenet of good statistical practice is violated in the test of part (a)?

5. A study to determine the effectiveness of a drug (serum) for arthritis resulted in the comparison of two groups each consisting of two hundred arthritic patients. One group was inoculated with the serum while the other received a placebo (an inoculation that appears to contain serum but actually is nonactive). After a period of time, each person in the study was asked to state whether his arthritic condition was improved. The following results were observed:

	TREATED	UNTREATED
IMPROVED	117	74
NOT IMPROVED	83	126

Do these data present sufficient evidence to indicate that the serum was effective in improving the condition of arthritic patients?
(a) Test using the X^2 statistic.   Use $\alpha = .05$.
(b) Using the z-test in Section 8.11.

6. A radio station conducted a survey to study the relationship between the number of radios per household and family income. The survey based upon $n = 1000$ interviews, produced the following results:

NUMBER OF RADIOS PER HOUSEHOLD	FAMILY INCOME (IN DOLLARS)			
	less than 4000	4000–7000	7000–10,000	more than 10,000
1	126	362	129	78
2	29	138	82	56

Do the data present sufficient evidence to indicate that the number of radios per household is dependent upon family income? Test at the $\alpha = .10$ level of significance.

7. A group of three hundred six people were interviewed to determine their opinion concerning a particular current American foreign-policy issue. At the same time, their political affiliation was recorded.   The data are shown below.

PARTY \ OPINION	APPROVE OF POLICY	DO NOT APPROVE OF POLICY	NO OPINION
REPUBLICANS	114	53	17
DEMOCRATS	87	27	8

Do the data present sufficient evidence to indicate a dependence between party affiliation and the opinion expressed for the sampled population?

8. A survey of student opinion concerning a resolution presented to the student council was studied to determine whether the resulting opinion was independent of fraternity and sorority affiliation. Two hundred students were interviewed with the following results:

AFFILIATION \ OPINION	IN FAVOR	OPPOSED	UNDECIDED
FRATERNITY	37	16	5
SORORITY	30	22	8
NO AFFILIATION	32	44	6

Do these data present sufficient evidence to indicate that student opinion concerning the resolution was dependent upon affiliation with fraternities or sororities? Test using $\alpha = .05$.

9. The responses for the data in Exercise 8 were reclassified according to whether the student was male or female.

AFFILIATION \ OPINION	IN FAVOR	OPPOSED	UNDECIDED
FEMALE	39	46	9
MALE	60	36	10

Do the data present sufficient evidence to indicate that student reaction to the resolution varied for the various opinion categories depending upon whether the student was male or female?

10. A manufacturer of buttons wished to determine whether the fraction of defective buttons produced by three machines varied from machine to machine. Samples of four hundred buttons were selected from each of the three machines and the number of defectives counted for each sample. The results are shown below.

MACHINE NUMBER	1	2	3
NUMBER OF DEFECTIVES	16	24	9

Do these data present sufficient evidence to indicate that the fraction of defective buttons varies from machine to machine? Test using $\alpha = .05$.

11. A survey was conducted by an auto repairman to determine whether various auto ills were dependent upon the make of the auto. His survey, restricted to this year's model, produced the following results:

MAKE	TYPE OF REPAIR		
	ELECTRICAL	FUEL SUPPLY	OTHER
A	17	19	7
B	14	7	9
C	6	21	12
D	33	44	19
E	7	9	6

Do these data present sufficient evidence to indicate a dependency between auto makes and type of repair for these new-model cars? Note that the repairman was not utilizing all of the information available when he conducted his survey. In conducting a study of this type, what other factors should be recorded?

12. A manufacturer of floor polish conducted a consumer-preference experiment to see whether a new floor polish, A, was superior to those produced by four of his competitors. A sample of one hundred housewives viewed five patches of flooring that had received the five polishes and each indicated the patch that she considered superior in appearance. The lighting, background, etc., were approximately the same for all five patches. The results of the survey are shown below.

POLISH	A	B	C	D	E
FREQUENCY	27	17	15	22	19

Do these data present sufficient evidence to indicate a preference for one or more of the polished patches of floor over the others? If one were to reject the hypothesis of "no preference" for this experiment, would this imply that polish A is superior to the others? Can you suggest a better method of conducting the experiment?

13. A sociologist conducted a survey to determine whether the incidence of various types of crime varied from one part of a particular city to another. The city was partitioned into three regions and the crimes classified as homicide, car theft, grand larceny, and others. An analysis of 1599 cases produced the following results:

TYPE OF CRIME

CITY REGION	HOMICIDE	AUTO THEFT	GRAND LARCENY (NEGLECTING AUTO THEFT)	PETTY LARCENY	OTHER
1	12	239	191	122	47
2	17	163	278	201	54
3	7	98	109	44	17

Do these data present sufficient evidence to indicate that the occurrence of various types of crime is dependent upon city region?

SUPPLEMENTARY EXERCISES

1. The chi-square test used in Exercise 5 is equivalent to the two-tailed z-test of Section 8.11 provided α is the same for the two tests. Show algebraically that the chi-square test statistic X^2 is the square of the test statistic z for the equivalent test.

2. It is often not clear whether all properties of a binomial experiment are actually met in a given application. A "goodness-of-fit" test is desirable for such cases. Suppose that an experiment consisting of 4 trials was repeated 100 times. The number of repetitions on which a given number of successes was obtained is recorded in the following table.

POSSIBLE RESULTS (NUMBER OF SUCCESSES)	0	1	2	3	4
NUMBER OF TIMES OBTAINED	11	17	42	21	9

Estimate p (assuming that the experiment was binomial), obtain estimates of the expected cell frequencies, and test for goodness of fit. To determine the appropriate number of degrees of freedom for X^2, note that p was estimated by a linear combination of the obtained frequencies.

REFERENCES

Anderson, R. L., and T. A. Bancroft, *Statistical Theory in Research.* New York: McGraw-Hill Book Co., Inc., 1952. Chapter 12.

Cochran, W. G., "The χ^2 Test of Goodness of Fit." *Ann. Math. Stat.*, Vol. XXIII (1952), pp. 315–345.

Dixon, W. J., and F. J. Massey, Jr., *Introduction to Statistical Analysis.* New York: McGraw-Hill Book Co., Inc., 1957. Chapter 13.

Kendall, M. G., and A. Stuart, *The Advanced Theory of Statistics*, Vol. 2. New York: Hafner Publishing Co., 1961. Chapter 30.

12

THE ANALYSIS
OF VARIANCE

12.1 Introduction

Many experiments are conducted to determine the effect of one or more variables on a response. A linear relationship between a response, y, and an independent variable, x, was studied in Chapter 10 and, in a more general sense, the comparison of means in Chapter 9 was a similar problem. For example, the comparison of the difference in the mean rate of human reaction for two stimuli in a psychological experiment is a study of the effect of an independent variable, "type of stimuli," on a response, y, which is the mean rate of reaction.

The preceding comments indicate that independent experimental variables may be one of two types, *quantitative* or *qualitative*. The former, as the name implies, are those familiar variables that are subject to a quantitative interpretation. Qualitative variables are not. Thus, pressure, temperature, number of employees, and blood count represent four quantitative variables. In contrast, the "manufacturer" of automobile tires is a variable that is likely to be related to the wearing characteristics of tires but there is no way to order or arrange five "manufacturers" on a continuum. Thus, "manufacturers" would be a qualitative independent variable.   Similarly, we may wish to determine whether the mean yield of chemical in a manufacturing operation varies depending upon the foreman managing the process and also whether it varies from one working shift to another.   Four foremen, Jones, Smith, Adams, and Green would represent "levels" or settings of a single qualitative variable, "foremen"; the three working shifts would identify levels of a second qualitative variable, "shifts."* The complete experiment would involve, therefore, a study of the effect of two independent qualitative variables, "foremen" and "shifts," on yield of chemical.

In this chapter, we consider the comparison of more than two means which, in the context of the previous discussion, implies a study of the effect of a single independent variable (quantitative or qualitative) on a response.   We will then extend the procedure to include the analysis of designed experiments involving two independent variables and will discuss a generalization of the procedure for more than two independent variables.

12.2   The Analysis of Variance

The methodology for the analysis of experiments involving several independent variables can best be explained in terms of the linear probabilistic model of Chapter 10.   Although elementary and unified, this approach is not susceptible to the condensation necessary for inclusion in an elementary text.   Instead, we will attempt an intuitive discussion using a procedure known as the *analysis of variance*.   Actually, the two approaches are connected and the analysis of variance can easily be explained in a general way in terms of the linear model.   The interested reader may consult the introductory text on this subject by Mendenhall (see References).

As the name implies, the analysis-of-variance procedure attempts to analyze the variation of a response and to assign portions of this variation to each of a set of independent variables.   The reasoning is that response variables vary only because of variation in a set of unknown independent variables.   Since the experimenter will rarely, if ever, include all of the variables affecting the response in his experiment, random variation in the response is observed even though all independent variables considered are held constant.   The objective of the analysis of variance is to locate important independent variables in a study and to determine how they interact and affect the response.

The rationale underlying the analysis of variance can be indicated best

---

* The word "level" is usually used to denote the intensity setting for a quantitative independent variable.   We use it in the present context to refer to the "settings" for either quantitative or qualitative independent variables.

with a symbolical discussion. The actual analysis of variance—that is, "how to do it"—can be illustrated with an example.

The reader will recall that the variability of a set of n measurements is proportional to the sum of squares of deviations, $\sum_{i=1}^{n} (y_i - \bar{y})^2$, and that this quantity is used to calculate the sample variance. The analysis of variance partitions the sum of squares of deviations, called the *total sum of squares of deviations*, into parts, each of which is attributed to one of the independent variables in the experiment, plus a remainder that is associated with random error. This may be shown diagrammatically as indicated in Figure 12.1 for three independent variables.

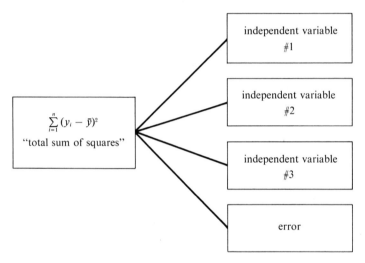

Figure 12.1. The Partitioning of the Total Sum of Squares of Deviations

If a multivariable linear model were written for the response, as suggested in Section 10.9, the portion of the total sum of squares of deviations assigned to error would be *SSE*.

For the cases which we consider, and when the independent variables are unrelated to the response, it can be shown that each of the pieces of the total sum of squares of deviations, divided by an appropriate constant, provides an independent and unbiased estimator of σ^2, the variance of the experimental error. When a variable is highly related to the response, its portion (called the "sum of squares" for the variable) will be inflated. This condition can be detected by comparing the estimate of σ^2 for a particular independent variable with that obtained from *SSE* using an

F test (see Section 9.7).   If the estimate for the independent variable is significantly larger, the *F* test will reject an hypothesis of "no effect for the independent variable" and produce evidence to indicate a relation to the response.

The mechanism involved in an analysis of variance can best be illustrated by considering a familiar example, say the comparison of means for the unpaired experiment, Section 9.4, for the special case where $n_1 = n_2$. This experiment, formerly analyzed by the use of Student's *t*, will now be approached from another point of view.   The total variation of the response measurements about their mean for the two samples is

$$\sum_{i=1}^{2} \sum_{j=1}^{n_1} (y_{ij} - \bar{y})^2,$$

where y_{ij} denotes the *j*th observation in the *i*th sample and $\bar{y}$ is the mean of all $2n_1 = n$ observations.   This quantity can be partitioned into two parts. That is,

$$\sum_{i=1}^{2} \sum_{j=1}^{n_1} (y_{ij} - \bar{y})^2 = n_1 \sum_{i=1}^{2} (\bar{y}_i - \bar{y})^2 + \sum_{i=1}^{2} \sum_{j=1}^{n_1} (y_{ij} - \bar{y}_i)^2$$

(proof deferred to Section 12.4), where $\bar{y}_i$ is the average of the observations in the *i*th sample, $i = 1, 2$, and the second quantity on the right-hand side of the equality is simply the pooled sum of squares of deviations used to calculate s^2.   (Recall that we assume equal population variances for this statistical method.)   We will denote this quantity as *SSE*.

The reader will note that we have partitioned the "total sum of squares" of deviations into two parts.   The one, SSE, can be used to obtain a pooled estimator of σ^2.   The other,

$$n_1 \sum_{i=1}^{2} (\bar{y}_i - \bar{y})^2 = \frac{n_1}{2} (\bar{y}_1 - \bar{y}_2)^2 = SST,$$

which we will call the *sum of squares for treatments*, will increase as $(\bar{y}_1 - \bar{y}_2)$ increases.   Thus, the larger *SST*, the greater the weight of evidence to indicate a difference in $(\mu_1 - \mu_2)$.

How large is "large?"   When will *SST* be large enough to indicate a real difference between μ_1 and μ_2 ?

As indicated in Chapter 9,

$$s^2 = MSE = \frac{SSE}{n_1 + n_2 - 2} = \frac{SSE}{2n_1 - 2} \qquad (\text{since } n_1 = n_2)$$

provides an unbiased estimator of σ^2.   Also, when the null hypothesis is true (that is, $\mu_1 = \mu_2$), *SST* divided by an appropriate number of degrees of freedom yields a second unbiased estimator of σ^2, which we will denote as

MST. For this example, the number of degrees of freedom for *MST* is equal to one. *Thus, when the null hypothesis is true, MSE (the mean square for error) and MST (the mean square for treatments) will estimate the same quantity and should be "roughly" of the same magnitude. When the null hypothesis is false and $\mu_1 \neq \mu_2$, MST will tend to be larger than MSE.*

The preceding discussion, along with a review of the variance ratio, Section 9.7, suggests the use of

$$\frac{MST}{MSE}$$

as a test statistic to test the hypothesis, $\mu_1 = \mu_2$, against the alternative, $\mu_1 \neq \mu_2$. Indeed, when both populations are normally distributed, it can be shown that *MST* and *MSE* are independent in a probabilistic sense and

$$F = \frac{MST}{MSE}$$

follows the *F*-probability distribution of Section 9.7. Disagreement with the null hypothesis is indicated by a large value of *F* and hence the rejection region for a given α will be,

$$F \geq F_\alpha.$$

Thus, the analysis of variance test results in a one-tailed *F* test. The degrees of freedom for the *F* will be those associated with *MST* and *MSE*, which we will denote as v_1 and v_2, respectively. Although we have not indicated how one determines v_1 and v_2, in general, $v_1 = 1$ and $v_2 = (2n_1 - 2)$ for the two-sample experiment described.

Example 12.1: The coded values for the measure of elasticity in plastic, prepared by two different processes, are given below for samples of six drawn randomly from each of the two processes.

PROCESS	A	B
	6.1	9.1
	7.1	8.2
	7.8	8.6
	6.9	6.9
	7.6	7.5
	8.2	7.9

Do the data present sufficient evidence to indicate a difference in mean elasticity for the two processes?

Solution: Although the Student's *t* could be used as the test statistic for this example, we will use our analysis-of-variance *F* test since it is more general and can be used to compare more than two means.

The three desired sums of squares of deviations are

$$\text{Total } SS = \sum_{i=1}^{2} \sum_{j=1}^{6} (y_{ij} - \bar{y})^2 = \sum_{i=1}^{2} \sum_{j=1}^{6} y_{ij}^2 - \frac{\left(\sum_{i=1}^{2} \sum_{j=1}^{6} y_{ij}\right)^2}{12}$$

$$= 711.35 - \frac{(91.9)^2}{12} = 7.5492,$$

$$SST = n_1 \sum_{i=1}^{2} (\bar{y}_i - \bar{y})^2 = 6 \sum_{i=1}^{2} (\bar{y}_i - \bar{y})^2 = 1.6875,$$

$$SSE = \sum_{i=1}^{2} \sum_{j=1}^{6} (y_{ij} - \bar{y}_i)^2 = 5.8617.$$

(The reader may verify that *SSE* is the pooled sum of squares of the deviations for the two samples. Also, note that Total $SS = SST + SSE$.) The mean squares for treatment and error are, respectively,

$$MST = \frac{SST}{1} = 1.6875,$$

$$MSE = \frac{SSE}{2n_1 - 2} = \frac{5.8617}{10} = .58617.$$

To test the null hypothesis, $\mu_1 = \mu_2$, we compute the test statistic

$$F = \frac{MST}{MSE} = \frac{1.6875}{.58617} = 2.88.$$

The critical value of the *F* statistic for $\alpha = .05$ is 4.96. Although the mean square for treatments is almost three times as large as the mean square for error, it is not large enough to reject the null hypothesis. Consequently, there is not sufficient evidence to indicate a difference between μ_1 and μ_2.

As noted, the purpose of the preceding example was to illustrate the computations involved in a simple analysis of variance. The *F* test for comparing two means is equivalent to a Student's *t* test because an *F* statistic with one degree of freedom in the numerator is equal to t^2. The reader can easily verify that the square of $t_{.025} = 2.228$ (used for the two-tailed test with $\alpha = .05$ and $v = 10$ degrees of freedom) is equal to $F_{.05} = 4.96$. Similarly, the value of the *t* statistic for Example 12.1 would equal the square root of the computed $F = 2.88$.

12.3   A Comparison of More Than Two Means

An analysis of variance to detect a difference in a set of more than two population means is a simple generalization of the analysis of variance of Section 12.2. The random selection of independent samples from p populations is known as a *completely randomized experimental design*.

Assume that independent random samples have been drawn from p normal populations with means $\mu_1, \mu_2, \ldots, \mu_p$, respectively, and variance σ^2. Thus all populations are assumed to possess equal variances. And, to be completely general, we will allow the sample sizes to be unequal and let $n_i, i = 1, 2, \ldots, p$, be the number in the sample drawn from the ith population. The total number of observations in the experiment will be $n = n_1 + n_2 + \ldots + n_p$.

Let y_{ij} denote the measured response on the jth experiment unit in the ith sample and let T_i and $\overline{T}_i$ represent the total and mean, respectively, for the observations in the ith sample. (The modification in the symbols for sample totals and averages will simplify the computing formulae for the sums of squares.) Then, as in the analysis of variance involving two means,

$$\text{Total } SS = SST + SSE$$

(Proof deferred to Section 12.4), where

$$\text{Total } SS = \sum_{i=1}^{p} \sum_{j=1}^{n_i} (y_{ij} - \bar{y})^2 = \sum_{i=1}^{p} \sum_{j=1}^{n_i} y_{ij}^2 - CM,$$

$$CM = \frac{(\text{Total of all observations})^2}{n} = \frac{\left(\sum_{i=1}^{p} \sum_{j=1}^{n_i} y_{ij}\right)^2}{n} = n\bar{y}^2$$

(the symbol CM denotes "correction for the mean"),

$$SST = \sum_{i=1}^{p} n_i(\overline{T}_i - \bar{y})^2 = \sum_{i=1}^{p} \frac{T_i^2}{n_i} - CM,$$

$$SSE = \text{Total } SS - SST.$$

Although the easy way to compute SSE is by subtraction as shown above, it is interesting to note that SSE is the pooled sum of squares for all p samples and is equal to

$$SSE = \sum_{i=1}^{p} \sum_{j=1}^{n_i} (y_{ij} - \overline{T}_i)^2.$$

The unbiased estimator of σ^2 based on $(n_1 + n_2 + \ldots + n_p - p)$ degrees of freedom is

$$s^2 = MSE = \frac{SSE}{n_1 + n_2 + \ldots + n_p - p}$$

The mean square treatments will possess $(p - 1)$ degrees of freedom, that is, one less than the number of means, and

$$MST = \frac{SST}{p - 1}.$$

To test the null hypothesis,

$$H_0: \mu_1 = \mu_2 = \ldots = \mu_p,$$

against the alternative that at least one of the equalities does not hold, MST is compared with MSE using the F-statistic based upon $v_1 = p - 1$ and $v_2 = \left(\sum_{i=1}^{p} n_i - p \right) = n - p$ degrees of freedom. The null hypothesis will be rejected if

$$F = \frac{MST}{MSE} > F_\alpha,$$

where F_α is the critical value of F for probability of a Type I error, α.

Intuitively, the greater the difference between the observed treatment means, $\bar{T}_1, \bar{T}_2, \ldots, \bar{T}_p$, the greater will be the evidence to indicate a difference between their corresponding population means. It can be seen from the above expression that $SST = 0$ when all of the observed treatment means are identical because then $\bar{T}_1 = \bar{T}_2 = \ldots = \bar{T}_p = \bar{y}$ and the deviations appearing in SST, $(\bar{T}_i - \bar{y})$, $i = 1, 2, \ldots, p$, will equal zero. As the treatment means get farther apart, the deviations $(\bar{T}_i - \bar{y})$ will increase in absolute value and SST will increase in magnitude. Consequently, the larger the value of SST, the greater will be the weight of evidence favoring a rejection of the null hypothesis. This same line of reasoning will apply to the F-tests employed in the analysis of variance for all designed experiments.

The assumptions underlying the analysis-of-variance F-tests should receive particular attention. The samples are assumed to have been randomly selected from the p populations in an independent manner. The populations are assumed to be normally distributed with equal variances σ^2 and means $\mu_1, \mu_2, \ldots, \mu_p$. Moderate departures from these assumptions will not seriously affect the properties of the test. This is particularly true of the normality assumption.

Example 12.2: Four groups of students were subjected to different teaching techniques and tested at the end of a specified period of time. Due to dropouts in the experimental groups (sickness, transfers, etc.), the number of students varied from group to group. Do the data shown below present sufficient evidence to indicate a difference in the mean achievement for the four teaching techniques?

	TECHNIQUES			
	1	2	3	4
	65	75	59	94
	87	69	78	89
	73	83	67	80
	79	81	62	88
	81	72	83	
	69	79	76	
		90		
T_i	454	549	425	351
$\bar{T}_i$	75.67	78.43	70.83	87.75

Solution:

$$CM = \frac{\left(\sum_{i=1}^{4} \sum_{j=1}^{n_i} y_{ij}\right)^2}{n} = \frac{(1779)^2}{23},$$

$$\text{Total SS} = \sum_{i=1}^{4} \sum_{j=1}^{n_i} y_{ij}^2 - CM = 139511 - 137601.8 = 1909.2,$$

$$SST = \sum_{i=1}^{4} \frac{T_i^2}{n_i} - CM = 138314.4 - 137601.8 = 712.6,$$

$$SSE = \text{Total SS} - SST = 1196.6.$$

The mean squares for treatment and error are

$$MST = \frac{SST}{p-1} = \frac{712.6}{3} = 237.5,$$

$$MSE = \frac{SSE}{n_1 + n_2 + \ldots + n_p - p} = \frac{SSE}{n-p} = \frac{1196.6}{19} = 63.0.$$

The test statistic for testing the hypothesis, $\mu_1 = \mu_2 = \mu_3 = \mu_4$, is

$$F = \frac{MST}{MSE} = \frac{237.5}{63.0} = 3.77,$$

where

$$v_1 = (p - 1) = 3,$$

$$v_2 = \sum_{i=1}^{p} n_i - 4 = 19.$$

The critical value of F for $\alpha = .05$ is $F_{.05} = 3.13$. Since the computed value of F exceeds $F_{.05}$, we reject the null hypothesis and conclude that the evidence is sufficient to indicate a difference in mean achievement for the four teaching procedures.

The reader may feel that the above conclusion could have been made on the basis of visual observation of the treatment means. It is not difficult to construct a set of data that will lead the "visual" decision maker to erroneous results.

12.4   Proof of Additivity of the Sums of Squares

The proof that

$$\text{Total } SS = SST + SSE$$

for the completely randomized design is presented in this section for the benefit of the interested reader. It may be omitted without loss of continuity.

The proof utilizes the three summation theorems of Chapter 2 and the device of adding and subtracting $\overline{T}_i$ within the expression for the Total SS. Thus,

$$\text{Total } SS = \sum_{i=1}^{p} \sum_{j=1}^{n_i} (y_{ij} - \bar{y})^2$$

$$= \sum_{i=1}^{p} \sum_{j=1}^{n_i} (y_{ij} - \overline{T}_i + \overline{T}_i - \bar{y})^2 = \sum_{i=1}^{p} \sum_{j=1}^{n_i} [(y_{ij} - \overline{T}_i) + (\overline{T}_i - \bar{y})]^2$$

$$= \sum_{i=1}^{p} \sum_{j=1}^{n_i} [(y_{ij} - \overline{T}_i)^2 + 2(y_{ij} - \overline{T}_i)(\overline{T}_i - \bar{y}) + (\overline{T}_i - \bar{y})^2].$$

Summing first over j, we obtain

$$\text{Total } SS = \sum_{i=1}^{p} \left[\sum_{j=1}^{n_i} (y_{ij} - \overline{T}_i)^2 + 2(\overline{T}_i - \bar{y}) \sum_{j=1}^{n_i} (y_{ij} - \overline{T}_i) + n_i(\overline{T}_i - \bar{y})^2 \right],$$

where

$$\sum_{j=1}^{n_i} (y_{ij} - \overline{T}_i) = T_i - n_i \overline{T}_i = T_i - T_i = 0.$$

Consequently, the middle term in the expression for the Total SS is equal to zero.

Then, summing over i, we obtain

$$\text{Total } SS = \sum_{i=1}^{p} \sum_{j=1}^{n_i} (y_{ij} - \overline{T}_i)^2 + \sum_{i=1}^{p} n_i(\overline{T}_i - \overline{y})^2,$$

$$\text{Total } SS = SSE + SST.$$

The first expression is SSE, the pooled sum of squares of deviations of the sample measurements about their respective means. The second is the formula for SST.

Proof of the additivity of the analysis-of-variance sums of squares for other experimental designs can be obtained in a similar manner. The procedure is tedious.

12.5   An Analysis-of-Variance Table for a Completely Randomized Design

The calculations of the analysis of variance are usually displayed in an analysis-of-variance (ANOVA or AOV) table.   The table for the design of Section 12.3 involving p treatment means is shown in Table 12.1.

Table 12.1.   ANOVA Table for a Comparison of Means

SOURCE	d.f.	SS	MS	F
Treatments	$p-1$	SST	$MST = SST/(p-1)$	MST/MSE
Error	$n-p$	SSE	$MSE = SSE/(n-p)$	
Total	$n-1$	$\sum_{i=1}^{p} \sum_{j=1}^{n} (y_{ij} - \overline{y})^2$		

Column 1 shows the source of each sum of squares of deviations; column 2 gives the respective degrees of freedom; columns 3 and 4 give the corresponding sums of squares and mean squares, respectively.   A calculated value of F, comparing MST and MSE, is usually shown in column 5. Note that the degrees of freedom and sums of squares add to their respective totals.

The ANOVA table for Example 12.2, shown in Table 12.2, gives a compact presentation of the appropriate computed quantities for the analysis of variance.

Table 12.2.   *ANOVA Table for Example 12.2*

SOURCE	d.f.	SS	MS	F
Treatments	3	712.6	237.5	3.77
Error	19	1196.6	63.0	
Total	22	1909.2		

12.6   Estimation for the Completely Randomized Design

Confidence intervals for a single treatment mean and the difference between a pair of treatment means, Section 12.3, are identical to those given in Chapter 9. The confidence interval for the mean of treatment i or the difference between treatments i and j are, respectively,

$$\overline{T}_i \pm t_{\alpha/2} s / \sqrt{n_i}$$

and

$$(\overline{T}_i - \overline{T}_j) \pm t_{\alpha/2} s \sqrt{\frac{1}{n_i} + \frac{1}{n_j}},$$

where

$$s = \sqrt{s^2} = \sqrt{MSE} = \sqrt{\frac{SSE}{n_1 + n_2 + \ldots + n_p - p}}$$

and $t_{\alpha/2}$ is based upon $(n - p)$ degrees of freedom.

Note that the confidence intervals stated above are appropriate for single treatment means or a comparison of a pair of means selected prior to observation of the data. The stated confidence coefficients are based on random sampling. If one were to look at the data and always compare the largest and smallest sample means, the assumption of randomness would be disturbed. Certainly the difference between the largest and smallest sample means is expected to be larger than for a pair selected at random.

Example 12.3: Find a 95% confidence interval for the mean score for teaching technique number 1, Example 12.2.

Solution: The 95% confidence interval for the mean score is

$$\overline{T}_1 \pm t_{.025} s / \sqrt{6}$$

or

$$75.67 \pm \frac{(2.093)(7.94)}{\sqrt{6}}$$

or

$$75.67 \pm 6.78.$$

Example 12.4: Find a 95% confidence interval for the difference in mean score for teaching techniques 1 and 4, Example 12.2.

Solution: The 95% confidence interval for $(T_1 - T_4)$ is

$$(\bar{T}_1 - \bar{T}_4) \pm (2.093)(7.94)\sqrt{\frac{1}{6} + \frac{1}{4}}$$

or

$$-12.08 \pm 10.74.$$

12.7   A Randomized Block Design

The randomized block design is a generalization of the paired-difference design, Section 9.5. The purpose of this design is to make comparisons between a set of treatments within blocks of relatively homogeneous experimental material. Thus, in Section 9.5 two treatments (types of automobile tires) were compared within the relative homogeneity of a single automobile, which eliminated auto-to-auto variability.

The difference between a randomized block design and the completely randomized design can be demonstrated by considering an experiment designed to compare subject reaction to a set of four stimuli (treatments) in a stimulus-response psychological experiment. We will denote the treatments as T_1, T_2, T_3, and T_4 and also use these symbols to represent the treatment totals in the analysis of variance, Section 12.8.

Suppose that ten subjects are to be randomly assigned to each of the four treatments. Random assignment of subjects to treatments (or vice versa) randomly distributes errors due to person-to-person variability to the four treatments and yields four samples that are, for all practical purposes, random and independent. This would be a completely randomized experimental design and would require the analysis of Section 12.3.

The confidence interval for a comparison of means using the completely randomized design is dependent upon s, the estimated standard deviation of the experimental error. If one were able to reduce σ, the value of s would most probably decrease and the confidence interval would narrow, indicating an increase in information in the experiment. This would imply that a reduction is required in the magnitude of the random experimental errors that occur when making repeated measurements for a given treatment.

The random experimental error is composed of a number of components. Some of these are due to the difference between subjects, to the failure of repeated measurements within a subject to be identical (due to variations in physical and psychological conditions), to the failure of the experimenter to administer a given stimulus with exactly the same intensity in repeated measurements, and, finally, to errors of measurement. Reduction of any of these causes of error will increase the information in the experiment.

The subject-to-subject variation in the above experiment can be eliminated by using subjects as blocks. Thus, each subject would receive each of the four treatments assigned in a random sequence. The resulting randomized block design would appear as in Figure 12.2. Now only ten

SUBJECTS

1	2	3	4		10
T_2	T_4	T_1	T_1		T_2
T_1	T_2	T_3	T_4	$\cdots$	T_3
T_4	T_1	T_2	T_3		T_4
T_3	T_3	T_4	T_2		T_1

Figure 12.2.   A Randomized Block Design

subjects are required to acquire ten response measurements per treatment. Note that each treatment occurs exactly once in each block.

The word "randomization" in the name of the design implies that the treatments are randomly assigned within a block. For our experiment, position in the block would pertain to the position in the sequence when assigning the stimuli to a given subject over time. The purpose of the randomization (that is, position in the block) is to eliminate bias caused by fatigue or learning. However, it is well to note that if a sizable and identical trend in response does exist within blocks, more error might be introduced by blocking than that implied by subject-to-subject variability. If this were the case, the blocks would not be "relatively homogeneous" as formerly thought, and the randomized block design would not be appropriate.

Blocks may represent time, location, or experimental material. Thus, if three treatments are to be compared and there is a suspected trend in the mean response over time, a substantial part of the time-trend variation may be removed by blocking. All three treatments would be randomly applied to experimental units in one small block of time. This procedure would be repeated in succeeding blocks of time until the required amount of data is collected.   A comparison of the sale of competitive products in supermarkets should be made within supermarkets, thus using the super-markets as blocks and removing market-to-market variability.   Animal experiments in agriculture and medicine often utilize animal litters as blocks, applying all of the treatments, one each, to animals within a litter. Because of heredity, animals within a litter are more homogeneous than those between litters.   This type of blocking removes the litter-to-litter variation.

12.8   The Analysis of Variance for a Randomized Block Design

The randomized block design implies the presence of two qualitative independent variables, "blocks" and "treatments."   Consequently, the total sum of squares of deviations of the response measurements about their mean may be partitioned into three parts, the sums of squares for blocks, treatments, and error.

Denote the total and average of all observations in block i as B_i and $\bar{B}_i$, respectively.   Then, for a randomized block design involving b blocks and p treatments,

$$\text{Total } SS = SSB + SST + SSE,$$

$$\text{Total } SS = \sum_{i=1}^{b} \sum_{j=1}^{p} (y_{ij} - \bar{y})^2 = \sum_{i=1}^{b} \sum_{j=1}^{p} y_{ij}^2 - CM,$$

$$SSB = p \sum_{i=1}^{b} (\bar{B}_i - \bar{y})^2 = \frac{\sum_{i=1}^{b} B_i^2}{p} - CM,$$

$$SST = b \sum_{j=1}^{p} (\bar{T}_j - \bar{y})^2 = \frac{\sum_{j=1}^{p} T_j^2}{b} - CM,$$

where

$$\bar{y} = (\text{average of all } n = bp \text{ observations}) = \frac{\sum_{i=1}^{b} \sum_{j=1}^{p} y_{ij}}{n}$$

and

$$CM = \frac{(\text{total of all observations})^2}{n} = \frac{\left(\sum_{i=1}^{b} \sum_{j=1}^{p} y_{ij} \right)^2}{n}.$$

The analysis of variance for the randomized block design is presented in Table 12.2. The degrees of freedom associated with each sum of squares is shown in the second column. Mean squares are calculated by dividing the sums of squares by their respective degrees of freedom.

Table 12.2.   ANOVA Table for a Randomized Block
Design

SOURCE	d.f.	SS	MS
Blocks	$b-1$	SSB	$SSB/(b-1)$
Treatments	$p-1$	SST	$SST/(p-1)$
Error	$n-b-p+1$	SSE	MSE
Total	$n-1$	Total SS	

To test the null hypothesis, "there is no difference in treatment means," we use the F statistic,

$$F = \frac{MST}{MSE}$$

and reject if $F > F_\alpha$ based on $v_1 = (p-1)$ and $v_2 = (n-b-p+1)$ degrees of freedom.

Blocking not only reduces the experimental error, it also provides an opportunity to see whether evidence exists to indicate a difference in the mean response for blocks. Under the null hypothesis that there is no difference in mean response for blocks, MSB provides an unbiased estimator for σ^2 based on $(b-1)$ degrees of freedom. Where a real difference exists in the treatment means, MSB will tend to be inflated in comparison with MSE and

$$F = \frac{MSB}{MSE}$$

provides a test statistic. As in the test for treatments, the rejection region for the test will be

$$F > F_\alpha,$$

based on $v_1 = b-1$ and $v_2 = n-b-p+1$ degrees of freedom.

Example 12.5: A stimulus-response experiment involving three treatments was laid out in a randomized block design using four subjects. The response was the length of time to reaction measured in seconds. The data are shown below.

SUBJECT

1	2	3	4
T_1 1.7	T_3 2.1	T_1 .1	T_2 2.2
T_3 2.3	T_1 1.5	T_2 2.3	T_1 .6
T_2 3.4	T_2 2.6	T_3 .8	T_3 1.6

Do the data present sufficient evidence to indicate a difference in the mean response for stimuli (treatments)?   Subjects?

Solution: The sums of squares for the analysis of variance are shown individually below, and jointly on the analysis of variance table.   Thus,

$$CM = \frac{(\text{Total})^2}{n} = \frac{(21.2)^2}{12} = 37.45,$$

$$\text{Total } SS = \sum_{i=1}^{4} \sum_{j=1}^{3} (y_{ij} - \bar{y})^2 = \sum_{i=1}^{4} \sum_{j=1}^{3} y_{ij}^2 - CM = 46.86 - 37.45 = 9.41,$$

$$SSB = \frac{\sum_{i=1}^{4} B_i^2}{3} - CM = 40.93 - 37.45 = 3.48,$$

$$SST = \frac{\sum_{j=1}^{3} T_j^2}{4} - CM = 42.93 - 37.45 = 5.48,$$

$$SSE = \text{Total } SS - SSB - SST$$

$$= 9.41 - 3.48 - 5.48 = .45.$$

ANOVA Table

SOURCE	d.f.	SS	MS	F
Blocks	3	3.48	1.16	15.47
Treatments	2	5.48	2.74	36.53
Error	6	.45	.075	
Total	11	9.41		

We use the ratio of mean square treatments to mean square error to test an hypothesis of no difference in the expected response for treatments. Thus,

$$F = \frac{MST}{MSE} = \frac{2.74}{.075} = 36.53.$$

The critical value of the F statistic ($\alpha = .05$) for $v_1 = 2$ and $v_2 = 6$ degrees of freedom is $F_{.05} = 5.14$. Since the computed value of F exceeds the critical value, there is sufficient evidence to reject the null hypothesis and conclude that a real difference does exist in the expected response for the four stimuli.

A similar test may be conducted for the null hypothesis that no difference exists in the mean response for subjects. Rejection of this hypothesis would imply that subject-to-subject variability does exist, and that blocking is desirable. The computed value of F based on $v_1 = 3$ and $v_2 = 6$ degrees of freedom is

$$F = \frac{MSB}{MSE} = \frac{1.16}{.075} = 15.47.$$

Since this value of F exceeds the corresponding tabulated critical value, $F_{.05} = 4.76$, we reject the null hypothesis and conclude that a real difference exists in the expected response in the group of subjects.

12.9 Estimation for the Randomized Block Design

The confidence interval for the difference between a pair of means is exactly the same as for the completely randomized design, Section 12.5. It is

$$(\overline{T}_i - \overline{T}_j) \pm t_{\alpha/2} s \sqrt{\frac{2}{b}},$$

where $n_i = n_j = b$, the number of observations contained in a treatment mean. The difference between the confidence intervals for the completely randomized and the randomized block designs is that s, appearing in the expressions above, will tend to be smaller than for the completely randomized design.

Similarly, one may construct a $(1 - \alpha)$ confidence interval for the difference between a pair of block means. Each block contains p observations corresponding to the p treatments. Therefore, the confidence interval is

$$(\bar{B}_i - \bar{B}_j) \pm t_{\alpha/2} s \sqrt{\frac{2}{p}}.$$

Example 12.6: Construct a 95% confidence interval for the difference between treatments 1 and 2, Example 12.5.

Solution: The confidence interval for the difference in mean response for a pair of treatments is

$$(\bar{T}_i - \bar{T}_j) \pm t_{\alpha/2} s \sqrt{\frac{2}{b}},$$

where, for our example, $t_{.025}$ is based upon 6 degrees of freedom. Then

$$(.98 - 2.63) \pm (2.447)(.27) \sqrt{\frac{2}{4}}$$

or

$$-1.65 \pm .47 .$$

12.10   Selecting the Sample Size

Selecting the sample size for the completely randomized or the randomized block design is an extension of the procedure of Section 8.9. We confine our attention to the case of equal sample sizes, $n_1 = n_2 = \ldots = n_p$, for the p treatments of the completely randomized design. The number of observations per treatment is equal to b for the randomized block design. Thus the problem is to select n_1 or b for these two designs so as to purchase a specified quantity of information.

The selection of sample size follows a similar procedure for both designs; hence we will outline a general method. First, the experimenter must decide on the parameter (or parameters) of major interest. Usually he will wish to compare a pair of treatment means. Second, he must specify a bound on the error of estimation that he is willing to tolerate. Once determined, he need only select n_i (the number of observations in a treatment mean) or, correspondingly, b (the number of blocks in the randomized block design) that will reduce the half-width of the confidence interval for the parameter so that it is less than or equal to the specified bound on the error of estimation. It should be emphasized that the sample-size solution will *always* be an approximation, since σ is unknown and s is unknown until the sample is acquired. The best available value will be used for s in order to produce an approximate solution. We will illustrate the procedure with an example.

Example 12.7: A completely randomized design is to be conducted to compare five teaching techniques on classes of equal size. Estimation of the difference in mean response to an achievement test is desired correct to within 30 test-score points, with probability equal to .95. It is expected that the test scores for a given teaching technique will possess a range approximately equal to 240. Find the approximate number of observations required for each sample in order to acquire the specified information.

Solution: The confidence interval for the difference between a pair of treatment means is

$$(\overline{T}_i - \overline{T}_j) \pm t_{\alpha/2} s \sqrt{\frac{1}{n_i} + \frac{1}{n_j}}.$$

Therefore, we will wish to select n_i and n_j so that

$$t_{\alpha/2} s \sqrt{\frac{1}{n_i} + \frac{1}{n_j}} \le 30.$$

The value of σ is unknown and s is a random variable. However, an approximate solution for $n_i = n_j$ can be obtained by guessing s to be roughly equal to one-fourth of the range. Thus $s \approx (240)/4 = 60$. The value of $t_{\alpha/2}$ will be based upon $(n_1 + n_2 + \ldots + n_5 - 5)$ degrees of freedom, and for even moderate values of n_i, $t_{.025}$ will approximately equal 2. Then

$$t_{.025} s \sqrt{\frac{1}{n_i} + \frac{1}{n_j}} = 2(60) \sqrt{\frac{2}{n_i}} \le 30$$

or

$$n_i = 32, \qquad i = 1, 2, \ldots, 5.$$

Example 12.8: An experiment is to be conducted to compare the toxic effect of three chemicals on the skin of rats. The resistance to the chemicals was expected to vary substantially from rat to rat. Therefore all three chemicals were to be tested on each rat, thereby blocking out rat-to-rat variability.

The standard deviation of the experimental error was unknown, but prior experimentation involving several applications of a given chemical on the same rat suggested a range of response measurements equal to 5 units.

Find a value for b such that the error of estimating the difference between a pair of treatment means is less than one unit, with probability equal to .95.

Solution: A very approximate value for s would be one-fourth the range, or $s \approx 1.25$. Then we wish to select b so that

$$t_{.025}s\sqrt{\frac{1}{b} + \frac{1}{b}} = t_{.025}s\sqrt{\frac{2}{b}} \leq 1.$$

Since $t_{.025}$ will depend upon the degrees of freedom associated with s^2, which will be $(n - b - p + 1)$, we will guess $t_{.025} \approx 2$. Then

$$2(1.25)\sqrt{\frac{2}{b}} \leq 1$$

or

$$b \approx 13, \qquad i = 1, 2, 3.$$

Thus, approximately thirteen rats will be required to obtain the required information.

The degrees of freedom associated with s^2 will be 24 based on this solution. Therefore, the guessed value of t would seem to be adequate for this approximate solution.

The sample-size solutions for Examples 12.7 and 12.8 are very approximate, and are intended to provide only a rough estimate of approximate size and consequent cost of the experiment. The experimenter will obtain information on σ as the data are being collected and can recalculate a better approximation to n as he proceeds.

12.11   Summary and Comments

The completely randomized and the randomized block designs are illustrations of two experiments involving one and two qualitative independent variables, respectively. The analysis of variance partitions the total sum of squares of deviations of the response measurements about their mean into portions associated with each independent variable and the experimental error. The former may be compared with the sum of squares for error, using mean squares and the F-statistic, to see whether the mean squares for the independent variables are unusually large and thereby indicative of an effect on the response.

This chapter has presented a very brief introduction to the analysis of variance and its associated subject, the design of experiments. Experiments can be designed to investigate the effect of many quantitative and qualitative variables on a response. These may be variables of primary interest to the experimenter as well as nuisance variables, such as blocks, which we attempt to separate from the experimental error. They are subject to an analysis of variance when properly designed. A more extensive coverage of the basic concepts of experimental design and the analysis of experiments will be found in the References, page 293.

EXERCISES

1. Analyze the data of Exercise 25 in Chapter 9 by the procedure outlined in Section 12.2. Determine whether there is evidence of a difference in mean strengths between the two kinds of material. Test at the $\alpha = .05$ level of significance.

2. State the assumptions underlying the analysis of variance of a completely randomized design.

3. Refer to Example 12.2. Calculate SSE by pooling the sums of squares of deviations within each of the four samples, and compare with the value obtained by subtraction. Note that this is an extension of the pooling procedure used in the two-sample case discussed in Section 12.2.

4. To compare the strengths of concrete produced by four experimental mixes, three specimens were prepared from each type of mix. Each of the twelve specimens was subjected to increasing compressive loads until breakdown. The following compressive loads in tons per square inch were attained at breakdown. Specimen numbers 1–12 are indicated in parentheses for identification purposes.

COMPRESSIVE LOAD AT BREAKDOWN (TONS PER SQUARE INCH)

MIX A		MIX B		MIX C		MIX D	
(1)	2.30	(2)	2.20	(3)	2.15	(4)	2.25
(5)	2.20	(6)	2.10	(7)	2.15	(8)	2.15
(9)	2.25	(10)	2.20	(11)	2.20	(12)	2.25

Assuming that the requirements for a completely randomized design are met, analyze the data. State whether there is statistical support at the $\alpha = .05$ level of significance for the conclusion that the four types of concrete differ in average strength.

5. Refer to Exercise 4. Let μ_A and μ_B denote the mean strengths of concrete specimens prepared from mix A and mix B, respectively.
(a) Find a 90% confidence interval for μ_A.
(b) Find a 95% confidence interval for $\mu_A - \mu_B$.

6. A clinical psychologist wished to compare three methods for reducing hostility levels in university students. A certain psychological test (HLT) was used to measure the degree of hostility. High scores on this test were taken to indicate great hostility. Eleven students obtaining high and nearly equal scores were used in the experiment. Five were selected at random from among the eleven problem cases and treated by method A. Three were taken at random from the remaining six students and treated by method B. The other three students were treated by method C. All treatments continued throughout a semester. Each student was given the HLT test again at the end of the semester, with the following results:

SCORES ON THE HLT TEST

METHOD A	METHOD B	METHOD C
73	54	79
83	74	95
76	71	87
68		
80		

(a) Perform an analysis of variance for this experiment.
(b) Do the data provide sufficient evidence to indicate a difference in mean student response for the three methods after treatment?

7. Refer to Exercise 6. Let μ_A and μ_B, respectively, denote the mean scores at the end of the semester for the populations of extremely hostile students who are treated throughout that semester by method A and method B.
(a) Find a 95% confidence interval for μ_A.
(b) Find a 95% confidence interval for μ_B.
(c) Find a 95% confidence interval for $\mu_A - \mu_B$.
(d) Is it correct to claim that the confidence intervals found in parts (a), (b), and (c) are jointly valid?

8. Refer to Exercise 4. Suppose that the sand used in the mixes for samples 1, 2, 3, and 4 came from pit A, that the sand used for samples 5, 6, 7, and 8 came from pit B, and that sand for the other samples came from pit C. Analyze the data, assuming that the requirements for a randomized block are met with three blocks consisting respectively of samples 1, 2, 3, and 4; samples 5, 6, 7, and 8; and samples 9, 10, 11, and 12.
(a) At the 5% level, is there evidence of differences in concrete strength due to the sand used?
(b) Is there evidence at the 5% level that the four types of concrete differ in average strength?
(c) Does the conclusion of part (b) contradict the conclusion obtained in Exercise 4?

9. Refer to Exercise 8. Let μ_A and μ_B, respectively, denote the mean strengths of concrete specimens prepared from mix A and mix B.
   (a) Find a 95% confidence interval for $\mu_A - \mu_B$.
   (b) Is the interval found in part (a) the same interval found in Exercise 5(b)? Explain.

10. A study was initiated to investigate the effect of two drugs, administered simultaneously, in reducing human blood pressure. It was decided to utilize three levels of each drug and to include all nine combinations in the experiment. Nine high-blood-pressure patients were selected for the experiment, and one was randomly assigned to each of the nine drug combinations. The response observed was a drop in blood pressure over a fixed interval of time.
   (a) Is this a randomized block design?
   (b) Suppose that two patients were assigned to each of the nine drug combinations. What type of experimental design is this?

11. Refer to Exercise 10. Suppose that prior experimentation suggests that $\sigma = 20$.
   (a) How many replications would be required to estimate any treatment (drug combination) mean correct to within plus or minus ten?
   (b) How many degrees of freedom will be available for estimating σ^2 when using the number of replications determined in part (a)?
   (c) Give the approximate half-width of a confidence interval for the difference in mean response for two treatments when using the number of replications determined in part (a).

12. A dealer has in stock three cars (car A, car B, and car C) of the same make and model. Wishing to compare these cars in gas consumption, a customer arranged to test each car with each of three brands of gasoline (brand A, brand B, and brand C). In each trial, a gallon of gasoline was added to an empty tank and the car was driven without stopping until it ran out of gasoline. The following table shows the number of miles covered in each of the nine trials.

BRAND OF GASOLINE	DISTANCE IN MILES		
	CAR A	CAR B	CAR C
A	22.4	17.0	19.2
B	20.8	19.4	20.2
C	21.5	18.7	21.2

   (a) Should the customer conclude that the three cars differ in gas mileage? Test at the $\alpha = .05$ level.
   (b) Do the data indicate that the brand of gasoline affects gas mileage?

13. Refer to Exercise 12. Suppose that gas mileage is unrelated to brand of gasoline; carry out an analysis of the data appropriate for a completely randomized design with three treatments.
    (a) Should the customer conclude that the three cars differ in gas mileage? Test at the $\alpha = .05$ level.
    (b) Comparing your answer for part (a) in Exercise 12 with your answer for part (a) above, can you suggest a reason why blocking may be unwise in certain cases?

14. A portion of a questionnaire was constructed to enable judges to evaluate a certain aspect of observed classroom teaching. Four films portraying teaching performances, and differing markedly in the teaching characteristic under study, were viewed by each of eight judges. The order of viewing the four films was assigned in a random manner to each judge. The data obtained are shown below.

FILM SCORES OBTAINED FROM COMPLETED QUESTIONNAIRES

| | JUDGES | | | | | | | |
FILMS	1	2	3	4	5	6	7	8
1	9	10	7	5	12	7	8	6
2	4	9	3	0	6	8	2	4
3	12	16	10	9	11	10	10	14
4	9	11	7	8	12	7	7	8

(a) Give the type of design employed for this experiment and justify your diagnosis.
(b) How many degrees of freedom are available for estimating σ^2? Perform an analysis of variance on the data.
(c) Do the data provide sufficient evidence to indicate that the mean questionnaire score varies from film to film? Test using $\alpha = .05$.
(d) Suppose that the data did provide sufficient evidence to indicate differences among the mean questionnaire scores for the four films. Would this imply that the questionnaire was able to detect a difference in the teaching characteristic exhibited in the four films?

15. Refer to Exercise 4. About how many specimens per mix should be prepared to allow estimation of the difference in mean strengths for a preselected pair of specimen types to within .02 tons per square inch? Assume knowledge of the data given in Exercise 4.

16. Refer to Exercise 14. About how many judges should be used to allow estimation of the difference in mean questionnaire scores for a preselected pair of films to within one unit. Assume knowledge of the data given in Exercise 14.

REFERENCES

Guenther, W. C., *Analysis of Variance.*   Englewood Cliffs, N. J. : Prentice-Hall, Inc., 1964.

Hicks, C. R., *Fundamental Concepts in the Design of Experiments.*   New York : Holt, Rinehart and Winston, Inc., 1964.

Li, J. C. R., *Introduction to Statistical Inference.*   Ann Arbor, Mich. : J. W. Edwards, Publisher, Inc., 1961.

Mendenhall, W., *An Introduction to Linear Models and the Design and Analysis of Experiments.*   Belmont, Calif : Wadsworth Publishing Company, Inc., 1967.

13

NONPARAMETRIC STATISTICS

13.1 Introduction

Some experiments yield response measurements that defy quantification. That is, they generate response measurements that can be ordered (ranked), but the location of the response on a scale of measurement is arbitrary. Although experiments of this type occur in almost all fields of study, they are particularly evident in social-science research and in studies of consumer preference. For example, suppose that a judge is employed to evaluate and rank the instructional abilities of four teachers, the edibility and taste characteristics of five brands of corn flakes, or the relative merits of 53 Miss America contestants. Since it is clearly impossible to give an exact measure of teacher competence, "tastability" of food, or beauty, the response measurements are of a completely different character from those presented in preceding chapters. *Nonparametric* statistical methods are useful for analyzing this type of data.

The word "nonparametric" evolves from the type of hypothesis usually tested when dealing with ranked data of the type described above. *Parametric hypotheses* are those concerned with the population parameters. *Nonparametric hypotheses* do not involve the population parameters but are concerned with the form of the population frequency distribution. Tests of hypotheses concerning the binomial parameter p, the tests concerning μ, σ^2, and the analysis-of-variance tests were parametric. On the other hand, an hypothesis that a particular population possesses a normal distribution (without specification of parameter values) would be nonparametric. Similarly, an hypothesis that the distributions for two populations are identical would be nonparametric.

This latter hypothesis would be pertinent to the three ranking problems previously described. Even though we do not have an exact measure of teacher competence, we can imagine that one exists and that in repeated performances a given teacher would generate a population of such measurements. An hypothesis that the four probability distributions for the populations (associated with the four teachers) are identical would imply no difference in the instructional ability of the teachers. Similarly, we would imagine that a scale of tastability for corn flakes does exist (even if unknown to us) and that a population of responses representing the reactions of a very large set of prospective consumers corresponds to each brand. An hypothesis that the distributions of "tastability" for the five brands are identical implies no difference in consumer preference for these products.

The preceding illustrations suggest that the hypotheses not only are nonparametric but indicate that the underlying population distributions are unknown. Although Kendall and Stuart (see References) suggest that statistical procedures appropriate for this latter condition be called *distribution-free*, it has become common to classify statistical methods for either nonparametric hypotheses or populations of unknown distributional form as *nonparametric methods*—in spite of the fact that these two conditions are in many respects unrelated (one deals with the null hypothesis and the other with the dependence of a test procedure on knowledge of the population distributional forms). However, we will conform with common usage of the term "nonparametric statistical methods" and will think of procedures applicable to situations where the form of the population distribution is unknown or where the case involves a nonparametric hypothesis.

Nonparametric statistical procedures apply not only to data that are difficult to quantify. They are particularly useful in making inferences in situations where serious doubt exists about the assumptions underlying standard methodology. For example, the t-test for comparing a pair of means, Section 9.4, is based on the assumption that both populations are normally distributed with equal variances. Now, admittedly, the experimenter will never know whether these assumptions hold in a practical situation, but he will often be reasonably certain that departures from the assumptions will be small enough so that the properties of his statistical procedure will be undisturbed.   That is, α and β will be approximately what he thinks they are.   On the other hand, it is not uncommon for the experimenter seriously to question his assumptions and wonder whether he is using a valid statistical procedure.   This difficulty may be circumvented by using a nonparametric statistical test and thereby avoiding reliance on a very uncertain set of assumptions.

It is a hard fact of life that one rarely gets "something for nothing." Circumventing the assumptions usually requires a rephrasing of one's hypothesis, a price that often is not difficult to pay.   Instead of hypothesizing that $\mu_1 = \mu_2$, we hypothesize that "the population distributions are identical."   Note that the practical implications of the two hypotheses are not equivalent because the latter hypothesis is less clearly defined.   Two distributions could differ and still possess the same mean.   A second and less obvious price exacted by the nonparametric procedures is that they usually use a smaller amount of information in the sample than do corresponding parametric methods.   Consequently, they are less efficient. This means that in testing with a given α, the probability of a Type II error, β, for a specified alternative will be larger for the nonparametric test.   We will have more to say on this point after giving an example of a nonparametric procedure.

13.2   The Sign Test for Comparing Two Populations

Without emphasizing the point, we employed a nonparametric statistical test as an alternative procedure for determining whether evidence existed to indicate a difference in the mean wear for the two types of tires in the paired difference experiment, Section 9.5.   Each pair of responses was compared and y (the number of times A exceeded B) was used as the test statistic.   This nonparametric test is known as the *sign test* because y is the number of positive (or negative) signs associated with the differences. The implied null hypothesis is that the two population distributions are identical and the resulting technique is completely independent of the form of the distribution of differences.   Thus, regardless of the distribution of differences, the probability that A exceeds B for a given pair will be $p = .5$ when the null hypothesis is true (that is, when the distributions for A and B are identical).   Then y will possess a binomial probability distribution and a rejection region for y can be obtained using the binomial probability distribution of Chapter 6.   (We will illustrate this point in the example that follows.)

The sign test is appropriate for the comparison of two populations using either paired or unpaired data.   We will illustrate the procedure using Exercise 22, Chapter 6, as an example.

Example 13.1: The number of defective electrical fuses proceeding from each of two production lines, A and B, was recorded daily for a period of 10 days with the following results:

DAY	A	B
1	172	201
2	165	179
3	206	159
4	184	192
5	174	177
6	142	170
7	190	182
8	169	179
9	161	169
10	200	210

Assume that both production lines produced the same daily output. Compare the number of defectives produced by A and B each day and let y equal the number of days when A exceeded B. Do the data present sufficient evidence to indicate that production line B produces more defectives, on the average, than A? State the null hypothesis to be tested and use y as a test statistic.

Solution: Pair the observations as they appear in the data tabulation and let y be the number of times that the observation for production line A exceeds that for B in a given day. Under the null hypothesis that the two distributions of defectives are identical, the probability, p, that A exceeds B for a given pair is $p = .5$. Or, equivalently, we may wish to test an hypothesis that the binomial parameter, p, equals .5.

Very large or very small values of y are most contradictory to the null hypothesis. Therefore, the rejection region for the test will be located by including the most extreme values of y that at the same time provide an α that is feasible for the test.

Suppose that we would like α to be somewhere on the order of .05 or .10. We would commence the selection of the rejection region by including $y = 0$ and $y = 10$ and calculate the α associated with this region using $p(y)$ (the probability distribution for the binomial random variable, Chapter 6). Thus, with $n = 10$, $p = .5$,

$$\alpha = p(0) + p(10) = C_0^{10}(.5)^{10} + C_{10}^{10}(.5)^{10} = .002.$$

Since this value of α is too small, the region will be expanded by including the next pair of y values most contradictory to the null hypothesis, $y = 1$

and $y = 9$. The value of α for this region ($y = 0, 1, 9, 10$) may be obtained from Table I, Appendix II.

$$\alpha = p(0) + p(1) + p(9) + p(10) = .022.$$

This also is too small, so we will again expand the region to include $y = 0, 1, 2, 8, 9, 10$. The reader may verify that the corresponding value of α is .11. We will suppose that this value of α is acceptable to the experimenter (and the reader) and will employ $y = 0, 1, 2, 8, 9, 10$ as the rejection region for the test.

From the data, we observe that $y = 2$ and therefore we reject the null hypothesis. Thus we conclude that sufficient evidence exists to indicate that the population distributions of number of defects are not identical and that the number for production line B tends to exceed that for A. The probability of rejecting the null hypothesis when true is only $\alpha = .11$, and therefore we are reasonably confident of our conclusion.

The experimenter in this example is using the test procedure as a rough tool for detecting faulty production lines. The rather large value of α is not likely to disturb him because he can easily collect additional data if he is concerned about making a Type I error in reaching his conclusion.

Example 13.1 was a paired or blocked experimental design because the numbers of defectives for the two production lines were paired by collecting them for a given day. Although the nonparametric procedure is exactly the same for either the completely randomized or the blocked experimental designs, the latter will contain more information (if, indeed, a substantial difference does exist between blocks) and this may increase the probability of rejecting the null hypothesis if it is false.

The values of α associated with the sign test can be obtained by using the normal approximation to the binomial probability distribution discussed in Section 7.4. The reader can verify (by comparison of exact probabilities with their approximations) that these approximations will be quite adequate for n as small as 10. This is due to the symmetry of the binomial probability distribution for $p = .5$. For $n \geq 25$, the z-test of Chapters 7 and 8 will be quite adequate where

$$z = \frac{y - np}{\sqrt{npq}} = \frac{y - n/2}{\frac{1}{2}\sqrt{n}}.$$

This would be testing the null hypothesis $p = .5$ against the alternative, $p \neq .5$, and would utilize the familiar rejection regions of Chapter 8.

What should be done in case of ties between the paired observations? This difficulty is circumvented by omitting tied pairs and thereby reducing n, the number of pairs.

Suppose that the two populations were normally distributed with equal variances. Will the sign test detect a difference in the populations as effectively as the Student's t-test? Intuitively, we would suspect that the answer is "no," and this is correct, because the Student's t test utilizes comparatively more information. In addition to giving the sign of the difference, the t test uses the magnitudes of the observations to obtain a more accurate value of the sample means and variances. Thus, one might say that the sign test is not as "efficient" as Student's t test, but this statement is meaningful only if the populations conform to the assumptions stated above; that is, they are normally distributed with equal variances. The sign test might be more efficient for some other unusual combination of population distributions.

Summarizing, the sign test is a very easily applied nonparametric procedure for comparing two populations. No assumptions are made concerning the underlying population distributions. The value of the test statistic can be quickly obtained by a visual count and the rejection region can be easily located by using a table of binomial probabilities. Furthermore, the data need not be ordinal. That is, we need not know the exact values of pairs of responses.

13.3 A Comparison of Statistical Tests

We have introduced two statistical test procedures utilizing given data for the same hypothesis, and we are now faced with the problem of comparison of tests. Which is better? One method would be to hold the sample size and α constant for both procedures and compare β, the probability of a type II error. Actually, statisticians prefer a comparison of the *power of a test* where

$$\text{Power} = 1 - \beta.$$

Since β is the probability of failing to reject the null hypothesis when it is false, the power of the test is the probability of rejecting the null hypothesis when it is false and some specified alternative is true. It is the probability that the test will do what it was designed to do; that is, detect a departure from the null hypothesis when a departure exists.

Probably the most common method of comparing two test procedures is in terms of the *relative efficiency* of a pair of tests. Relative efficiency is the ratio of the sample sizes for the two test procedures required to achieve the same α and β for a given alternative to the null hypothesis. This method of comparison is meaningful from a practical point of view but poses difficulties for some hypotheses because the number of alternatives may be infinitely large and difficult to tabulate. Which "relative efficiency" should one give in comparing the test procedures?

The asymptotic relative efficiency of a pair of tests is a quantity approached by the relative efficiency as the alternative hypothesis specifies parameter values closer and closer to the value implied by H_0. Although asymptotic relative efficiency will in general depend on α and β, in many important cases this is not so. This quantity is, indeed, compact, but is meaningless because the experimenter is not concerned with minute departures from the null hypothesis and actually is not dealing with infinitely large samples. Several other attempts to package the comparison of a pair of statistical tests in a single number have been proposed and are subject to the same criticism. To be useful, the method of comparison must consider the experimenter and his testing problem.

The above discussion is not intended to suggest that tests should not or cannot be compared. They should be compared in a given experimental situation by calculating the relative efficiency for the alternative of interest to the experimenter. Another way to look at tests is to view them as microscopes that are utilized to detect departures from an hypothesized theory. One need not know the exact power of a microscope to use it in a biological investigation, and the same applies to statistical tests. If the test procedure detects a departure from the null hypothesis, we are delighted. If not, we can increase the power of the microscope (test) by increasing the sample size.

13.4   The Rank Sum Test for Comparing Two Population Distributions

The sign test for comparing two population distributions ignores the actual magnitudes of the paired observations and thereby discards information that would be useful in detecting a departure from the null hypothesis. A statistical test that partially circumvents this loss by utilizing the relative magnitudes of the observations was proposed by F. Wilcoxon as a rank sum test. The procedure will be illustrated with an example.

Example 13.2: The bacteria counts per unit volume are shown below for two types of cultures, A and B. Four observations were made for each culture.

A	B
27	32
31	29
26	35
25	28

Let n_1 and n_2 represent the number of observations in samples A and B, respectively. Then the rank sum procedure ranks each of the $(n_1 + n_2) = n$ measurements in order of magnitude and uses T, the sum of the ranks for A (or B), as the test statistic. Thus, for the data given above, the corresponding ranks are

A	B
3	7
6	5
2	8
1	4
Rank Sum 12	24

Do these data present sufficient evidence to indicate a difference in the population distributions for A and B?

Solution: Let T equal the rank sum for sample A (for this sample, $T = 12$). Certainly very small or very large values of T will provide evidence to indicate a difference between the two population distributions, and hence T, the *rank sum*, will be employed as a test statistic.

The rejection region for a given test will be obtained in the same manner as for the sign test. We will commence by selecting the most contradictory values of T as the rejection region and will add to these until α is of sufficient size.

The minimum rank sum would include the ranks 1, 2, 3, 4, or $T = 10$. Similarly, the maximum would include 5, 6, 7, 8, with $T = 26$. We will commence by including these two values of T in the rejection region. What is the corresponding value of α?

Finding the value of α is a probability problem that can be solved by using the methods of Chapter 4. If the populations are identical, every permutation of the eight ranks will represent a sample point and will be equally likely. Then α will represent the sum of the probabilities of the sample points (arrangements) which imply $T = 10$ or $T = 26$ in sample A. The total number of permutations of the eight ranks is 8!. The number of different arrangements of the ranks, 1, 2, 3, 4 in sample A with the 5, 6, 7, 8 of sample B is (4! 4!). Similarly, the number of arrangements that place the maximum value of T in sample A (ranks 5, 6, 7, 8) is (4! 4!). Then the probability that $T = 10$ or $T = 26$ is

$$p = p(10) + p(26)$$

$$= \frac{2(4!)(4!)}{8!} = \frac{2}{C_4^8} = \frac{1}{35} = .029.$$

If this value of α is too small, the rejection region can be enlarged to include the next smallest and largest rank sums, $T = 11$ and $T = 25$. The rank sum $T = 11$ will include the ranks 1, 2, 3, 5, and

$$p(11) = \frac{4!\,4!}{8!} = \frac{1}{70}.$$

Similarly,

$$p(25) = \frac{1}{70}.$$

Then

$$\alpha = p(10) + p(11) + p(25) + p(26) = \frac{2}{35} = .057.$$

Expansion of the rejection region to include 12 and 24 will substantially increase the value of α. The set of sample points giving a rank of 12 will be all sample points associated with rankings of $(1, 2, 3, 6)$ and $(1, 2, 4, 5)$. Thus,

$$p(12) = \frac{2(4!)(4!)}{8!} = \frac{1}{35}.$$

and

$$\alpha = p(10) + p(11) + p(12) + p(24) + p(25) + p(26)$$

$$= \frac{1}{70} + \frac{1}{70} + \frac{1}{35} + \frac{1}{35} + \frac{1}{70} + \frac{1}{70} = \frac{4}{35} = .114.$$

This value of α might be considered too large for practical purposes. In this case, we would be better satisfied with the rejection region $T = 10$, 11, 25, and 26.

The rank sum for the sample, $T = 12$, falls in the nonrejection region, and hence we do not have sufficient evidence to reject the hypothesis that the population distributions of bacteria counts for the two cultures are identical.

Mann and Whitney (1947) proposed a nonparametric test statistic for the comparison of two population distributions that at first glance appears to be different from Wilcoxon's statistic but actually is a function of T. Consequently, the two tests are equivalent. As a matter of interest, we will present the Mann-Whitney U test in Section 13.5 along with tables of critical values of U for various sample sizes. This will eliminate the need for a similar table for Wilcoxon's T.

13.5 The Mann-Whitney U Test

The Mann-Whitney statistic, U, is obtained by ordering all $(n_1 + n_2)$ observations according to their magnitude and counting the number of observations in sample A that precede each observation in sample B. The U statistic is the sum of these counts.

For example, the eight observations of Example 13.2 are

$$25, \quad 26, \quad 27, \quad 28, \quad 29, \quad 31, \quad 32, \quad 35,$$
$$A \quad\ A \quad\ A \quad\ B \quad\ B \quad\ A \quad\ B \quad\ B$$

The smallest B observation is 28, and $u_1 = 3$ observations from sample A precede it. Similarly, $u_2 = 3$ A observations precede the second B observation and $u_3 = 4$ and $u_4 = 4$ A observations precede the third and fourth B observations, respectively (32 and 35). Then $U = u_1 + u_2 + u_3 + u_4 = 14$.

Very large or small values of U will imply a separation of the ordered A and B observations and will provide evidence to indicate a difference between the population distributions for A and B.

The probabilities required for calculating α for small samples (n_1 and $n_2 \leq 10$) are included in Table 8, Appendix II. A large sample approximation is given in the latter part of this section. Entries in Table 8 are $P[U \leq U_0]$. Thus, for example, $P[U \leq 1] = .024$ for $n_1 = 3$ and $n_2 = 6$. The rejection region for a two-tailed test such as that implied in Example 13.2 would require doubling the tabulated one-tail probability to find α. The test procedure would require calculating the smaller value of U and using the lower tail of the U distribution as the rejection region.

If $n_1 = 6$ and $n_2 = 8$, one could use the smaller value of U and reject when $U \leq 9$. The tabulated value gives $P[U \leq 9] = .030$. This probability must be doubled in calculating α to take into account the corresponding large values of U that would be included in the rejection region for a two-tailed test. Then $\alpha = .060$.

A shortcut procedure for calculating U can be obtained by ranking the observations as for the Wilcoxon rank sum test, letting the smallest observation have a rank of 1, and using the formulae

$$U = n_1 n_2 + \frac{n_1(n_1 + 1)}{2} - T_A$$

or

$$U = n_1 n_2 + \frac{n_2(n_2 + 1)}{2} - T_B,$$

where T_A and T_B are the rank sums of samples A and B, respectively.

The first value of U will be the number of A observations preceding the B observations, and the second will be the total count of the B observations preceding the A's. Thus, for our example,

$$U = n_1 n_2 + \frac{n_1(n_1 + 1)}{2} - T_A$$

$$= (4)(4) + \frac{4(5)}{2} - 12 = 14$$

and

$$U = n_1 n_2 + \frac{n_2(n_2 + 1)}{2} - T_B$$

$$= (4)(4) + \frac{4(5)}{2} - 24 = 2.$$

We have agreed to use the smaller sum and hence would use $U = 2$ as the test statistic.

The expressions given above not only give an easy way of calculating U but also indicate the very simple relationship between the U statistic and the rank sum T of the Wilcoxon test. For all practical purposes, the tests are equivalent.

Ties in the observations can be handled by averaging the ranks that would have been assigned to the tied observations and assigning this average to each. Thus, if three observations are tied and are due to receive ranks 3, 4, 5, we would assign the rank of 4 to all three. The next observation in the sequence would receive the rank of 6, and ranks 3 and 5 would not appear. Similarly, if two observations are tied for ranks 3 and 4, each would receive a rank of 3.5, and ranks 3 and 4 would not appear.

Example 13.3: Test the hypothesis of no difference in the distribution of strengths for the two types of packaging material, Exercise 25, Chapter 9.

Solution: The data for this example are shown below. The rank associated with each observation is given alongside in parentheses.

Although this is not a blocked (paired) experiment, the reader will observe that each A observation in a pair exceeds its corresponding B measurement. Thus, knowledge of the nonparametric sign test would quickly indicate that A exceeds B in nine out of nine pairs and would imply rejection of the hypothesis of no difference in the population distribution of strengths for the two types of packaging material. Certainly this procedure, which required less than thirty seconds to discuss, was much more rapid than the calculations involved in the Student's t test, Chapter 9.

A	B
(15) 1.25	.89 (1)
(11) 1.16	1.01 (7)
(18) 1.33	.97 (4)
(10) 1.15	.95 (3)
(14) 1.23	.94 (2)
(12) 1.20	1.02 (8)
(17) 1.32	.98 (5.5)
(16) 1.28	1.06 (9)
(13) 1.21	.98 (5.5)
Rank Sum 126	45

Although we have tested our hypothesis using the sign test, we will show that the same result can be quickly obtained using the more powerful Mann-Whitney U Test. Thus,

$$n_1 = n_2 = 9$$

and

$$U = n_1 n_2 + \frac{n_1(n_1 + 1)}{2} - T_A = (9)(9) + \frac{(9)(10)}{2} - 126 = 0.$$

From Table 8, $P[U = 0]$ for $n_1 = n_2 = 9$ is .000. The value of α for a two-tailed test and a rejection region of $U = 0$ and $U = 81$ is $\alpha = .000$.

A simplified large sample test can be obtained by using the familiar z statistic of Chapter 8. When the population distributions are identical, it can be shown that the U statistic has expected value and variance,

$$E(U) = \frac{n_1 n_2}{2}$$

and

$$V(U) = \frac{n_1 n_2 (n_1 + n_2 + 1)}{12},$$

and the distribution of

$$z = \frac{U - E(U)}{\sigma_U}$$

tends to normality with mean zero and variance equal to one as n_1 and n_2 become large. This approximation will be adequate when n_1 and n_2 are both larger than, say, 10. Thus, for a two-tailed test with $\alpha = .05$, we would reject the null hypothesis if $|z| \geq 1.96$.

What constitutes an "adequate" approximation is a matter of opinion. The reader will observe that the z-statistic will reach the same conclusion as the exact U test for Example 13.3. Thus,

$$z = \frac{0 - \dfrac{(9)(9)}{2}}{\sqrt{\dfrac{(9)(9)(9 + 9 + 1)}{12}}} = \frac{-45}{\sqrt{128.25}} = -3.97.$$

This value of z falls in the rejection region ($|z| \geq 1.96$) and hence agrees with the sign test and the U test using the exact tabulated values for the rejection region.

13.6 The Wilcoxon Rank Sum Test for a Paired Experiment

The Wilcoxon test (or equivalently, the Mann-Whitney U-test) can be adapted to the paired-difference experiment of Section 9.5 by considering the paired differences of the two treatments A and B. Under the null hypothesis of no differences in the distributions for A and B, the expected number of negative differences between pairs would be $n/2$ (where n is the number of pairs), and positive and negative differences of equal absolute magnitude should occur with equal probability. Thus, if one were to order the differences according to their absolute values and rank them from smallest to largest, the expected rank sums for the negative and positive differences would be equal. Sizable departures of the rank sum of the positive (or negative) differences from its expected value would provide evidence to indicate a difference between the distributions of responses for the two treatments, A and B.

The rank sum T of the positive (or negative) differences contains the information provided by the sign test statistic and, in addition, gives information on the relative magnitude of the differences. For example, a low rank sum for negative differences indicates that both the number and absolute values of negative differences are small.

The probabilities associated with rank sums for the paired-difference experiment can be calculated using the probability laws of Chapter 4.

Thus, if we let

$$n = \text{number of pairs}$$

$$y = \text{number of positive differences}$$

$$T = \text{rank sum for the positive differences,}$$

and observe that a particular value of T is the union of the mutually exclusive events ($y = 0$ and the rank sum equals T), ($y = 1$ and the rank sum equals T),...,($y = n$ and the rank sum equals T), then

$$P(T) = P[y = 0,T] + P[y = 1,T] + \ldots + P[y = n,T].$$

Each of the events $[y = j,T]$, $j = 1,\ldots, n$, is an intersection of the events, $y = j$ and "the rank sum equals T." Then

$$P[y = j,T] = P[y = j]P[T/y = j]$$

where $p(y) = C_y^n (1/2)^n$ is the binomial probability distribution with $p = 1/2$ when the null hypothesis is true and the two population distributions are identical. Since T and U are related by a one-to-one correspondence, $P[T/y = j]$ can be obtained (with a bit of difficulty) from Table 8.

Or, rather than use T, we could use the Mann-Whitney U and calculate

$$P[U] = P[y = 0,U] + P[y = 1,U] + \ldots + P[y = n,U]$$

The probabilities would be equivalent for corresponding values of T and U.

The critical values of T for the Wilcoxon paired signed-ranks tests are given in Table 9, where T is the smaller sum of ranks taking the same sign. For example, with $n = 17$ pairs, we would reject the hypothesis that the two population distributions are identical when $T \leq 35$ with $\alpha = .05$ using a two-tailed test. In calculating T, differences equal to zero are eliminated and the number of pairs, n, is reduced accordingly. Ties are treated in the same manner as for the unpaired comparison of two distributions.

Example 13.4: Test an hypothesis of no difference in population distributions of cake density for the paired-difference experiment, Exercise 28, Chapter 9.

Solution: The original data and differences in density for the six pairs of cakes are shown below:

DENSITY, OUNCES/CUBIC INCH

A	B	DIFFERENCE $A - B$	RANK
.135	.129	.006	3
.102	.120	− .018	5
.098	.112	− .004	1.5
.141	.152	− .011	4
.131	.135	− .004	1.5
.144	.163	− .019	6

The smaller rank sum is that for positive differences, and hence $T = 3$. From Table 9, the critical value of T for a two-tailed test, $\alpha = .10$, is $T = 2$. Since the observed value of T exceeds the critical value of T, there is not sufficient evidence to indicate a difference in the population distributions of density for the two types of cake mix.   (Values of T less than or equal to the critical value imply rejection.)   The lower power of the nonparametric test in comparison with the Student's t test is illustrated by this example because the t test led to rejection of the null hypothesis for these data.

When n is large (say 25), T will be approximately normally distributed with mean and variance

$$E(T) = \frac{n(n + 1)}{4},$$

$$V(T) = \frac{n(n + 1)(2n + 1)}{24}.$$

Then the z-statistic,

$$z = \frac{T - E(T)}{\sigma_T} = \frac{T - \dfrac{n(n + 1)}{4}}{\sqrt{\dfrac{n(n + 1)(2n + 1)}{24}}},$$

can be used as a test statistic.   Thus, for a two-tailed test and $\alpha = .05$, we would reject the hypothesis of "identical population distributions" when $|z| \geq 1.96$.

13.7   The Runs Test: A Test for Randomness

Consider a production process in which manufactured items emerge in sequence and each is classified as either defective (D) or nondefective

(N). We have studied how one might compare the fraction defective over two equal time intervals using the normal deviate test, Chapter 8, and extended this to a test of an hypothesis of constant p over two or more time intervals using the chi-square test of Chapter 11. The purpose of these tests was to detect a change or trend in the fraction defective, p. Evidence to indicate increasing fraction defective might indicate the need for a process study to locate the source of difficulty. A decreasing value might suggest that a process quality control program was having a beneficial effect in reducing the fraction defective.

Trends in fraction defective (or other quality measures) are not the only indication of lack of process control. A process may be causing periodic runs of defectives with the average fraction defective remaining constant, for all practical purposes, over long periods of time. For example, photoflash lamps are manufactured on a rotating machine with a fixed number of positions for bulbs. A bulb is placed on the machine at a given position, the air is removed, oxygen is pumped into the bulb, and the glass base is flame sealed. If a machine contains twenty positions, and several adjacent positions are faulty (too much heat in the sealing process), surges of defective lamps will emerge from the process in a periodic manner. Tests to compare the process fraction defective over equal intervals of time will not detect this periodic difficulty in the process. The periodicity, indicated by runs of defectives, is indicative of nonrandomness in the occurrence of defectives over time and can be detected by a *test for randomness*. The statistical test that we present, known as the runs test, is discussed in detail by A. Wald and J. Wolfowitz (see References). Other practical applications of the run test will follow.

As the name implies, the runs test studies a sequence of events where each element in the sequence may assume one of two outcomes, say success (S) or failure (F). If we think of the sequences of items emerging from a manufacturing process as defective (F) or nondefective (S), the observation of twenty items might yield

$$S\ S\ S\ S\ S\ F\ F\ S\ S\ S\ F\ F\ F\ S\ S\ S\ S\ S\ S\ S.$$

We notice the groupings of defectives and nondefectives and wonder whether this implies nonrandomness and, consequently, lack of process control. A *run* is defined to be a maximal subsequence of like elements. For example, the first five successes is a subsequence of five like elements and it is maximal in the sense that it includes the maximum number of like elements before encountering an F. (The first four elements form a subsequence of like elements but it is not maximal because the fifth element could also be included.) Consequently, the twenty elements shown above are arranged in five runs, the first containing five S's, the second containing two F's, and so on.

A very small or very large number of runs in a sequence would indicate nonrandomness. Therefore let R (the number of runs in a sequence) be the test statistic, and let the rejection region be $R \leq k_1$ and $R \geq k_2$ as indicated in Figure 13.1. Let m denote the maximum possible number of runs.

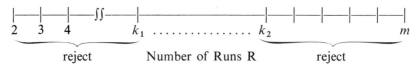

Figure 13.1.　The Rejection Region for the Runs Test

We must then find the probability distribution for $R, p(R)$, in order to calculate α and to locate a suitable rejection region for the test.

Suppose that the complete sequence contains n_1 S elements, and n_2 F elements, resulting in y_1 S runs and y_2 F runs, where $(y_1 + y_2) = R$. Then, for a given y_1, y_2 can equal y_1, $(y_1 - 1)$, or $(y_1 + 1)$, and $m = 2n_1$ if $n_1 = n_2$ and $m = 2n_1 + 1$ if $n_1 < n_2$. We will suppose that every distinguishable arrangement of the $(n_1 + n_2)$ elements in the sequence constitutes a simple event for the experiment and that the sample points are equiprobable. It then remains for us to count the number of sample points that imply R runs.

The total number of distinguishable arrangements of n_1 S elements and n_2 F elements is $C_{n_1}^{n_1 + n_2}$ and, therefore, the probability per sample point is $1/C_{n_1}^{n_1 + n_2}$. The number of ways of achieving y_1 S runs is equal to the number of distinguishable arrangements of n_1 indistinguishable elements in y_1 cells, none of which is empty. The situation is represented in Figure 13.2.

$$|S|SSSS|SS| \ldots \ldots |SS|SSS|S|$$

Figure 13.2.　Distribution of n_1 S Elements in y_1 Cells
(None Empty)

The reader will note that this is equal to the number of ways of distributing the $(y_1 - 1)$ identical inner bars in the $(n_1 - 1)$ spaces between the S elements (the outer two bars remain fixed). Consequently, it is equal to the number of ways of selecting $(y_1 - 1)$ spaces (for the bars) out of the $(n_1 - 1)$ spaces available. This will equal $C_{y_1 - 1}^{n_1 - 1}$.

The number of ways of observing y_1 S runs and y_2 F runs, obtained by applying the mn rule, is

$$(C_{y_1-1}^{n_1-1})(C_{y_2-1}^{n_2-1}).$$

The probability of exactly y_1 S runs and y_2 F runs would be

$$P(y_1,y_2) = \frac{(C_{y_1-1}^{n_1-1})(C_{y_2-1}^{n_2-1})}{C_{n_1}^{n_1+n_2}}.$$

Then $P(R)$ equals the sum of $P(y_1, y_2)$ over all values of y_1 and y_2 such that $(y_1 + y_2) = R$.

To illustrate the use of the formula, the event $R = 4$ could occur when $y_1 = 2$ and $y_2 = 2$ with either the S or F elements commencing the sequences. Consequently,

$$p(4) = 2P[y_1 = 2, y_2 = 2].$$

On the other hand, $R = 5$ could occur when $y_1 = 2$ and $y_2 = 3$, or $y_1 = 3$, or $y_2 = 2$, and these points are mutually exclusive. Then

$$p(5) = P[y_1 = 3, y_2 = 2] + P[y_1 = 2, y_2 = 3].$$

Example 13.5: Suppose that a sequence consists of $n_1 = 5$ S elements and $n_2 = 3$ F elements. Calculate the probability of observing $R = 3$ runs. Also, calculate $P[R \leq 3]$.

Solution: Three runs could occur when $y_1 = 2$ and $y_2 = 1$, or $y_1 = 1$ and $y_2 = 2$. Then

$$p(3) = P[y_1 = 2, y_2 = 1] + P[y_1 = 1, y_2 = 2]$$

$$= \frac{(C_1^4)(C_0^2)}{C_5^8} + \frac{(C_0^4)(C_1^2)}{C_5^8}$$

$$= \frac{4}{56} + \frac{2}{56} = .107.$$

Next, we require $P[R \leq 3] = p(2) + p(3)$. Accordingly, note that

$$p(2) = 2P[y_1 = 1, y_2 = 1]$$

$$= 2\frac{(C_0^4)(C_0^2)}{C_5^8} = \frac{2}{56} = .036.$$

Thus, the probability of 3 or less runs is .143.

The values of $P[R \leq a]$ are given in Table 10 for all combinations of n_1 and n_2 where n_1 and n_2 are less than or equal to 10. These can be used to locate the rejection regions for a one- or two-tailed test. We will illustrate with an example.

Example 13.6: A true-false examination was constructed with the answers running in the following sequence:

$$T\ F\ FT\ FT\ FT\ TT\ FT\ FFT\ FT\ FTT\ F.$$

Does this sequence indicate a departure from randomness in the arrangement of T and F answers?

Solution: The sequence contains $n_1 = 10$ T and $n_2 = 10$ F answers with $y = 16$ runs. Nonrandomness can be indicated by either an unusually small or an unusually large number of runs, and, consequently, we will be concerned with a two-tailed test.

Suppose that we wish to use α approximately equal to .05 with .025 or less in each tail of the rejection region. Then from Table 10 with $n_1 = n_2 = 10$, we note $P[R \leq 6] = .019$ and $P[R \leq 15] = .981$. Then $P[R \geq 16] = .019$, and we would reject the hypothesis of randomness if $R \leq 6$ or $R \geq 16$. Since $R = 16$ for the observed data, we conclude that evidence exists to indicate nonrandomness in the professor's arrangement of answers. His attempt to mix the answers was overdone.

A second application of the runs test is in detecting nonrandomness of a sequence of quantitative measurements over time. These sequences, known as *time series*, occur in many fields. For example, the measurement of a quality characteristic of an industrial product, blood pressure of a human, and the price of a stock on the stock market all vary over time. Departures in randomness in a series, caused either by trends or periodicities, can be detected by examining the *deviations* of the time-series measurements from their average. Negative and positive deviations could be denoted by S and F, respectively, and we could then test this time sequence of deviations for nonrandomness. We will illustrate with an example.

Example 13.7: Paper is produced in a continuous process. Suppose that a brightness measurement, y, is made on the paper once every hour and that the results appear as shown in Figure 13.3.

The average for the fifteen sample measurements, $\bar{y}$, appears as shown. Note the deviations about $\bar{y}$. Do these indicate a lack of randomness and thereby suggest periodicity in the process and lack of control?

Solution: The sequence of negative (S) and positive (F) deviations as indicated in Figure 13.1 is

$$S\ S\ S\ S\ F\ F\ S\ F\ F\ S\ F\ S\ S\ S\ S$$

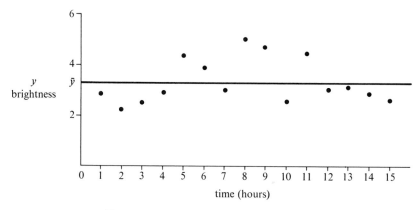

Figure 13.3.   Paper Brightness versus Time

Then $n_1 = 10$, $n_2 = 5$ and $R = 7$.   Consulting Table 10, $P[R \leq 7] = .455$. This value of R is not improbable, assuming the hypothesis of randomness to be true.   Consequently, there is not sufficient evidence to indicate nonrandomness in the sequence of brightness measurements.

The runs test can also be used to compare two population frequency distributions for a two-sample unpaired experiment.   Thus, it provides an alternative to the sign test, Section 13.2, and the Mann-Whitney U test, Section 13.5.   If the measurements for the two samples are arranged in order of magnitude, they will form a sequence.   The measurements for samples 1 and 2 can be denoted as S and F, respectively, and we are once again concerned with a test for randomness.   If all measurements for sample 1 are smaller than those for sample 2, the sequence will result in $S\,S\,S\,S\ldots S\,F\,F\,F\ldots F$, or $R = 2$ runs.   Thus, a small value of R will provide evidence of a difference in population frequency distributions, and the rejection region chosen would be $R \leq a$.   This rejection region would imply a one-tailed statistical test.   An illustration of the application of the run test to compare two population frequency distributions will be left as an exercise for the reader.

As in the case of the other nonparametric test statistics studied in earlier sections of this chapter, the probability distribution for R tends to normality as n_1 and n_2 become large.   The approximation is good when n_1 and n_2 are both greater than 10.   Consequently, we may use the z-statistic as a large sample test statistic where

$$z = \frac{R - E(R)}{\sqrt{V(R)}}$$

and

$$E(R) = \frac{2n_1 n_2}{n_1 + n_2} + 1,$$

$$V(R) = \frac{2n_1 n_2 (2n_1 n_2 - n_1 - n_2)}{(n_1 + n_2)^2 (n_1 + n_2 - 1)}$$

are the expected value of R and variance of R_1, respectively. The rejection region for a two-tailed test, $\alpha = .05$, is $|z| \geq 1.96$.

13.8 Rank Correlation Coefficient

In preceding sections we have used ranks to indicate the relative magnitude of observations in nonparametric tests for comparison of treatments. We will now employ the same technique in testing for a relation between two ranked variables. Two common rank correlation coefficients are the Spearman r_s and the Kendall τ. We will present the Spearman r_s because its computation is identical to that for the sample correlation coefficient, r, of Chapter 10. Kendall's rank correlation coefficient is discussed in detail in Kendall (1948).

Suppose that eight elementary science teachers have been ranked by a judge according to their teaching ability and all have taken a "national teachers' examination." The data are shown below.

TEACHER	JUDGE'S RANK	EXAMINATION SCORE
1	7	44
2	4	72
3	2	67
4	6	70
5	1	93
6	3	82
7	8	67
8	5	80

Do the data suggest an agreement between the judge's ranking and the examination score? Or one might express this question by asking whether a correlation exists between ranks and test scores.

The two variables of interest are rank and test score. The former is already in rank form, and the test scores may be ranked similarly as shown below. The ranks for tied observations are obtained by averaging the ranks that the tied observations would occupy as for the Mann-Whitney U statistic.

TEACHER	JUDGE'S RANK (x_i)	TEST RANK (y_i)
1	7	1
2	4	5
3	2	2.5
4	6	4
5	1	8
6	3	7
7	8	2.5
8	5	6

The Spearman rank correlation coefficient, r_s, is calculated using the ranks as the paired measurements on the two variables, x and y, in the formula for r, Chapter 10.   Thus,

$$r_s = \frac{n\sum_{i=1}^{n} x_i y_i - \left(\sum_{i=1}^{n} x_i\right)\left(\sum_{i=1}^{n} y_i\right)}{\sqrt{\left[n\sum_{i=1}^{n} x_i^2 - \left(\sum_{i=1}^{n} x_i\right)^2\right]\left[n\sum_{i=1}^{n} y_i^2 - \left(\sum_{i=1}^{n} y_i\right)^2\right]}}.$$

The formula for r_s can be simplified because the sum of the ranks, $\sum_{i=1}^{n} x_i$ and $\sum_{i=1}^{n} y_i$, will be the sum of the integers from 1 to n, which is

$$\sum_{x=1}^{n} x = \sum_{y=1}^{n} y = \frac{n(n+1)}{2}.$$

Similarly, the sum of squares of integers from 1 to n is

$$\sum_{x}^{n} x^2 = \sum_{y=1}^{n} y^2 = \frac{n(n+1)(2n+1)}{6}.$$

The formula for $\sum_{x=1}^{n} x^2 = \sum_{y=1}^{n} y^2$ applies only when no ties are present. When ties occur, these sums of squares can be acquired easily on a desk calculator.

Example 13.8: Calculate r_s for the teacher-judge test-score data.

Solution: Using the formula for the sum of the eight integers,

$$\sum_{i=1}^{8} x_i = \sum_{i=1}^{8} y_i = \frac{8(8+1)}{2} = 36.$$

The sum of squares and cross-products are given in the table below.

TEACHER	x_i^2	y_i^2	$x_i y_i$
1	49	1	7
2	16	25	20
3	4	6.25	5
4	36	16	24
5	1	64	8
6	9	49	21
7	64	6.25	20
8	25	36	30
	204	203.50	135

$$r_s = \frac{n \sum_i x_i y_i - \sum_i x_i \sum_i y_i}{\sqrt{\left[n \sum_i x_i^2 - \left(\sum_i x_i \right)^2 \right] \left[n \sum_i y_i^2 - \left(\sum_i y_i \right)^2 \right]}}$$

$$= \frac{8(135) - (36)(36)}{\sqrt{[8(204) - (36)^2][8(203.5) - (36)^2]}}$$

$$= \frac{-216}{\sqrt{(336)(332)}} = -.65.$$

The Spearman rank correlation coefficient may be employed as a test statistic to test an hypothesis of "no association" between two populations. We assume that the n pairs of observations, (x_i, y_i), have been randomly selected and therefore "no association between the populations" would imply a random assignment of the n ranks within each sample. Each random assignment (for the two samples) would represent a sample point associated with the experiment and a value of r_s could be calculated for each. Thus it is possible to calculate the probability that r_s assumes a large absolute value due solely to chance and thereby suggests an association between populations when none exists.

We will spare the reader the details involved in calculating the probability that r_s exceeds some critical value, say r_0, and will present the critical values for $\alpha = .05$ and $\alpha = .01$ in Table 11. The tabulated values give r_0 such that $P[r_s > r_0] \approx .05$ or $.01$ as indicated. Therefore, they represent the critical values for a one-tailed test. The α for a two-tailed test would require doubling the tabulated probabilities.

Example 13.9: Test an hypothesis of "no association" between the populations for Example 13.8.

Solution: The critical value of r_s for a one-tailed test with $\alpha = .05$ and

$n = 8$ is .643.   Let us assume that a correlation between judge's rank and the teachers' test scores could not possibly be positive.   (Low rank means good teaching and should be associated with a high test score if the judge and test measure teaching ability.)   The alternative hypothesis would be that the population correlation coefficient, ρ, is less than zero, and we would be concerned with a one-tailed statistical test.   Thus α for the test would be the tabulated value .05, and we would reject the null hypothesis if $r_s \leq -.643$.

Since the tabulated value of $r_s = -.65$ is less than the critical value, we reject the hypothesis of "no association."   It appears that some agreement does exist between the judge's rankings and the test scores.   However, it should be noted that this agreement could exist when *neither* provides an adequate yardstick for measuring teaching ability.   For example, the association could exist if both the judge and those who constructed the teachers' examination possessed a completely erroneous, but identical, concept of the characteristics of good teaching.

13.9   Some General Comments on Nonparametric Statistical Tests

The nonparametric statistical tests presented in the preceding pages represent only a few of the many nonparametric statistical measures of inference available.   A much larger collection of nonparametric test procedures, along with worked examples, is given by Siegel (1956), and an extensive bibliography of publications dealing with nonparametric statistical methods has been presented by Savage (1953).   Both are listed in the references at the end of this chapter.

We have indicated that nonparametric statistical procedures are particularly useful when the experimental observations are susceptible to ordering but cannot be measured on a quantitative scale.   Parametric statistical procedures usually cannot be applied to this type of data, hence all inferential procedures must be based on nonparametric methods.

A second application of nonparametric statistical methods is in testing hypotheses associated with populations of quantitative data when uncertainty exists concerning the satisfaction of assumptions about the form of the population distributions.   Just how useful are nonparametric methods for this situation?

It is well known that many statistical test and estimation procedures are only slightly affected by moderate departures from the assumed form of the population frequency distribution and that parametric test procedures are more efficient than their nonparametric equivalents when the assumptions underlying parametric tests are true.   Furthermore, it is sometimes possible to transform statistical data and thereby make the population distributions of the transformed data satisfy the assumptions basic to a parametric procedure.   In spite of these positive arguments in favor of parametric procedures, nonparametric statistical methods possess definite advantages in some experimental situations.

Nonparametric statistical methods are rapid and often lead to an immediate decision in testing hypotheses, as indicated in Example 13.3. When experimental conditions depart substantially from the basic assumptions underlying parametric tests, the response measurements can often be transformed to alleviate the condition, but an unfortunate consequence often develops.   That is, the transformed response is no longer meaningful from a practical point of view, and analysis of the transformed data no longer answers the objectives of the experimenter. The use of non-parametric methods will often circumvent this difficulty.   Finally, one should note that many nonparametric methods are nearly as efficient as their parametric counterparts when the assumptions underlying the parametric procedures are true, and, as noted earlier, they could be more efficient when the assumptions are unsatisfied.   These reasons suggest that nonparametric techniques play a very useful role in statistical methodology.

EXERCISES

1. What significance levels between $\alpha = .01$ and $\alpha = .15$ are available for a two-tailed sign test utilizing 25 paired observations?   (Make use of tabulated values in Table 1, $n = 25$.)   What are the corresponding rejection regions?

2. Refer to Exercise 30, Chapter 9.   Solve that exercise by using a sign test with a level of significance as near as possible to $\alpha = .10$.

3. The coded values for a measure of brightness in paper (light reflectivity), prepared by two different processes, are given below for samples of size nine drawn randomly from each of the two processes:

PROCESS	A	B
	6.1	9.1
	9.2	8.2
	8.7	8.6
	8.9	6.9
	7.6	7.5
	7.1	7.9
	9.5	8.3
	8.3	7.8
	9.0	8.9

Do the data present sufficient evidence ($\alpha = .10$) to indicate a difference in the populations of brightness measurements for the two processes?
(a) Use the sign test.
(b) Use Student's t test.

4. To compare two junior high schools, A and B, in academic effectiveness, an experiment was designed requiring the use of 10 sets of identical twins, each twin having just completed the sixth grade. In each case, the twins in the same set had obtained their schooling in the same classrooms at each grade level   One child was selected at random from each set and assigned to school A.   The other children were sent to school B.   Near the end of the ninth grade, a certain achievement test was given to each child in the experiment.   The results are shown in the following table:

ACHIEVEMENT TEST SCORES

TWIN PAIR	A	B	TWIN PAIR	A	B
1	67	39	6	50	52
2	80	75	7	63	56
3	65	69	8	81	72
4	70	55	9	86	89
5	86	74	10	60	47

(a) Test (using the sign test) the hypothesis that the two schools are the same in academic effectiveness, as measured by scores on the achievement test, against the alternative that the schools are not equally effective. Use a level of significance as near as possible to $\alpha = .05$.
(b) Suppose it were known that junior high school A had a superior faculty and better learning facilities.   Test the hypothesis of equal academic effectiveness against the alternative that school A is superior.   Use a level of significance as near as possible to $\alpha = .05$.

5. Refer to Exercise 30, Chapter 9.   What answer is obtained if the U test is used in analyzing the data?   Use $\alpha = .10$.

6. Refer to Exercise 5.   Test the hypothesis of equivalance of population frequency distributions using the runs test with $\alpha = .10$.   Compare with the results of Exercise 5.

7. Refer to Exercise 3.   What answer is obtained if the Mann-Whitney U test is used in analyzing the data?   Compare with the answers to Exercise 3.

8. Refer to Exercise 3.   What answer is obtained if the runs test is used in analyzing the data?   Compare with the answers to Exercise 7.

9. Refer to Exercise 4.   What answers are obtained if Wilcoxon's T test is used in analyzing the data?   Compare with the answers to Exercise 4.

10. A psychological experiment was conducted to compare the lengths of response time (in seconds) for two different stimuli. In order to remove natural person-to-person variability in the responses, both stimuli were applied to each of nine subjects, thus permitting an analysis of the difference between stimuli *within* each person.

SUBJECT	STIMULUS 1	STIMULUS 2
1	9.4	10.3
2	7.8	8.9
3	5.6	4.1
4	12.1	14.7
5	6.9	8.7
6	4.2	7.1
7	8.8	11.3
8	7.7	5.2
9	6.4	7.8

(a) Use the sign test to determine whether sufficient evidence exists to indicate a difference in mean response for the two stimuli. Use a rejection region for which $\alpha \leq .05$.

(b) Test the hypothesis of no difference in mean response using Student's t test.

11. Refer to Exercise 10. Test the hypothesis that no difference exists in the distributions of responses for the two stimuli, using the Wilcoxon T test. Use a rejection region for which α is as near as possible to the α achieved in Exercise 10(a).

12. Four Republican and four Democratic politicians attended a civic banquet and selected their seats in the following order (left to right) : R, D, D, D, D, R, R, R. Does this seating sequence provide sufficient evidence to imply nonrandomness in the seating selection and a consequent grouping by party affiliation?

13. Fifteen experimental batteries were selected at random from a pilot lot at plant A, and fifteen standard batteries were selected at random from production at plant B. All thirty batteries were simultaneously placed under an electrical load of the same magnitude. The first battery to fail was an A, and second a B, the third a B, etc. The following sequence shows the order of failure for the thirty batteries :

$A B B B A B A A B B B B A B A B B B B A A B A A A B A A A A$

(a) Using the large sample theory for the U test, determine (use $\alpha = .05$) if there is sufficient evidence to conclude that the mean life for the experimental batteries is greater than the mean life for the standard batteries.

(b) If, indeed, the experimental batteries have the greater mean life, what would be the effect on the expected number of runs? Using the large sample theory for the runs test, test (using $\alpha = .05$) whether there is a difference in the distributions of battery life for the two populations.

14. The conditions (D for diseased, S for sound) of the individual trees in a row of ten poplars were found to be from left to right: $S, S, D, D, S, D, D, D,$ $S, S.$ Is there sufficient evidence to indicate nonrandomness in the sequence and therefore the possibility of contagion?

15. Items emerging from a continuous production process were classified as defective or nondefective. A sequence of items observed over time was as follows : $D, N, N, N, N, N, N, D, D, N, N, N, N, N, N, D, D, D, N, N, N, N$ $N, D, N, N, N, D, D, N, N, N, D, D.$
    (a) Give the appropriate probability that $R \leq 11$ where $n_1 = 11$ and $n_2 = 23$.
    (b) Do these data suggest lack of randomness in the occurrence of defectives (D) and nondefectives (N)? Use the large sample approximation for the runs test.

16. A quality control chart has been maintained for a certain measurable characteristic of items taken from a conveyor belt at a certain point in a production line. The measurements obtained today in order of time are :

$$68.2, 71.6, 69.3, 71.6, 70.4, 65.0, 63.6, 64.7,$$
$$65.3, 64.2, 67.6, 68.6, 66.8, 68.9, 66.8, 70.1.$$

    (a) Classify the measurements in this time series as above or below the sample mean and determine (use the runs test) whether consecutive observations suggest lack of stability in the production process.
    (b) Divide the time period into two equal parts and compare the means, using Student's t test. Do the data provide evidence of a shift in the mean level of the quality characteristics?

17. If (as in the case of measurements produced by two well-calibrated measuring instruments) the means of two populations are equal, it is possible to use the Mann-Whitney U statistic for testing hypotheses concerning the population variances as follows :
    (i) Rank the combined sample.
    (ii) Number the ranked observations " from the outside in "; that is, number the smallest observation 1; the largest, 2; the next-to-smallest, 3; the next-to-largest, 4; etc. This final sequence of numbers induces an ordering on the symbols A (population A items) and B (population B items). If $\sigma_A^2 > \sigma_B^2$, one would expect to find a preponderance of A's near the first of the sequence, and thus a relatively small "sum of ranks" for the A-observations.
    (a) Given the following measurements produced by well-calibrated precision instruments A and B, test at near the $\alpha = .05$ level to determine whether

the more expensive instrument, B, is more precise than A. (Note that this would imply a one-tailed test.) Use the Mann-Whitney U-test.

A	B
1060.21	1060.24
1060.34	1060.28
1060.27	1060.32
1060.36	1060.30
1060.40	

(b) Test, using the F-statistic of Section 9.7.

18. A large corporation selects college graduates for employment, using both interviews and a psychological-achievement test. Interviews conducted at the home office of the company were far more expensive than the tests which could be conducted on campus. Consequently, the personnel office was interested in determining whether the test scores were correlated with interview ratings and whether tests could be substituted for interviews. The idea was not to eliminate interviews but to reduce their number. To determine whether correlation was present, ten prospects were ranked during interviews, and tested. The paired scores are shown below.

SUBJECT	INTERVIEW RANK	TEST SCORE
1	8	74
2	5	81
3	10	66
4	3	83
5	6	66
6	1	94
7	4	96
8	7	70
9	9	61
10	2	86

Calculate the Spearman rank correlation coefficient, r_s. Rank 1 is assigned to the candidate judged to be the best.

19. Refer to Exercise 18. Do the data present sufficient evidence to indicate that the correlation between interview rankings and test scores is less than zero? If this evidence does exist, can we say that tests could be used to reduce the number of interviews?

20. A political scientist wished to examine the relationship of the voter image of a conservative political candidate and the distance between the residences of

the voter and the candidate. Each of twelve voters rated the candidate on a scale of 1 to 20.   The data are shown below.

VOTER	RATING	DISTANCE
1	12	75
2	7	165
3	5	300
4	19	15
5	17	180
6	12	240
7	9	120
8	18	60
9	3	230
10	8	200
11	15	130
12	4	130

Calculate the Spearman rank correlation coefficient, r_s.

21. Refer to Exercise 20.   Do these data provide sufficient evidence to indicate a negative correlation between rating and distance?

SUPPLEMENTARY EXERCISES

1. Calculate the probability that $U \leq 2$ for $n_1 = n_2 = 5$.   Assume that no ties will be present.

2. Calculate the probability that the Wilcoxon T, Section 13.6, is less than or equal to 2 for $n_1 = n_2 = 3$.   Assume that no ties will be present.

3. Calculate $P[R \leq 6]$ for the runs test where $n_1 = n_2 = 8$.

REFERENCES

Kendall, M. G., and A. Stuart, *The Advanced Theory of Statistics*, Vol. 2.   New York : Hafner Publishing Company, 1961.

Savage, I. R., "Bibliography of Nonparametric Statistics and Related Topics," *Journal of the American Statistical Association*, 48 : 844–906, 1953.

Siegel, S., *Nonparametric Statistics for the Behavioral Sciences.* New York: McGraw-Hill Book Company, Inc., 1956.

Wald, A., and J. Wolfowitz, "On a Test Whether Two Samples are from the Same Population," *Annals of Mathematical Statistics*, 2 : 147–162, 1940.

14

A SUMMARY
AND CONCLUSION

The preceding thirteen chapters construct a picture of statistics centered about the dominant feature of the subject, statistical inference. Inference, the objective of statistics, runs as a thread through the entire book, from the phrasing of the inference through the discussion of the probabilistic mechanism and the presentation of the reasoning involved in making the inference, to the formal elementary discussion of the theory of statistical inference presented in Chapter 8. What is statistics, what is its purpose, and how does it accomplish its objective? If we have answered these questions to the satisfaction of the reader, if each chapter and section seems to fulfill a purpose and to complete a portion of the picture, we have in some measure accomplished our instructional objective.

Chapter 1 presented statistics as a scientific tool utilized in making inferences, a prediction, or a decision concerning a population of measurements based upon information contained in a sample. Thus statistics is employed in the evolutionary process known as the scientific method—which in essence is the observation of nature—in order that we may form inferences or theories concerning the structure of nature and test the theories against repeated observation. Inherent in this objective is the sampling and experimentation that purchase a quantity of information which, hopefully, will be employed to provide the best inferences concerning the population from which the sample was drawn.

The method of phrasing the inference, that is, describing a set of measurements, was presented in Chapter 3 in terms of a frequency distribution and associated numerical descriptive measures. In particular we noted that the frequency distribution is subject to a probabilistic interpretation and that the numerical descriptive measures are more suitable for inferential purposes because we can more easily associate with them a measure of their goodness. Finally, a secondary but extremely important result of our study of numerical descriptive measures involved the notion of variation, its measurement in terms of a standard deviation, and its interpretation by using Tchebysheff's Theorem and the Empirical Rule. Thus, while concerned with describing a set of measurements, namely the population, we provided the basis for a description of the sampling distributions of estimators and the z-test statistic to be considered as we progressed in our study.

The mechanism involved in making an inference—a decision—concerning the parameters of a population of die throws was introduced in Chapter 4. We hypothesized the population of die throws to be known, that is, that the die was perfectly balanced, and then drew a sample of $n = 10$ tosses from the population. Observing ten ones, we concluded that the observed sample was highly improbable, assuming our hypothesis to be true, and we therefore rejected the hypothesis and concluded that the die was unbalanced. Thus we noted that the theory of probability assumes the population known, and reasons from the population to the sample. Statistical inference, using probability, observes the sample and attempts to make inferences concerning the population. Fundamental to this procedure is a probabilistic model for the frequency distribution of the population, the acquisition of which was considered in Chapters 4 and 5.

The methodology of Chapters 4 and 5 was employed in Chapter 6 in the construction of a probability distribution, that is, a model for the frequency distribution, of a discrete random variable generated by the binomial experiment. The binomial experiment was chosen as an example because the acquisition of the probabilities, $p(x)$, is a task easily handled by the beginner and thus gives the reader an opportunity to utilize his probabilistic tools. In addition, it was chosen because of its utility, which was exemplified by the cold vaccine and lot acceptance sampling problems. Particularly, the inferential aspects of these problems were noted, with emphasis upon the reasoning involved.

Study of a useful continuous random variable in Chapter 7 centered about the Central Limit Theorem, its suggested support of the Empirical Rule, and its use in describing the probability distribution of sample means and sums. Indeed, we used the Central Limit Theorem to justify the use of the Empirical Rule and the normal probability distribution as an approximation to the binomial probability distribution when the number of trials, n, is large. Through examples we attempted to reinforce the probabilistic concept of statistical inference introduced in preceding chapters and induce the reader, as a matter of intuition, to employ statistical reasoning in making inferences.

Chapter 8 formally discussed statistical inference, estimation and tests of hypotheses, the methods of measuring the goodness of the inference, and presented a number of estimators and test statistics which, because of the Central Limit Theorem, possess approximately a normal probability distribution in repeated sampling. These notions were carried over to the discussion of the small sample tests and estimators in Chapter 9.

Chapters 10 and 11 attempted, primarily, to broaden the view of the beginner, presenting two rather interesting and unique inferential problems. While stress was placed upon the relation between two variables, y and x, in Chapter 10, we were primarily interested in studying the use of the method of least squares in obtaining an equation for predicting y as a function of many variables. Thus, while the methodology appropriate to a single variable is useful, it was not the sole objective of our discussion. The analysis of enumerative data presents a methodology that is interesting and extremely useful in the social sciences as well as in many other areas. The analysis of variance, Chapter 12, extended the comparison of treatment means in the completely random and blocked designs (Chapter 9) to more than two treatments. Simultaneously, it introduced a completely new way to view the analysis of data through the analysis (or partitioning) of variance. Nonparametric statistical methods, Chapter 13, provided a discussion of some very useful statistical test procedures that are particularly appropriate for ordinal data.

Finally, we note that the methodology presented in this introduction to statistics represents a very small sample of the population of statistical methodology that is available to the researcher. It is a bare introduction and nothing more. The design of experiments—an extremely useful topic—was barely touched. Indeed, the methodology presented, while very useful, is intended primarily to serve as a vehicle suitable for conveying to the reader the philosophy involved.

APPENDIX I

USEFUL STATISTICAL TESTS AND CONFIDENCE INTERVALS

I. Inferences concerning the mean of a population.
   1. Sample size, n, is large ($n > 30$).
      A. Test:
         Null hypothesis: $\mu = \mu_0$.
         Alternative hypothesis: $\mu \neq \mu_0$.
         Test statistic:

$$z = \frac{\bar{y} - \mu_0}{\sigma/\sqrt{n}}.$$

If σ is unknown and the sample is large, use

$$s = \sqrt{\frac{\sum\limits_{i=1}^{n}(y_i - \bar{y})^2}{n - 1}}$$

as an estimate of σ.

Rejection region:
   Reject if z is greater than 1.96
   Reject if z is less than -1.96 $\Big\}$ For $\alpha = .05$.

B. $(1 - \alpha)$ confidence interval:

$$\bar{y} \pm z_{\alpha/2}\sigma/\sqrt{n}.$$

2. Small samples, $n < 30$ and the observations are nearly normally distributed.

A. Test:

Null hypothesis: $\mu = \mu_0$.
Alternative hypothesis: $\mu \neq \mu_0$.
Test statistic:

$$t = \frac{\bar{y} - \mu_0}{s/\sqrt{n}}.$$

Rejection region: See t-tables.

B. $(1 - \alpha)$ confidence interval:

$$\bar{y} \pm t_{\alpha/2}s/\sqrt{n}.$$

II. Inferences concerning the difference between the means of two populations.

1. Large samples.

A. Assumptions:

(a) Population I has mean equal to μ_1 and variance equal to σ_1^2.
(b) Population II has mean equal to μ_2 and variance equal to σ_2^2.

B. Some results:

(a) Let $\bar{y}_1$ be the mean of a random sample of n_1 observations from population I, and $\bar{y}_2$ be the mean of an independent and random sample of n_2 observations from population II. Consider the difference, $(\bar{y}_1 - \bar{y}_2)$.
(b) It can be shown that the mean of $(\bar{y}_1 - \bar{y}_2)$ is $\mu_1 - \mu_2$ and its variance is $\dfrac{\sigma_1^2}{n_1} + \dfrac{\sigma_2^2}{n_2}$. Furthermore, for large samples, $\bar{y}_1 - \bar{y}_2$ will be approximately normally distributed.

C. Test:

Null hypothesis: $\mu_1 - \mu_2 = D_0$. (Note: We are usually testing the hypothesis that $\mu_1 - \mu_2 = 0$, i.e., $\mu_1 = \mu_2$.)

Alternative hypothesis: $\mu_1 - \mu_2 \neq D_0$.
Test statistic:

$$z = \frac{(\bar{y}_1 - \bar{y}_2) - D_0}{\sqrt{\sigma_1^2/n_1 + \sigma_2^2/n_2}}.$$

If the null hypothesis is that $\mu_1 = \mu_2$, then $D_0 = 0$ and

$$z = \frac{\bar{y}_1 - \bar{y}_2}{\sqrt{\sigma_1^2/n_1 + \sigma_2^2/n_2}}.$$

If σ_1^2 and σ_2^2 are unknown and n is large, use s_1^2 and s_2^2 as estimates.

Rejection region:

$$\left.\begin{array}{l} \text{Reject if } z > \quad 1.96 \\ \text{or} \quad z < -1.96 \end{array}\right\} \text{For } \alpha = .05.$$

D. $(1 - \alpha)$ confidence interval:

$$(\bar{y}_1 - \bar{y}_2) \pm z_{\alpha/2} \sqrt{\frac{\sigma_1^2}{n_1} + \frac{\sigma_2^2}{n_1}}.$$

2. Small sample size.

A. Assumptions: Both populations approximately normally distributed and

$$\sigma_1^2 = \sigma_2^2.$$

B. Test

Null hypothesis: $\mu_1 - \mu_2 = D_0$.
Alternative hypothesis: $\mu_1 - \mu_2 \neq D_0$,

$$t = \frac{\bar{y}_1 - \bar{y}_2 - D_0}{s\sqrt{\dfrac{1}{n_1} + \dfrac{1}{n_2}}},$$

where s is a pooled estimate of σ.

$$s = \sqrt{\frac{(n_1 - 1)s_1^2 + (n_2 - 1)s_2^2}{n_1 + n_2 - 2}}.$$

Rejection region: See t-tables.

C. $(1 - \alpha)$ confidence interval:

$$(\bar{y}_1 - \bar{y}_2) \pm t_{\alpha/2}s\sqrt{\frac{1}{n_1} + \frac{1}{n_2}}.$$

III. Inferences concerning a probability, p.
  1. Assumptions for a "binomial experiment":

  A. Experiment consists of n identical trials each resulting in one of two outcomes, say success and failure.

  B. The probability of success is equal to p and remains the same from trial to trial.

  C. The trials are independent of each other.

  D. The variable measured is $y =$ number of successes observed during the n trials.

  2. Results:

  A. The estimator of p is $\hat{p} = \dfrac{y}{n}$.

  B. The average value of $\hat{p}$ is p.

  C. The variance of $\hat{p}$ is equal to $\dfrac{pq}{n}$.

  3. Test (n large):

  Null hypothesis: $p = p_0$.
  Alternative hypothesis: $p \neq p_0$ (two-tailed test).
  Test statistic:

  $$z = \frac{\dfrac{y}{n} - p_0}{\sqrt{\dfrac{p_0 q_0}{n}}}.$$

  Rejection region: Reject if $|z| \geq 1.96$.   Note: $\alpha = .05$.

  4. $(1 - \alpha)$ confidence interval (n large):

  $$\hat{p} \pm z_{\alpha/2}\sqrt{\frac{\hat{p}\hat{q}}{n}}.$$

IV. Inferences comparing two probabilities, p_1 and p_2.

1. Assumption: Independent random samples are drawn from each of two binomial populations.

	Pop. I	Pop. II
Probability of success	p_1	p_2
Sample size	n_1	n_2
Observed successes	y_1	y_2

2. Results:

A. The estimated difference between p_1 and p_2 is

$$\hat{p}_1 - \hat{p}_2 = \frac{y_1}{n_1} - \frac{y_2}{n_2}.$$

B. The average value of $\hat{p}_1 - \hat{p}_2$ is $p_1 - p_2$.

C. The variance of $\hat{p}_1 - \hat{p}_2$ is

$$\frac{p_1 q_1}{n_1} + \frac{p_2 q_2}{n_2}.$$

3. Test (n_1 and n_2 large):

Null hypothesis: $p_1 = p_2 = p$.
Alternative hypothesis: $p_1 \neq p_2$ (two-tailed test).
Test statistic:

$$z = \frac{\dfrac{y_1}{n_1} - \dfrac{y_2}{n_2}}{\sqrt{\hat{p}\hat{q}\left(\dfrac{1}{n_1} + \dfrac{1}{n_2}\right)}} \quad \text{where} \quad \hat{p} = \frac{y_1 + y_2}{n_1 + n_2}.$$

Rejection region: Reject if $|z| \geq 1.96$.   Note: $\alpha = .05$.

4. $(1 - \alpha)$ confidence interval (n_1 and n_2 large):

$$(\hat{p}_1 - \hat{p}_2) \pm z_{\alpha/z}\sqrt{\frac{\hat{p}_1 \hat{q}_1}{n_1} + \frac{\hat{p}_2 \hat{q}_2}{n_2}}.$$

V. Inferences concerning the variance of a population.

1. Assumption: Population measurements are normally distributed.

2. Test:

Null hypothesis: $\sigma^2 = \sigma_0^2$.

Alternative hypothesis: $\sigma^2 > \sigma_0^2$. (Note that this implies a one-tailed test.)
Test statistic:

$$\chi^2 = \frac{(n-1)s^2}{\sigma_0^2}.$$

Rejection region:
Reject if χ^2 is greater than or equal to χ_α^2 (see table of χ^2 values). For example, if $\alpha = .05$ and $n = 10$, reject if χ^2 is greater than 16.919.

3. $(1 - \alpha)$ confidence interval:

$$\frac{(n-1)s^2}{\chi_U^2} < \sigma^2 < \frac{(n-1)s^2}{\chi_L^2}.$$

VI. Tests for comparing the equality of two variances.

1. Assumptions:

A. Population I has a normal distribution with mean μ_1 and variance σ_1^2.

B. Population II has a normal distribution with mean μ_2 and variance σ_2^2.

C. Two independent random samples are drawn, n_1 measurements from population I, n_2 from population II.

2. Test:
Null hypothesis: $\sigma_1^2 = \sigma_2^2$.
Alternative hypothesis: $\sigma_1^2 > \sigma_2^2$.
   (one-tailed test)
Test statistic:

$$F = \frac{s_1^2}{s_2^2}.$$

Rejection region: Reject if F is greater than or equal to $F_\alpha(n_1 - 1, n_2 - 1)$.

3. $(1 - \alpha)$ confidence interval:

$$\frac{s_1^2}{s_2^2} \cdot \frac{1}{F_{v_1, v_2}} < \frac{\sigma_1^2}{\sigma_2^2} < \frac{s_1^2}{s_2^2} \cdot F_{v_2, v_1}.$$

APPENDIX II

TABLES

TABLE 1 (a, b, c, d, e):
BINOMIAL PROBABILITY TABLES

Tabulated values are $\sum\limits_{y=0}^{a} P(Y)$ (Computations are rounded at third decimal place)

(a) $n = 5$

a \ P	0.01	0.05	0.10	0.20	0.30	0.40	0.50	0.60	0.70	0.80	0.90	0.95	0.99
0	.951	.774	.590	.328	.168	.078	.031	.010	.002	.000	.000	.000	.000
1	.999	.977	.919	.737	.528	.337	.188	.087	.031	.007	.000	.000	.000
2	1.000	.999	.991	.942	.837	.683	.500	.317	.163	.058	.009	.001	.000
3	1.000	1.000	1.000	.993	.969	.913	.812	.663	.472	.263	.081	.023	.001
4	1.000	1.000	1.000	1.000	.998	.990	.969	.922	.832	.672	.410	.226	.049

(b) $n = 10$

a	0.01	0.05	0.10	0.20	0.30	0.40	0.50	0.60	0.70	0.80	0.90	0.95	0.99
0	.904	.599	.349	.107	.028	.006	.001	.000	.000	.000	.000	.000	.000
1	.996	.914	.736	.376	.149	.046	.011	.002	.000	.000	.000	.000	.000
2	1.000	.988	.930	.678	.383	.167	.055	.012	.002	.000	.000	.000	.000
3	1.000	.999	.987	.879	.650	.382	.172	.055	.011	.001	.000	.000	.000
4	1.000	1.000	.998	.967	.850	.633	.377	.166	.047	.006	.000	.000	.000
5	1.000	1.000	1.000	.994	.953	.834	.623	.367	.150	.033	.002	.000	.000
6	1.000	1.000	1.000	.999	.989	.945	.828	.618	.350	.121	.013	.001	.000
7	1.000	1.000	1.000	1.000	.998	.988	.945	.833	.617	.322	.070	.012	.000
8	1.000	1.000	1.000	1.000	1.000	.998	.989	.954	.851	.624	.264	.086	.004
9	1.000	1.000	1.000	1.000	1.000	1.000	.999	.994	.972	.893	.651	.401	.096

(c) $n = 15$

a \ P	0.01	0.05	0.10	0.20	0.30	0.40	0.50	0.60	0.70	0.80	0.90	0.95	0.99	P \ a
0	.860	.463	.206	.035	.005	.000	.000	.000	.000	.000	.000	.000	.000	0
1	.990	.829	.549	.167	.035	.005	.000	.000	.000	.000	.000	.000	.000	1
2	1.000	.964	.816	.398	.127	.027	.004	.000	.000	.000	.000	.000	.000	2
3	1.000	.995	.944	.648	.297	.091	.018	.002	.000	.000	.000	.000	.000	3
4	1.000	.999	.987	.836	.515	.217	.059	.009	.001	.000	.000	.000	.000	4
5	1.000	1.000	.998	.939	.722	.403	.151	.034	.004	.000	.000	.000	.000	5

6	.000	.000	.000	.001	.015	.095	.304	.610	.869	.982	1.000	1.000	1.000
7	.000	.000	.000	.004	.050	.213	.500	.787	.950	.996	1.000	1.000	1.000
8	.000	.000	.000	.018	.131	.390	.696	.905	.985	.999	1.000	1.000	1.000
9	.000	.000	.002	.061	.278	.597	.849	.966	.996	1.000	1.000	1.000	1.000
10	.000	.001	.013	.164	.485	.783	.941	.991	.999	1.000	1.000	1.000	1.000
11	.000	.005	.056	.352	.703	.909	.982	.998	1.000	1.000	1.000	1.000	1.000
12	.000	.036	.184	.602	.873	.973	.996	1.000	1.000	1.000	1.000	1.000	1.000
13	.010	.171	.451	.833	.965	.995	1.000	1.000	1.000	1.000	1.000	1.000	1.000
14	.140	.537	.794	.965	.995	1.000	1.000	1.000	1.000	1.000	1.000	1.000	1.000

(d) $n = 20$

a \ P	0.01	0.05	0.10	0.20	0.30	0.40	0.50	0.60	0.70	0.80	0.90	0.95	0.99
0	.818	.358	.122	.002	.001	.000	.000	.000	.000	.000	.000	.000	.000
1	.983	.736	.392	.069	.008	.001	.000	.000	.000	.000	.000	.000	.000
2	.999	.925	.677	.206	.035	.004	.000	.000	.000	.000	.000	.000	.000
3	1.000	.984	.867	.411	.107	.016	.001	.000	.000	.000	.000	.000	.000
4	1.000	.997	.957	.630	.238	.051	.006	.000	.000	.000	.000	.000	.000
5	1.000	1.000	.989	.804	.416	.126	.021	.002	.000	.000	.000	.000	.000
6	1.000	1.000	.998	.913	.608	.250	.058	.006	.000	.000	.000	.000	.000
7	1.000	1.000	1.000	.968	.772	.416	.132	.021	.001	.000	.000	.000	.000
8	1.000	1.000	1.000	.990	.887	.596	.252	.057	.005	.000	.000	.000	.000

9	.000	.000	.000	.001	.017	.128	.412	.755	.952	.997	1.000	1.000	1.000
10	.000	.000	.000	.003	.048	.245	.588	.872	.983	.999	1.000	1.000	1.000
11	.000	.000	.000	.010	.113	.404	.748	.943	.995	1.000	1.000	1.000	1.000
12	.000	.000	.000	.032	.228	.584	.868	.979	.999	1.000	1.000	1.000	1.000
13	.000	.000	.002	.087	.392	.750	.942	.994	1.000	1.000	1.000	1.000	1.000
14	.000	.000	.011	.196	.584	.874	.979	.998	1.000	1.000	1.000	1.000	1.000
15	.000	.003	.043	.370	.762	.949	.994	1.000	1.000	1.000	1.000	1.000	1.000
16	.000	.016	.133	.589	.893	.984	.999	1.000	1.000	1.000	1.000	1.000	1.000
17	.000	.075	.323	.794	.965	.996	1.000	1.000	1.000	1.000	1.000	1.000	1.000
18	.001	.264	.608	.931	.992	.999	1.000	1.000	1.000	1.000	1.000	1.000	1.000
19	.182	.642	.878	.988	.999	1.000	1.000	1.000	1.000	1.000	1.000	1.000	1.000

(e) $n = 25$

a \ P	0.01	0.05	0.10	0.20	0.30	0.40	0.50	0.60	0.70	0.80	0.90	0.95	0.99
0	.778	.277	.072	.004	.000	.000	.000	.000	.000	.000	.000	.000	.000
1	.974	.642	.271	.027	.002	.000	.000	.000	.000	.000	.000	.000	.000
2	.998	.873	.537	.092	.009	.000	.000	.000	.000	.000	.000	.000	.000
3	1.000	.966	.764	.234	.033	.002	.000	.000	.000	.000	.000	.000	.000
4	1.000	.993	.902	.421	.090	.009	.000	.000	.000	.000	.000	.000	.000
5	1.000	.999	.967	.617	.193	.029	.002	.000	.000	.000	.000	.000	.000
6	1.000	1.000	.991	.780	.341	.074	.007	.000	.000	.000	.000	.000	.000
7	1.000	1.000	.998	.891	.512	.154	.022	.001	.000	.000	.000	.000	.000
8	1.000	1.000	1.000	.953	.677	.274	.054	.004	.000	.000	.000	.000	.000
9	1.000	1.000	1.000	.983	.811	.425	.115	.013	.000	.000	.000	.000	.000
10	1.000	1.000	1.000	.994	.902	.586	.212	.034	.002	.000	.000	.000	.000
11	1.000	1.000	1.000	.998	.956	.732	.345	.078	.006	.000	.000	.000	.000

	12	13	14	15	16	17	18	19	20	21	22	23	24
12	.000	.000	.000	.000	.017	.154	.500	.846	.983	1.000	1.000	1.000	1.000
13	.000	.000	.000	.002	.044	.268	.655	.922	.994	1.000	1.000	1.000	1.000
14	.000	.000	.000	.006	.098	.414	.788	.966	.998	1.000	1.000	1.000	1.000
15	.000	.000	.000	.017	.189	.575	.885	.987	1.000	1.000	1.000	1.000	1.000
16	.000	.000	.000	.047	.323	.726	.946	.996	1.000	1.000	1.000	1.000	1.000
17	.000	.000	.002	.109	.488	.846	.978	.999	1.000	1.000	1.000	1.000	1.000
18	.000	.000	.009	.220	.659	.926	.993	1.000	1.000	1.000	1.000	1.000	1.000
19	.000	.001	.033	.383	.807	.971	.998	1.000	1.000	1.000	1.000	1.000	1.000
20	.000	.007	.098	.579	.910	.991	1.000	1.000	1.000	1.000	1.000	1.000	1.000
21	.000	.034	.236	.766	.967	.998	1.000	1.000	1.000	1.000	1.000	1.000	1.000
22	.002	.127	.463	.902	.991	1.000	1.000	1.000	1.000	1.000	1.000	1.000	1.000
23	.026	.358	.729	.973	.998	1.000	1.000	1.000	1.000	1.000	1.000	1.000	1.000
24	.222	.723	.928	.996	1.000	1.000	1.000	1.000	1.000	1.000	1.000	1.000	1.000

TABLE 2

X	e^{-x}	X	e^{-x}	X	e^{-x}	X	e^{-x}
0.00	1.000000	2.60	.074274	5.10	.006097	7.60	.000501
0.10	.904837	2.70	.067206	5.20	.005517	7.70	.000453
0.20	.818731	2.80	.060810	5.30	.004992	7.80	.000410
0.30	.740818	2.90	.055023	5.40	.004517	7.90	.000371
0.40	.670320	3.00	.049787	5.50	.004087	8.00	.000336
0.50	.606531	3.10	.045049	5.60	.003698	8.10	.000304
0.60	.548812	3.20	.040762	5.70	.003346	8.20	.000275
0.70	.496585	3.30	.036883	5.80	.003028	8.30	.000249
0.80	.449329	3.40	.033373	5.90	.002739	8.40	.000225
0.90	.406570	3.50	.030197	6.00	.002479	8.50	.000204
1.00	.367879	3.60	.027324	6.10	.002243	8.60	.000184
1.10	.332871	3.70	.024724	6.20	.002029	8.70	.000167
1.20	.301194	3.80	.022371	6.30	.001836	8.80	.000151
1.30	.272532	3.90	.020242	6.40	.001661	8.90	.000136
1.40	.246597	4.00	.018316	6.50	.001503	9.00	.000123
1.50	.223130	4.10	.016573	6.60	.001360	9.10	.000112
1.60	.201897	4.20	.014996	6.70	.001231	9.20	.000101
1.70	.182684	4.30	.013569	6.80	.001114	9.30	.000091
1.80	.165299	4.40	.012277	6.90	.001008	9.40	.000083
1.90	.149569	4.50	.011109	7.00	.000912	9.50	.000075
2.00	.135335	4.60	.010052	7.10	.000825	9.60	.000068
2.10	.122456	4.70	.009095	7.20	.000747	9.70	.000061
2.20	.110803	4.80	.008230	7.30	.000676	9.80	.000056
2.30	.100259	4.90	.007447	7.40	.000611	9.90	.000050
2.40	.090718	5.00	.006738	7.50	.000553	10.00	.000045
2.50	.082085						

TABLE 3: NORMAL CURVE AREAS

z	.00	.01	.02	.03	.04	.05	.06	.07	.08	.09
0.0	.0000	.0040	.0080	.0120	.0160	.0199	.0239	.0279	.0319	.0359
0.1	.0398	.0438	.0478	.0517	.0557	.0596	.0636	.0675	.0714	.0753
0.2	.0793	.0832	.0871	.0910	.0948	.0987	.1026	.1064	.1103	.1141
0.3	.1179	.1217	.1255	.1293	.1331	.1368	.1406	.1443	.1480	.1517
0.4	.1554	.1591	.1628	.1664	.1700	.1736	.1772	.1808	.1844	.1879
0.5	.1915	.1950	.1985	.2019	.2054	.2088	.2123	.2157	.2190	.2224
0.6	.2257	.2291	.2324	.2357	.2389	.2422	.2454	.2486	.2517	.2549
0.7	.2580	.2611	.2642	.2673	.2704	.2734	.2764	.2794	.2823	.2852
0.8	.2881	.2910	.2939	.2967	.2995	.3023	.3051	.3078	.3106	.3133
0.9	.3159	.3186	.3212	.3238	.3264	.3289	.3315	.3340	.3365	.3389
1.0	.3413	.3438	.3461	.3485	.3508	.3531	.3554	.3577	.3599	.3621
1.1	.3643	.3665	.3686	.3708	.3729	.3749	.3770	.3790	.3810	.3830
1.2	.3849	.3869	.3888	.3907	.3925	.3944	.3962	.3980	.3997	.4015
1.3	.4032	.4049	.4066	.4082	.4099	.4115	.4131	.4147	.4162	.4177
1.4	.4192	.4207	.4222	.4236	.4251	.4265	.4279	.4292	.4306	.4319
1.5	.4332	.4345	.4357	.4370	.4382	.4394	.4406	.4418	.4429	.4441
1.6	.4452	.4463	.4474	.4484	.4495	.4505	.4515	.4525	.4535	.4545
1.7	.4554	.4564	.4573	.4582	.4591	.4599	.4608	.4616	.4625	.4633
1.8	.4641	.4649	.4656	.4664	.4671	.4678	.4686	.4693	.4699	.4706
1.9	.4713	.4719	.4726	.4732	.4738	.4744	.4750	.4756	.4761	.4767
2.0	.4772	.4778	.4783	.4788	.4793	.4798	.4803	.4808	.4812	.4817
2.1	.4821	.4826	.4830	.4834	.4838	.4842	.4846	.4850	.4854	.4857
2.2	.4861	.4864	.4868	.4871	.4875	.4878	.4881	.4884	.4887	.4890
2.3	.4893	.4896	.4898	.4901	.4904	.4906	.4909	.4911	.4913	.4916
2.4	.4918	.4920	.4922	.4925	.4927	.4929	.4931	.4932	.4934	.4936
2.5	.4938	.4940	.4941	.4943	.4945	.4946	.4948	.4949	.4951	.4952
2.6	.4953	.4955	.4956	.4957	.4959	.4960	.4961	.4962	.4963	.4964
2.7	.4965	.4966	.4967	.4968	.4969	.4970	.4971	.4972	.4973	.4974
2.8	.4974	.4975	.4976	.4977	.4977	.4978	.4979	.4979	.4980	.4981
2.9	.4981	.4982	.4982	.4983	.4984	.4984	.4985	.4985	.4986	.4986
3.0	.4987	.4987	.4987	.4988	.4988	.4989	.4989	.4989	.4990	.4990

This table is abridged from Table I of *Statistical Tables and Formulas*, by A. Hald (New York: John Wiley & Sons, Inc., 1952). Reproduced by permission of A. Hald and the publishers, John Wiley & Sons, Inc.

TABLE 4: CRITICAL VALUES OF t

n	$t_{.100}$	$t_{.050}$	$t_{.025}$	$t_{.010}$	$t_{.005}$	$d.f.$
2	3.078	6.314	12.706	31.821	63.657	1
3	1.886	2.920	4.303	6.965	9.925	2
4	1.638	2.353	3.182	4.541	5.841	3
5	1.533	2.132	2.776	3.747	4.604	4
6	1.476	2.015	2.571	3.365	4.032	5
7	1.440	1.943	2.447	3.143	3.707	6
8	1.415	1.895	2.365	2.998	3.499	7
9	1.397	1.860	2.306	2.896	3.355	8
10	1.383	1.833	2.262	2.821	3.250	9
11	1.372	1.812	2.228	2.764	3.169	10
12	1.363	1.796	2.201	2.718	3.106	11
13	1.356	1.782	2.179	2.681	3.055	12
14	1.350	1.771	2.160	2.650	3.012	13
15	1.345	1.761	2.145	2.624	2.977	14
16	1.341	1.753	2.131	2.602	2.947	15

(Table 4 continued)

17	1.333	1.746	2.120	2.583	2.921	16
18	1.333	1.740	2.110	2.567	2.898	17
19	1.330	1.734	2.101	2.552	2.878	18
20	1.328	1.729	2.093	2.539	2.861	19
21	1.325	1.725	2.086	2.528	2.845	20
22	1.323	1.721	2.080	2.518	2.831	21
23	1.321	1.717	2.074	2.508	2.819	22
24	1.319	1.714	2.069	2.500	2.807	23
25	1.318	1.711	2.064	2.492	2.797	24
26	1.316	1.708	2.060	2.485	2.787	25
27	1.315	1.706	2.056	2.479	2.779	26
28	1.314	1.703	2.052	2.473	2.771	27
29	1.313	1.701	2.048	2.467	2.763	28
30	1.311	1.699	2.045	2.462	2.756	29
inf.	1.282	1.645	1.960	2.326	2.576	inf.

From "Table of Percentage Points of the t-Distribution." Computed by Maxine Merrington, *Biometrika*, Vol. 32 (1941), p. 300. Reproduced by permission of Professor E. S. Pearson.

TABLE 5: CRITICAL VALUES OF CHI-SQUARE

d.f.	$\chi^2 0.995$	$\chi^2 0.990$	$\chi^2 0.975$	$\chi^2 0.950$	$\chi^2 0.900$
1	0.0000393	0.0001571	0.0009821	0.0039321	0.0157908
2	0.0100251	0.0201007	0.0506356	0.102587	0.210720
3	0.0717212	0.114832	0.215795	0.351846	0.584375
4	0.206990	0.297110	0.484419	0.710721	1.063623
5	0.411740	0.554300	0.831211	1.145476	1.61031
6	0.675727	0.872085	1.237347	1.63539	2.20413
7	0.989265	1.239043	1.68987	2.16735	2.83311
8	1.344419	1.646482	2.17973	2.73264	3.48954
9	1.734926	2.087912	2.70039	3.32511	4.16816
10	2.15585	2.55821	3.24697	3.94030	4.86518
11	2.60321	3.05347	3.81575	4.57481	5.57779
12	3.07382	3.57056	4.40379	5.22603	6.30380
13	3.56503	4.10691	5.00874	5.89186	7.04150
14	4.07468	4.66043	5.62872	6.57063	7.78953
15	4.60094	5.22935	6.26214	7.26094	8.54675
16	5.14224	5.81221	6.90766	7.96164	9.31223
17	5.69724	6.40776	7.56418	8.67176	10.0852
18	6.26481	7.01491	8.23075	9.39046	10.8649
19	6.84398	7.63273	8.90655	10.1170	11.6509
20	7.43386	8.26040	9.59083	10.8508	12.4426
21	8.03366	8.89720	10.28293	11.5913	13.2396
22	8.64272	9.54249	10.9823	12.3380	14.0415
23	9.26042	10.19567	11.6885	13.0905	14.8479
24	9.88623	10.8564	12.4011	13.8484	15.6587
25	10.5197	11.5240	13.1197	14.6114	16.4734
26	11.1603	12.1981	13.8439	15.3791	17.2919
27	11.8076	12.8786	14.5733	16.1513	18.1138
28	12.4613	13.5648	15.3079	16.9279	18.9392
29	13.1211	14.2565	16.0471	17.7083	19.7677
30	13.7867	14.9535	16.7908	18.4926	20.5992
40	20.7065	22.1643	24.4331	26.5093	29.0505
50	27.9907	29.7067	32.3574	34.7642	37.6886
60	35.5346	37.4848	40.4817	43.1879	46.4589
70	43.2752	45.4418	48.7576	51.7393	55.3290
80	51.1720	53.5400	57.1532	60.3915	64.2778
90	59.1963	61.7541	65.6466	69.1260	73.2912
100	67.3276	70.0648	74.2219	77.9295	82.3581

$\chi^2 0.100$	$\chi^2 0.050$	$\chi^2 0.025$	$\chi^2 0.010$	$\chi^2 0.005$	d.f.
2.70554	3.84146	5.02389	6.63490	7.87944	1
4.60517	5.99147	7.37776	9.21034	10.5966	2
6.25139	7.81473	9.34840	11.3449	12.8381	3
7.77944	9.48773	11.1433	13.2767	14.8602	4
9.23635	11.0705	12.8325	15.0863	16.7496	5
10.6446	12.5916	14.4494	16.8119	18.5476	6
12.0170	14.0671	16.0128	18.4753	20.2777	7
13.3616	15.5073	17.5346	20.0902	21.9550	8
14.6837	16.9190	19.0228	21.6660	23.5893	9
15.9871	18.3070	20.4831	23.2093	25.1882	10
17.2750	19.6751	21.9200	24.7250	26.7569	11
18.5494	21.0261	23.3367	26.2170	28.2995	12
19.8119	22.3621	24.7356	27.6883	29.8194	13
21.0642	23.6848	26.1190	29.1413	31.3193	14
22.3072	24.9958	27.4884	30.5779	32.8013	15
23.5418	26.2962	28.8454	31.9999	34.2672	16
24.7690	27.5871	30.1910	33.4087	35.7185	17
25.9894	28.8693	31.5264	34.8053	37.1564	18
27.2036	30.1435	32.8523	36.1908	38.5822	19
28.4120	31.4104	34.1696	37.5662	39.9968	20
29.6151	32.6705	35.4789	38.9321	41.4010	21
30.8133	33.9244	36.7807	40.2894	42.7956	22
32.0069	35.1725	38.0757	41.6384	44.1813	23
33.1963	36.4151	39.3641	42.9798	45.5585	24
34.3816	37.6525	40.6465	44.3141	46.9278	25
35.5631	38.8852	41.9232	45.6417	48.2899	26
36.7412	40.1133	43.1944	46.9630	49.6449	27
37.9159	41.3372	44.4607	48.2782	50.9933	28
39.0875	42.5569	45.7222	49.5879	52.3356	29
40.2560	43.7729	46.9792	50.8922	53.6720	30
51.8050	55.7585	59.3417	63.6907	66.7659	40
63.1671	67.5048	71.4202	76.1539	79.4900	50
74.3970	79.0819	83.2976	88.3794	91.9517	60
85.5271	90.5312	95.0231	100.425	104.215	70
96.5782	101.879	106.629	112.329	116.321	80
107.565	113.145	118.136	124.116	128.299	90
118.498	124.342	129.561	135.807	140.169	100

From "Tables of the Percentage Points of the χ^2-Distribution." *Biometrika*, Vol. 32 (1941), pp. 188–189, by Catherine M. Thompson. Reproduced by permission of Professor E. S. Pearson.

TABLE 6: PERCENTAGE POINTS OF THE F DISTRIBUTION

Degrees of Freedom $\alpha = .05$

ν_1 / ν_2	1	2	3	4	5	6	7	8	9
1	161.4	199.5	215.7	224.6	230.2	234.0	236.8	238.9	240.5
2	18.51	19.00	19.16	19.25	19.30	19.33	19.35	19.37	19.38
3	10.13	9.55	9.28	9.12	9.01	8.94	8.89	8.85	8.81
4	7.71	6.94	6.59	6.39	6.26	6.16	6.09	6.04	6.00
5	6.61	5.79	5.41	5.19	5.05	4.95	4.88	4.82	4.77
6	5.99	5.14	4.76	4.53	4.39	4.28	4.21	4.15	4.10
7	5.59	4.74	4.35	4.12	3.97	3.87	3.79	3.73	3.68
8	5.32	4.46	4.07	3.84	3.69	3.58	3.50	3.44	3.39
9	5.12	4.26	3.86	3.63	3.48	3.37	3.29	3.23	3.18
10	4.96	4.10	3.71	3.48	3.33	3.22	3.14	3.07	3.02
11	4.84	3.98	3.59	3.36	3.20	3.09	3.01	2.95	2.90
12	4.75	3.89	3.49	3.26	3.11	3.00	2.91	2.85	2.80
13	4.67	3.81	3.41	3.18	3.03	2.92	2.83	2.77	2.71
14	4.60	3.74	3.34	3.11	2.96	2.85	2.76	2.70	2.65
15	4.54	3.68	3.29	3.06	2.90	2.79	2.71	2.64	2.59
16	4.49	3.63	3.24	3.01	2.85	2.74	2.66	2.59	2.54
17	4.45	3.59	3.20	2.96	2.81	2.70	2.61	2.55	2.49
18	4.41	3.55	3.16	2.93	2.77	2.66	2.58	2.51	2.46
19	4.38	3.52	3.13	2.90	2.74	2.63	2.54	2.48	2.42
20	4.35	3.49	3.10	2.87	2.71	2.60	2.51	2.45	2.39
21	4.32	3.47	3.07	2.84	2.68	2.57	2.49	2.42	2.37
22	4.30	3.44	3.05	2.82	2.66	2.55	2.46	2.40	2.34
23	4.28	3.42	3.03	2.80	2.64	2.53	2.44	2.37	2.32
24	4.26	3.40	3.01	2.78	2.62	2.51	2.42	2.36	2.30
25	4.24	3.39	2.99	2.76	2.60	2.49	2.40	2.34	2.28
26	4.23	3.37	2.98	2.74	2.59	2.47	2.39	2.32	2.27
27	4.21	3.35	2.96	2.73	2.57	2.46	2.37	2.31	2.25
28	4.20	3.34	2.95	2.71	2.56	2.45	2.36	2.29	2.24
29	4.18	3.33	2.93	2.70	2.55	2.43	2.35	2.28	2.22
30	4.17	3.32	2.92	2.69	2.53	2.42	2.33	2.27	2.21
40	4.08	3.23	2.84	2.61	2.45	2.34	2.25	2.18	2.12
60	4.00	3.15	2.76	2.53	2.37	2.25	2.17	2.10	2.04
120	3.92	3.07	2.68	2.45	2.29	2.17	2.09	2.02	1.96
∞	3.84	3.00	2.60	2.37	2.21	2.10	2.01	1.94	1.88

10	12	15	20	24	30	40	60	120	∞	ν_1 / ν_2
241.9	243.9	245.9	248.0	249.1	250.1	251.1	252.2	253.3	254.3	1
19.40	19.41	19.43	19.45	19.45	19.46	19.47	19.48	19.49	19.50	2
8.79	8.74	8.70	8.66	8.64	8.62	8.59	8.57	8.55	8.53	3
5.96	5.91	5.86	5.80	5.77	5.75	5.72	5.69	5.66	5.63	4
4.74	4.68	4.62	4.56	4.53	4.50	4.46	4.43	4.40	4.36	5
4.06	4.00	3.94	3.87	3.84	3.81	3.77	3.74	3.70	3.67	6
3.64	3.57	3.51	3.44	3.41	3.38	3.34	3.30	3.27	3.23	7
3.35	3.28	3.22	3.15	3.12	3.08	3.04	3.01	2.97	2.93	8
3.14	3.07	3.01	2.94	2.90	2.86	2.83	2.79	2.75	2.71	9
2.98	2.91	2.85	2.77	2.74	2.70	2.66	2.62	2.58	2.54	10
2.85	2.79	2.72	2.65	2.61	2.57	2.53	2.49	2.45	2.40	11
2.75	2.69	2.62	2.54	2.51	2.47	2.43	2.38	2.34	2.30	12
2.67	2.60	2.53	2.46	2.42	2.38	2.34	2.30	2.25	2.21	13
2.60	2.53	2.46	2.39	2.35	2.31	2.27	2.22	2.18	2.13	14
2.54	2.48	2.40	2.33	2.29	2.25	2.20	2.16	2.11	2.07	15
2.49	2.42	2.35	2.28	2.24	2.19	2.15	2.11	2.06	2.01	16
2.45	2.38	2.31	2.23	2.19	2.15	2.10	2.06	2.01	1.96	17
2.41	2.34	2.27	2.19	2.15	2.11	2.06	2.02	1.97	1.92	18
2.38	2.31	2.23	2.16	2.11	2.07	2.03	1.98	1.93	1.88	19
2.35	2.28	2.20	2.12	2.08	2.04	1.99	1.95	1.90	1.84	20
2.32	2.25	2.18	2.10	2.05	2.01	1.96	1.92	1.87	1.81	21
2.30	2.23	2.15	2.07	2.03	1.98	1.94	1.89	1.84	1.78	22
2.27	2.20	2.13	2.05	2.01	1.96	1.91	1.86	1.81	1.76	23
2.25	2.18	2.11	2.03	1.98	1.94	1.89	1.84	1.79	1.73	24
2.24	2.16	2.09	2.01	1.96	1.92	1.87	1.82	1.77	1.71	25
2.22	2.15	2.07	1.99	1.95	1.90	1.85	1.80	1.75	1.69	26
2.20	2.13	2.06	1.97	1.93	1.88	1.84	1.79	1.73	1.67	27
2.19	2.12	2.04	1.96	1.91	1.87	1.82	1.77	1.71	1.65	28
2.18	2.10	2.03	1.94	1.90	1.85	1.81	1.75	1.70	1.64	29
2.16	2.09	2.01	1.93	1.89	1.84	1.79	1.74	1.68	1.62	30
2.08	2.00	1.92	1.84	1.79	1.74	1.69	1.64	1.58	1.51	40
1.99	1.92	1.84	1.75	1.70	1.65	1.59	1.53	1.47	1.39	60
1.91	1.83	1.75	1.66	1.61	1.55	1.50	1.43	1.35	1.25	120
1.83	1.75	1.67	1.57	1.52	1.46	1.39	1.32	1.22	1.00	∞

From "Tables of Percentage Points of the Inverted Beta (F) Distribution," *Biometrika*, Vol. 33 (1943), pp. 73–88, by Maxine Merrington and Catherine M. Thompson.   Reproduced by permission of Professor E. S. Pearson.

TABLE 7: PERCENTAGE POINTS OF
THE F DISTRIBUTION

Degrees of Freedom $\alpha = .01$

ν_2 \ ν_1	1	2	3	4	5	6	7	8	9
1	4052	4999.5	5403	5625	5764	5859	5928	5982	6022
2	98.50	99.00	99.17	99.25	99.30	99.33	99.36	99.37	99.39
3	34.12	30.82	29.46	28.71	28.24	27.91	27.67	27.49	27.35
4	21.20	18.00	16.69	15.98	15.52	15.21	14.98	14.80	14.66
5	16.26	13.27	12.06	11.39	10.97	10.67	10.46	10.29	10.16
6	13.75	10.92	9.78	9.15	8.75	8.47	8.26	8.10	7.98
7	12.25	9.55	8.45	7.85	7.46	7.19	6.99	6.84	6.72
8	11.26	8.65	7.59	7.01	6.63	6.37	6.18	6.03	5.91
9	10.56	8.02	6.99	6.42	6.06	5.80	5.61	5.47	5.35
10	10.04	7.56	6.55	5.99	5.64	5.39	5.20	5.06	4.94
11	9.65	7.21	6.22	5.67	5.32	5.07	4.89	4.74	4.63
12	9.33	6.93	5.95	5.41	5.06	4.82	4.64	4.50	4.39
13	9.07	6.70	5.74	5.21	4.86	4.62	4.44	4.30	4.19
14	8.86	6.51	5.56	5.04	4.69	4.46	4.28	4.14	4.03
15	8.68	6.36	5.42	4.89	4.56	4.32	4.14	4.00	3.89
16	8.53	6.23	5.29	4.77	4.44	4.20	4.03	3.89	3.78
17	8.40	6.11	5.18	4.67	4.34	4.10	3.93	3.79	3.68
18	8.29	6.01	5.09	4.58	4.25	4.01	3.84	3.71	3.60
19	8.18	5.93	5.01	4.50	4.17	3.94	3.77	3.63	3.52
20	8.10	5.85	4.94	4.43	4.10	3.87	3.70	3.56	3.46
21	8.02	5.78	4.87	4.37	4.04	3.81	3.64	3.51	3.40
22	7.95	5.72	4.82	4.31	3.99	3.76	3.59	3.45	3.35
23	7.88	5.66	4.76	4.26	3.94	3.71	3.54	3.41	3.30
24	7.82	5.61	4.72	4.22	3.90	3.67	3.50	3.36	3.26
25	7.77	5.57	4.68	4.18	3.85	3.63	3.46	3.32	3.22
26	7.72	5.53	4.64	4.14	3.82	3.59	3.42	3.29	3.18
27	7.68	5.49	4.60	4.11	3.78	3.56	3.39	3.26	3.15
28	7.64	5.45	4.57	4.07	3.75	3.53	3.36	3.23	3.12
29	7.60	5.42	4.54	4.04	3.73	3.50	3.33	3.20	3.09
30	7.56	5.39	4.51	4.02	3.70	3.47	3.30	3.17	3.07
40	7.31	5.18	4.31	3.83	3.51	3.29	3.12	2.99	2.89
60	7.08	4.98	4.13	3.65	3.34	3.12	2.95	2.82	2.72
120	6.85	4.79	3.95	3.48	3.17	2.96	2.79	2.66	2.56
∞	6.63	4.61	3.78	3.32	3.02	2.80	2.64	2.51	2.41

(Table 7 continued)

10	12	15	20	24	30	40	60	120	∞	ν_1
										ν_2
6056	6106	6157	6209	6235	6261	6287	6313	6339	6366	1
99.40	99.42	99.43	99.45	99.46	99.47	99.47	99.48	99.49	99.50	2
27.23	27.05	26.87	26.69	26.60	26.50	26.41	26.32	26.22	26.13	3
14.55	14.37	14.20	14.02	13.93	13.84	13.75	13.65	13.56	13.46	4
10.05	9.89	9.72	9.55	9.47	9.38	9.29	9.20	9.11	9.02	5
7.87	7.72	7.56	7.40	7.31	7.23	7.14	7.06	6.97	6.88	6
6.62	6.47	6.31	6.16	6.07	5.99	5.91	5.82	5.74	5.65	7
5.81	5.67	5.52	5.36	5.28	5.20	5.12	5.03	4.95	4.86	8
5.26	5.11	4.96	4.81	4.73	4.65	4.57	4.48	4.40	4.31	9
4.85	4.71	4.56	4.41	4.33	4.25	4.17	4.08	4.00	3.91	10
4.54	4.40	4.25	4.10	4.02	3.94	3.86	3.78	3.69	3.60	11
4.30	4.16	4.01	3.86	3.78	3.70	3.62	3.54	3.45	3.36	12
4.10	3.96	3.82	3.66	3.59	3.51	3.43	3.34	3.25	3.17	13
3.94	3.80	3.66	3.51	3.43	3.35	3.27	3.18	3.09	3.00	14
3.80	3.67	3.52	3.37	3.29	3.21	3.13	3.05	2.96	2.87	15
3.69	3.55	3.41	3.26	3.18	3.10	3.02	2.93	2.84	2.75	16
3.59	3.46	3.31	3.16	3.08	3.00	2.92	2.83	2.75	2.65	17
3.51	3.37	3.23	3.08	3.00	2.92	2.84	2.75	2.66	2.57	18
3.43	3.30	3.15	3.00	2.92	2.84	2.76	2.67	2.58	2.49	19
3.37	3.23	3.09	2.94	2.86	2.78	2.69	2.61	2.52	2.42	20
3.31	3.17	3.03	2.88	2.80	2.72	2.64	2.55	2.46	2.36	21
3.26	3.12	2.98	2.83	2.75	2.67	2.58	2.50	2.40	2.31	22
3.21	3.07	2.93	2.78	2.70	2.62	2.54	2.45	2.35	2.26	23
3.17	3.03	2.89	2.74	2.66	2.58	2.49	2.40	2.31	2.21	24
3.13	2.99	2.85	2.70	2.62	2.54	2.45	2.36	2.27	2.17	25
3.09	2.96	2.81	2.66	2.58	2.50	2.42	2.33	2.23	2.13	26
3.06	2.93	2.78	2.63	2.55	2.47	2.38	2.29	2.20	2.10	27
3.03	2.90	2.75	2.60	2.52	2.44	2.35	2.26	2.17	2.06	28
3.00	2.87	2.73	2.57	2.49	2.41	2.33	2.23	2.14	2.03	29
2.98	2.84	2.70	2.55	2.47	2.39	2.30	2.21	2.11	2.01	30
2.80	2.66	2.52	2.37	2.29	2.20	2.11	2.02	1.92	1.80	40
2.63	2.50	2.35	2.20	2.12	2.03	1.94	1.84	1.73	1.60	60
2.47	2.34	2.19	2.03	1.95	1.86	1.76	1.66	1.53	1.38	120
2.32	2.18	2.04	1.88	1.79	1.70	1.59	1.47	1.32	1.00	∞

From "Tables of Percentage Points of the Inverted Beta (F) Distribution," *Biometrika*, Vol. 33 (1943), pp. 73–88, by Maxine Merrington and Catherine M. Thompson. Reproduced by permission of Professor E. S. Pearson.

TABLE 8: DISTRIBUTION FUNCTION OF U, $P(U \leq U_0)$; U_0 IS THE ARGUMENT
$$n_1 \leq n_2 \qquad 3 \leq n_2 \leq 10$$

$n_2 = 3$

U_0 \ n_1	1	2	3
0	.25	.10	.05
1	.50	.20	.10
2		.40	.20
3		.60	.35
4			.50

$n_2 = 4$

U_0 \ n_1	1	2	3	4
0	.2000	.0667	.0286	.0143
1	.4000	.1333	.0571	.0286
2	.6000	.2667	.1143	.0571
3		.4000	.2000	.1000
4		.6000	.3143	.1714
5			.4286	.2429
6			.5714	.3429
7				.4429
8				.5571

$n_2 = 5$

U_0 \ n_1	1	2	3	4	5
0	.1667	.0476	.0179	.0079	.0040
1	.3333	.0952	.0357	.0159	.0079
2	.5000	.1905	.0714	.0317	.0159
3		.2857	.1250	.0556	.0278
4		.4286	.1964	.0952	.0476
5		.5714	.2857	.1429	.0754
6			.3929	.2063	.1111
7			.5000	.2778	.1548
8				.3651	.2103
9				.4524	.2738
10				.5476	.3452
11					.4206
12					.5000

$n_2 = 6$

U_0 \ n_1	1	2	3	4	5	6
0	.1429	.0357	.0119	.0048	.0022	.0011
1	.2857	.0714	.0238	.0095	.0043	.0022
2	.4286	.1429	.0476	.0190	.0087	.0043
3	.5714	.2143	.0833	.0333	.0152	.0076
4		.3214	.1310	.0571	.0260	.0130
5		.4286	.1905	.0857	.0411	.0206
6		.5714	.2738	.1286	.0628	.0325
7			.3571	.1762	.0887	.0465
8			.4524	.2381	.1234	.0660
9			.5476	.3048	.1645	.0898
10				.3810	.2143	.1201
11				.4571	.2684	.1548
12				.5429	.3312	.1970
13					.3961	.2424
14					.4654	.2944
15					.5346	.3496
16						.4091
17						.4686
18						.5314

$n_2 = 7$

U_0 \ n_1	1	2	3	4	5	6	7
0	.1250	.0278	.0083	.0030	.0013	.0006	.0003
1	.2500	.0556	.0167	.0061	.0025	.0012	.0006
2	.3750	.1111	.0333	.0121	.0051	.0023	.0012
3	.5000	.1667	.0583	.0212	.0088	.0041	.0020
4		.2500	.0917	.0364	.0152	.0070	.0035
5		.3333	.1333	.0545	.0240	.0111	.0055
6		.4444	.1917	.0818	.0366	.0175	.0087
7		.5556	.2583	.1152	.0530	.0256	.0131
8			.3333	.1576	.0745	.0367	.0189
9			.4167	.2061	.1010	.0507	.0265
10			.5000	.2636	.1338	.0688	.0364
11				.3242	.1717	.0903	.0487
12				.3939	.2159	.1171	.0641
13				.4636	.2652	.1474	.0825
14				.5364	.3194	.1830	.1043
15					.3775	.2226	.1297
16					.4381	.2669	.1588
17					.5000	.3141	.1914
18						.3654	.2279
19						.4178	.2675
20						.4726	.3100
21						.5274	.3552
22							.4024
23							.4508
24							.5000

$n_2 = 8$

U_0 \ n_1	1	2	3	4	5	6	7	8
0	.1111	.0222	.0061	.0020	.0008	.0003	.0002	.0001
1	.2222	.0444	.0121	.0040	.0016	.0007	.0003	.0002
2	.3333	.0889	.0242	.0081	.0031	.0013	.0006	.0003
3	.4444	.1333	.0424	.0141	.0054	.0023	.0011	.0005
4	.5556	.2000	.0667	.0242	.0093	.0040	.0019	.0009
5		.2667	.0970	.0364	.0148	.0063	.0030	.0015
6		.3556	.1394	.0545	.0225	.0100	.0047	.0023
7		.4444	.1879	.0768	.0326	.0147	.0070	.0035
8		.5556	.2485	.1071	.0466	.0213	.0103	.0052
9			.3152	.1414	.0637	.0296	.0145	.0074
10			.3879	.1838	.0855	.0406	.0200	.0103
11			.4606	.2303	.1111	.0539	.0270	.0141
12			.5394	.2848	.1422	.0709	.0361	.0190
13				.3414	.1772	.0906	.0469	.0249
14				.4040	.2176	.1142	.0603	.0325
15				.4667	.2618	.1412	.0760	.0415
16				.5333	.3108	.1725	.0946	.0524
17					.3621	.2068	.1159	.0652
18					.4165	.2454	.1405	.0803
19					.4716	.2864	.1678	.0974
20					.5284	.3310	.1984	.1172
21						.3773	.2317	.1393
22						.4259	.2679	.1641
23						.4749	.3063	.1911
24						.5251	.3472	.2209
25							.3894	.2527
26							.4333	.2869
27							.4775	.3227
28							.5225	.3605
29								.3992
30								.4392
31								.4796
32								.5204

$n_2 = 9$

U_0 \ n_1	1	2	3	4	5	6	7	8	9
0	.1000	.0182	.0045	.0014	.0005	.0002	.0001	.0000	.0000
1	.2000	.0364	.0091	.0028	.0010	.0004	.0002	.0001	.0000
2	.3000	.0727	.0182	.0056	.0020	.0008	.0003	.0002	.0001
3	.4000	.1091	.0318	.0098	.0035	.0014	.0006	.0003	.0001
4	.5000	.1636	.0500	.0168	.0060	.0024	.0010	.0005	.0002
5		.2182	.0727	.0252	.0095	.0038	.0017	.0008	.0004
6		.2909	.1045	.0378	.0145	.0060	.0026	.0012	.0006
7		.3636	.1409	.0531	.0210	.0088	.0039	.0019	.0009
8		.4545	.1864	.0741	.0300	.0128	.0058	.0028	.0014
9		.5455	.2409	.0993	.0415	.0180	.0082	.0039	.0020
10			.3000	.1301	.0559	.0248	.0115	.0056	.0028
11			.3636	.1650	.0734	.0332	.0156	.0076	.0039
12			.4318	.2070	.0949	.0440	.0209	.0103	.0053
13			.5000	.2517	.1199	.0567	.0274	.0137	.0071
14				.3021	.1489	.0723	.0356	.0180	.0094
15				.3552	.1818	.0905	.0454	.0232	.0122
16				.4126	.2188	.1119	.0571	.0296	.0157
17				.4699	.2592	.1361	.0708	.0372	.0200
18				.5301	.3032	.1638	.0869	.0464	.0252
19					.3497	.1942	.1052	.0570	.0313
20					.3986	.2280	.1261	.0694	.0385
21					.4491	.2643	.1496	.0836	.0470
22					.5000	.3035	.1755	.0998	.0567
23						.3445	.2039	.1179	.0680
24						.3878	.2349	.1383	.0807
25						.4320	.2680	.1606	.0951
26						.4773	.3032	.1852	.1112
27						.5227	.3403	.2117	.1290
28							.3788	.2404	.1487
29							.4185	.2707	.1701
30							.4591	.3029	.1933
31							.5000	.3365	.2181
32								.3715	.2447
33								.4074	.2729
34								.4442	.3024
35								.4813	.3332
36								.5187	.3652
37									.3981
38									.4317
39									.4657
40									.5000

$$n_2 = 10$$

U_0 \ n_1	1	2	3	4	5	6	7	8	9	10
0	.0909	.0152	.0035	.0010	.0003	.0001	.0001	.0000	.0000	.0000
1	.1818	.0303	.0070	.0020	.0007	.0002	.0001	.0000	.0000	.0000
2	.2727	.0606	.0140	.0040	.0013	.0005	.0002	.0001	.0000	.0000
3	.3636	.0909	.0245	.0070	.0023	.0009	.0004	.0002	.0001	.0000
4	.4545	.1364	.0385	.0120	.0040	.0015	.0006	.0003	.0001	.0001
5	.5455	.1818	.0559	.0180	.0063	.0024	.0010	.0004	.0002	.0001
6		.2424	.0804	.0270	.0097	.0037	.0015	.0007	.0003	.0002
7		.3030	.1084	.0380	.0140	.0055	.0023	.0010	.0005	.0002
8		.3788	.1434	.0529	.0200	.0080	.0034	.0015	.0007	.0004
9		.4545	.1853	.0709	.0276	.0112	.0048	.0022	.0011	.0005
10		.5455	.2343	.0939	.0376	.0156	.0068	.0031	.0015	.0008
11			.2867	.1199	.0496	.0210	.0093	.0043	.0021	.0010
12			.3462	.1518	.0646	.0280	.0125	.0058	.0028	.0014
13			.4056	.1868	.0823	.0363	.0165	.0078	.0038	.0019
14			.4685	.2268	.1032	.0467	.0215	.0103	.0051	.0026
15			.5315	.2697	.1272	.0589	.0277	.0133	.0066	.0034
16				.3177	.1548	.0736	.0351	.0171	.0086	.0045
17				.3666	.1855	.0903	.0439	.0217	.0110	.0057
18				.4196	.2198	.1099	.0544	.0273	.0140	.0073
19				.4725	.2567	.1317	.0665	.0338	.0175	.0093
20				.5275	.2970	.1566	.0806	.0416	.0217	.0116
21					.3393	.1838	.0966	.0506	.0267	.0144
22					.3839	.2139	.1148	.0610	.0326	.0177
23					.4296	.2461	.1349	.0729	.0394	.0216
24					.4765	.2811	.1574	.0864	.0474	.0262
25					.5235	.3177	.1819	.1015	.0564	.0315
26						.3564	.2087	.1185	.0667	.0376
27						.3962	.2374	.1371	.0782	.0446
28						.4374	.2681	.1577	.0912	.0526
29						.4789	.3004	.1800	.1055	.0615
30						.5211	.3345	.2041	.1214	.0716
31							.3698	.2299	.1388	.0827
32							.4063	.2574	.1577	.0952
33							.4434	.2863	.1781	.1088
34							.4811	.3167	.2001	.1237
35							.5189	.3482	.2235	.1399
36								.3809	.2483	.1575
37								.4143	.2745	.1763
38								.4484	.3019	.1965
39								.4827	.3304	.2179
40								.5173	.3598	.2406
41									.3901	.2644
42									.4211	.2894
43									.4524	.3153
44									.4841	.3421
45									.5159	.3697
46										.3980
47										.4267
48										.4559
49										.4853
50										.5147

Computed by M. Pagano, Department of Statistics, University of Florida.

TABLE 9: CRITICAL VALUES OF T IN THE WILCOXON MATCHED-PAIRS SIGNED-RANKS TEST $n = 5(1)50$

One sided	Two-sided	$n = 5$	$n = 6$	$n = 7$	$n = 8$	$n = 9$	$n = 10$
$P = .05$	$P = .10$	1	2	4	6	8	11
$P = .025$	$P = .05$		1	2	4	6	8
$P = .01$	$P = .02$			0	2	3	5
$P = .005$	$P = .01$				0	2	3

One-sided	Two-sided	$n = 11$	$n = 12$	$n = 13$	$n = 14$	$n = 15$	$n = 16$
$P = .05$	$P = .10$	14	17	21	26	30	36
$P = .025$	$P = .05$	11	14	17	21	25	30
$P = .01$	$P = .02$	7	10	13	16	20	24
$P = .005$	$P = .01$	5	7	10	13	16	19

One-sided	Two-sided	$n = 17$	$n = 18$	$n = 19$	$n = 20$	$n = 21$	$n = 22$
$P = .05$	$P = .10$	41	47	54	60	68	75
$P = .025$	$P = .05$	35	40	46	52	59	66
$P = .01$	$P = .02$	28	33	38	43	49	56
$P = .005$	$P = .01$	23	28	32	37	43	49

One-sided	Two-sided	$n = 23$	$n = 24$	$n = 25$	$n = 26$	$n = 27$	$n = 28$
$P = .05$	$P = .10$	83	92	101	110	120	130
$P = .025$	$P = .05$	73	81	90	98	107	117
$P = .01$	$P = .02$	62	69	77	85	93	102
$P = .005$	$P = .01$	55	68	68	76	84	92

One-sided	Two-sided	$n = 29$	$n = 30$	$n = 31$	$n = 32$	$n = 33$	$n = 34$
$P = .05$	$P = .10$	141	152	163	175	188	201
$P = .025$	$P = .05$	127	137	148	159	171	183
$P = .01$	$P = .02$	111	120	130	141	151	162
$P = .005$	$P = .01$	100	109	118	128	138	149

One-sided	Two-sided	$n = 35$	$n = 36$	$n = 37$	$n = 38$	$n = 39$
$P = .05$	$P = .10$	214	228	242	256	271
$P = .025$	$P = .05$	195	208	222	235	250
$P = .01$	$P = .02$	174	186	198	211	224
$P = .005$	$P = .01$	160	171	183	195	208

One-sided	Two-sided	$n = 40$	$n = 41$	$n = 42$	$n = 43$	$n = 44$	$n = 45$
$P = .05$	$P = .10$	287	303	319	336	353	371
$P = .025$	$P = .05$	264	279	295	311	327	344
$P = .01$	$P = .02$	238	252	267	281	297	313
$P = .005$	$P = .01$	221	234	248	262	277	292

One-sided	Two-sided	$n = 46$	$n = 47$	$n = 48$	$n = 49$	$n = 50$
$P = .05$	$P = .10$	389	408	427	446	466
$P = .025$	$P = .05$	361	379	397	415	434
$P = .01$	$P = .02$	329	345	362	380	398
$P = .005$	$P = .01$	307	323	339	356	373

From "Some Rapid Approximate Statistical Procedures" (1964), 28, F. Wilcoxon and R. A. Wilcox. Reproduced with the kind permission of R. A. Wilcox and the Lederle Laboratories.

TABLE 10: DISTRIBUTION OF THE TOTAL NUMBER OF RUNS R IN SAMPLES OF SIZE (n_1, n_2); $P[R \leq a]$

					a				
(n_1, n_2)	2	3	4	5	6	7	8	9	10
(2,3)	.200	.500	.900	1.000					
(2,4)	.133	.400	.800	1.000					
(2,5)	.095	.333	.714	1.000					
(2,6)	.071	.286	.643	1.000					
(2,7)	.056	.250	.583	1.000					
(2,8)	.044	.222	.533	1.000					
(2,9)	.036	.200	.491	1.000					
(2,10)	.030	.182	.455	1.000					
(3,3)	.100	.300	.700	.900	1.000				
(3,4)	.057	.200	.543	.800	.971	1.000			
(3,5)	.036	.143	.429	.714	.929	1.000			
(3,6)	.024	.107	.345	.643	.881	1.000			
(3,7)	.017	.083	.283	.583	.833	1.000			
(3,8)	.012	.067	.236	.533	.788	1.000			
(3,9)	.009	.055	.200	.491	.745	1.000			
(3,10)	.007	.045	.171	.455	.706	1.000			
(4,4)	.029	.114	.371	.629	.886	.971	1.000		
(4,5)	.016	.071	.262	.500	.786	.929	.992	1.000	
(4,6)	.010	.048	.190	.405	.690	.881	.976	1.000	
(4,7)	.006	.033	.142	.333	.606	.833	.954	1.000	
(4,8)	.004	.024	.109	.279	.533	.788	.929	1.000	
(4,9)	.003	.018	.085	.236	.471	.745	.902	1.000	
(4,10)	.002	.014	.068	.203	.419	.706	.874	1.000	
(5,5)	.008	.040	.167	.357	.643	.833	.960	.992	1.000
(5,6)	.004	.024	.110	.262	.522	.738	.911	.976	.998
(5,7)	.003	.015	.076	.197	.424	.652	.854	.955	.992
(5,8)	.002	.010	.054	.152	.347	.576	.793	.929	.984
(5,9)	.001	.007	.039	.119	.287	.510	.734	.902	.972
(5,10)	.001	.005	.029	.095	.239	.455	.678	.874	.958
(6,6)	.002	.013	.067	.175	.392	.608	.825	.933	.987
(6,7)	.001	.008	.043	.121	.296	.500	.733	.879	.966
(6,8)	.001	.005	.028	.086	.226	.413	.646	.821	.937
(6,9)	.000	.003	.019	.063	.175	.343	.566	.762	.902
(6,10)	.000	.002	.013	.047	.137	.288	.497	.706	.864
(7,7)	.001	.004	.025	.078	.209	.383	.617	.791	.922
(7,8)	.000	.002	.015	.051	.149	.296	.514	.704	.867
(7,9)	.000	.001	.010	.035	.108	.231	.427	.622	.806
(7,10)	.000	.001	.006	.024	.080	.182	.355	.549	.743
(8,8)	.000	.001	.009	.032	.100	.214	.405	.595	.786
(8,9)	.000	.001	.005	.020	.069	.157	.319	.500	.702
(8,10)	.000	.000	.003	.013	.048	.117	.251	.419	.621
(9,9)	.000	.000	.003	.012	.044	.109	.238	.399	.601
(9,10)	.000	.000	.002	.008	.029	.077	.179	.319	.510
(10,10)	.000	.000	.001	.004	.019	.051	.128	.242	.414

(n_1, n_2)	11	12	13	14	15	16	17	18	19	20
(2,3)										
(2,4)										
(2,5)										
(2,6)										
(2,7)										
(2,8)										
(2,9)										
(2,10)										
(3,3)										
(3,4)										
(3,5)										
(3,6)										
(3,7)										
(3,8)										
(3,9)										
(3,10)										
(4,4)										
(4,5)										
(4,6)										
(4,7)										
(4,8)										
(4,9)										
(4,10)										
(5,5)										
(5,6)	1.000									
(5,7)	1.000									
(5,8)	1.000									
(5,9)	1.000									
(5,10)	1.000									
(6,6)	.998	1.000								
(6,7)	.992	.999	1.000							
(6,8)	.984	.998	1.000							
(6,9)	.972	.994	1.000							
(6,10)	.958	.990	1.000							
(7,7)	.975	.996	.999	1.000						
(7,8)	.949	.988	.998	1.000	1.000					
(7,9)	.916	.975	.994	.999	1.000					
(7,10)	.879	.957	.990	.998	1.000					
(8,8)	.900	.968	.991	.999	1.000	1.000				
(8,9)	.843	.939	.980	.996	.999	1.000	1.000			
(8,10)	.782	.903	.964	.990	.998	1.000	1.000			
(9,9)	.762	.891	.956	.988	.997	1.000	1.000	1.000		
(9,10)	.681	.834	.923	.974	.992	.999	1.000	1.000	1.000	
(10,10)	.586	.758	.872	.949	.981	.996	.999	1.000	1.000	1.000

From "Tables for Testing Randomness of Grouping in a Sequence of Alternatives," C. Eisenhart and F. Swed, *Annals of Mathematical Statistics*, Volume 14 (1943). Reproduced with the kind permission of the Editor, *Annals of Mathematical Statistics*.

TABLE 11: CRITICAL VALUES OF SPEARMAN'S RANK CORRELATION COEFFICIENT

n	$\alpha = .05$	$\alpha = .025$	$\alpha = .01$	$\alpha = .005$
5	0.900	—	—	—
6	0.829	0.886	0.943	—
7	0.714	0.786	0.893	—
8	0.643	0.738	0.833	0.881
9	0.600	0.683	0.783	0.833
10	0.564	0.648	0.745	0.794
11	0.523	0.623	0.736	0.818
12	0.497	0.591	0.703	0.780
13	0.475	0.566	0.673	0.745
14	0.457	0.545	0.646	0.716
15	0.441	0.525	0.623	0.689
16	0.425	0.507	0.601	0.666
17	0.412	0.490	0.582	0.645
18	0.399	0.476	0.564	0.625
19	0.388	0.462	0.549	0.608
20	0.377	0.450	0.534	0.591
21	0.368	0.438	0.521	0.576
22	0.359	0.428	0.508	0.562
23	0.351	0.418	0.496	0.549
24	0.343	0.409	0.485	0.537
25	0.336	0.400	0.475	0.526
26	0.329	0.392	0.465	0.515
27	0.323	0.385	0.456	0.505
28	0.317	0.377	0.448	0.496
29	0.311	0.370	0.440	0.487
30	0.305	0.364	0.432	0.478

From "Distribution of Sums of Squares of Rank Differences for Small Samples," E. G. Olds, *Annals of Mathematical Statistics*, Volume 9 (1938). Reproduced with the kind permission of the Editor, *Annals of Mathematical Statistics*.

TABLE 12: SQUARES, CUBES AND ROOTS

Roots of numbers other than those given directly may be found by the following relations: $\sqrt{100n} = 10\sqrt{n}$; $\sqrt{1000n} = 10\sqrt{10n}$; $\sqrt{\frac{1}{10}n} = \frac{1}{10}\sqrt{10n}$;

$\sqrt{\frac{1}{100}}n = \frac{1}{10}\sqrt{n}$; $\sqrt{\frac{1}{1000}}n = \frac{1}{100}\sqrt{10n}$; $\sqrt[3]{1000n} = 10\sqrt[3]{n}$; $\sqrt[3]{10,000n} =$

$10\sqrt[3]{10n}$; $\sqrt[3]{100,000n} = 10\sqrt[3]{100n}$; $\sqrt[3]{\frac{1}{10}}n = \frac{1}{10}\sqrt[3]{100n}$; $\sqrt[3]{\frac{1}{100}}n = \frac{1}{10}\sqrt[3]{10n}$;

$\sqrt[3]{\frac{1}{1000}}n = \frac{1}{10}\sqrt[3]{n}$.

n	n^2	$\sqrt{n}$	$\sqrt{10n}$	n	n^2	$\sqrt{n}$	$\sqrt{10n}$
				30	900	5.477 226	17.32051
1	1	1.000 000	3.162 278	31	961	5.567 764	17.60682
2	4	1.414 214	4.472 136	32	1 024	5.656 854	17.88854
3	9	1.732 051	5.477 226	33	1 089	5.744 563	18.16590
4	16	2.000 000	6.324 555	34	1 156	5.830 952	18.43909
5	25	2.236 068	7.071 068	35	1 225	5.916 080	18.70829
6	36	2.449 490	7.745 967	36	1 296	6.000 000	18.97367
7	49	2.645 751	8.366 600	37	1 369	6.082 763	19.23538
8	64	2.828 427	8.944 272	38	1 444	6.164 414	19.49359
9	81	3.000 000	9.486 833	39	1 521	6.244 998	19.74842
10	100	3.162 278	10.00000	40	1 600	6.324 555	20.00000
11	121	3.316 625	10.48809	41	1 681	6.403 124	20.24846
12	144	3.464 102	10.95445	42	1 764	6.480 741	20.49390
13	169	3.605 551	11.40175	43	1 849	6.557 439	20.73644
14	196	3.741 657	11.83216	44	1 936	6.633 250	20.97618
15	225	3.872 983	12.24745	45	2 025	6.708 204	21.21320
16	256	4.000 000	12.64911	46	2 116	6.782 330	21.44761
17	289	4.123 106	13.03840	47	2 209	6.855 655	21.67948
18	324	4.242 641	13.41641	48	2 304	6.928 203	21.90890
19	361	4.358 899	13.78405	49	2 401	7.000 000	22.13594
20	400	4.472 136	14.14214	50	2 500	7.071 068	22.36068
21	441	4.582 576	14.49138	51	2 601	7.141 428	22.58318
22	484	4.690 416	14.83240	52	2 704	7.211 103	22.80351
23	529	4.795 832	15.16575	53	2 809	7.280 110	23.02173
24	576	4.898 979	15.49193	54	2 916	7.348 469	23.23790
25	625	5.000 000	15.81139	55	3 025	7.416 198	23.45208
26	676	5.099 020	16.12452	56	3 136	7.483 315	23.66432
27	729	5.196 152	16.43168	57	3 249	7.549 834	23.87467
28	784	5.291 503	16.73320	58	3 364	7.615 773	24.08319
29	841	5.385 165	17.02939	59	3 418	7.681 146	24.28992

n	n^2	$\sqrt{n}$	$\sqrt{10n}$	n	n^2	$\sqrt{n}$	$\sqrt{10n}$
60	3 600	7.745 967	24.49490	**100**	10 000	10.00000	31.62278
61	3 721	7.810 250	24.69818	101	10 201	10.04998	31.78050
62	3 844	7.874 008	24.89980	102	10 404	10.09950	31.93744
63	3 969	7.937 254	25.09980	103	10 609	10.14889	32.09361
64	4 096	8.000 000	25.29822	104	10 816	10.19804	32.24903
65	4 225	8.062 258	25.49510	105	11 025	10.24695	32.40370
66	4 356	8.124 038	25.69047	106	11 236	10.29563	32.55764
67	4 489	8.185 353	25.88436	107	11 449	10.34408	32.71085
68	4 624	8.246 211	26.07681	108	11 664	10.39230	32.86335
69	4 761	8.306 624	26.26785	109	11 881	10.44031	33.01515
70	4 900	8.366 600	26.45751	**110**	12 100	10.48809	33.16625
71	5 041	8.426 150	26.64583	111	12 321	10.53565	33.31666
72	5 184	8.485 281	26.83282	112	12 544	10.58301	33.46640
73	5 329	8.544 004	27.01851	113	12 769	10.63015	33.61547
74	5 476	8.602 325	27.20294	114	12 996	10.67708	33.76389
75	5 625	8.660 254	27.38613	115	13 225	10.72381	33.91165
76	5 776	8.717 798	27.56810	116	13 456	10.77033	34.05877
77	5 929	8.774 964	27.74887	117	13 689	10.81665	34.20526
78	6 084	8.831 761	27.92848	118	13 924	10.86278	34.35113
79	6 241	8.888 194	28.10694	119	14 161	10.90871	34.49638
80	6 400	8.944 272	28.28427	**120**	14 400	10.95445	34.64102
81	6 561	9.000 000	28.46050	121	14 641	11.00000	34.78505
82	6 724	9.055 385	28.63564	122	14 884	11.04536	34.92850
83	6 889	9.110 434	28.80972	123	15 129	11.09054	35 07136
84	7 056	9.165 151	28.98275	124	15 376	11.13553	35 21363
85	7 225	9.219 544	29.15476	125	15 625	11.18034	35.35534
86	7 396	9.273 618	29.32576	126	15 876	11.22497	35.49648
87	7 569	9.327 379	29.49576	127	16 129	11.26943	35.63706
88	7 744	9.380 832	29.66479	128	16 384	11.31371	35.77709
86	7 921	9.433 981	29.83287	129	16 641	11.35782	35.91657
90	8 100	9.486 833	30.00000	**130**	16 900	11.40175	36.05551
91	8 281	9.539 392	30.16621	131	17 161	11.44552	36.19392
92	8 464	9.591 663	30.33150	132	17 424	11.48913	36.33180
93	8 649	9.643 651	30.49590	133	17 689	11.53256	36.46917
94	8 836	9.695 360	30.65942	134	17 956	11.57584	36.60601
95	9 025	9.746 794	30.82207	135	18 225	11.61895	36.74235
96	9 216	9.797 959	30.98387	136	18 496	11.66190	36.87818
97	9 409	9.848 858	31.14482	137	18 769	11.70470	37.01351
98	9 604	9.899 495	31.30495	138	19 044	11.74734	37.14835
99	9 801	9.949 874	31.46427	139	19 321	11.78983	37.28270

n	n^2	$\sqrt{n}$	$\sqrt{10n}$	n	n^2	$\sqrt{n}$	$\sqrt{10n}$
140	19 600	11.83216	37.41657	**180**	32 400	13.41641	42.42641
141	19 881	11.87434	37.54997	181	32 761	13.45362	42.54409
142	20 164	11.91638	37.68289	182	33 124	13.49074	42.66146
143	20 449	11.95826	37.81534	183	33 489	13.52775	42.77850
144	20 736	12.00000	37.94733	184	33 856	13.56466	42.89522
145	21 025	12.04159	38.07887	185	34 225	13.60147	43.01163
146	21 316	12.08305	38.20995	186	34 596	13.63818	43.12772
147	21 609	12.12436	38.34058	187	34 969	13.67479	43.24350
148	21 904	12.16553	38.47077	188	35 344	13.71131	43.35897
149	22 201	12.20656	38.60052	189	35 721	13.74773	43.47413
150	22 500	12.24745	38.72983	**190**	36 100	13.78405	43.58899
151	22 801	12.28821	38.85872	191	36 481	13.82027	43.70355
152	23 104	12.32883	38.98718	192	36 864	13.85641	43.81780
153	23 409	12.36932	39.11521	193	37 249	13.89244	34.93177
154	23 716	12.40967	39.24283	194	37 636	13.92839	44.04543
155	24 025	12.44990	39.37004	195	38 025	13.96424	44.15880
156	24 336	12.49000	39.49684	196	38 416	14.00000	44.27189
157	24 649	12.52996	39.62323	197	38 809	14.03567	44.38468
158	24 964	12.56981	39.74921	198	39 204	14.07125	44.49719
159	25 281	12.60952	39.87480	199	39 601	14.10674	44.60942
160	25 600	12.64911	40.00000	**200**	40 000	14.14214	44.72136
161	25 921	12.68858	40.12481	201	40 401	14.17745	44.83302
162	26 244	12.72792	40.24922	202	40 804	14.21267	44.94441
163	26 569	12.76715	40.37326	203	41 209	14.24781	45.05552
164	26 806	12.80625	40.49691	204	41 616	14.28286	45.16636
165	27 225	12.84523	40.62019	205	42 025	14.31782	45.27693
166	27 556	12.88410	40.74310	206	42 436	14.35270	45.38722
167	27 889	12.92285	40.86563	207	42 849	14.38749	45.49725
168	28 224	12.96148	40.98780	208	43 264	14.42221	45.60702
169	28 561	13.00000	41.10961	209	43 681	14.45683	45.71652
170	28 900	13.03840	41.23106	**210**	44 100	14.49138	45.82576
171	29 241	13.07670	41.35215	211	44 521	14.52584	45.93474
172	29 584	13.11488	41.47288	212	44 944	14.56022	46.04346
173	29 929	13.15295	41.59327	213	45 369	14.59452	46.15192
174	30 276	13.19091	41.71331	214	45 796	14.62874	46.26013
175	30 625	13.22876	41.83300	215	46 225	14.66288	46.36809
176	30 976	13.26650	41.95235	216	46 656	14.69694	46.47580
177	31 329	13.30413	42.07137	217	47 089	14.73092	46.58326
178	31 684	13.34166	42.19005	218	47 524	14.76482	46.69047
179	32 041	13.37909	42.30829	219	47 961	14.79865	46.79744

n	n^2	$\sqrt{n}$	$\sqrt{10n}$	n	n^2	$\sqrt{n}$	$\sqrt{10n}$
220	48 400	14.83240	46.90416	**260**	67 600	16.12452	50.99020
221	48 841	14.86607	47.01064	261	68 121	16.15549	51.08816
222	49 284	14.89966	47.11688	262	68 644	16.18641	51.18594
223	49 729	14.93318	47.22288	263	69 169	16.21727	51.28353
224	50 176	14.96663	47.32864	264	69 696	16.24808	51.38093
225	50 625	15.00000	47.43416	265	70 225	16.27882	51.47815
226	51 076	15.03330	47.53946	266	70 756	16.30951	51.57519
227	51 529	15.06652	47.64452	267	71 289	16.34013	51.67204
228	51 984	15.09967	47.74935	268	71 824	16.37071	51.76872
229	52 441	15.13275	47.85394	269	72 361	16.40122	51.86521
230	52 900	15.16575	47.95832	**270**	72 900	16.43168	51.96152
231	53 361	15.19868	48.06246	271	73 441	16.46208	52.05766
232	53 824	15.23155	48.16638	272	73 984	16.49242	52.15362
233	54 289	15.26434	48.27007	273	74 529	16.52271	52.24940
234	54 756	15.29706	48.37355	274	75 076	16.55295	52.34501
235	55 225	15.32971	48.47680	275	75 625	16.58312	52.44044
236	55 696	15.36229	48.57983	276	76 176	16.61235	52.53570
237	56 169	15.39480	48.68265	277	76 729	16.64332	52.63079
238	56 644	15.42725	48.78524	278	77 284	16.67333	52.72571
239	57 121	15.45962	48.88763	279	77 841	16.70329	52.82045
240	57 600	15.49193	48.98979	**280**	78 400	16.73320	52.91503
241	58 081	15.52417	49.09175	281	78 961	16.76305	53.00943
242	58 564	15.55635	49.19350	282	79 524	16.79286	53.10367
243	59 049	15.58846	49.29503	283	80 089	16.82260	53.19774
244	59 536	15.62050	49.39636	284	80 656	16.85230	53.29165
245	60 025	15.65248	49.49747	285	81 225	16.88194	53.38539
246	60 516	15.68439	49.59839	286	81 796	16.91153	53.47897
247	61 009	15.71623	49.69909	287	82 369	16.94107	53.57238
248	61 504	15.74902	49.79960	288	82 944	16.97056	53.66563
249	62 001	15.77973	49.89990	289	83 521	17.00000	53.75872
250	62 500	15.81139	50.00000	**290**	84 100	17.02939	53.85165
251	63 001	15.84298	50.09990	291	84 681	17.05872	53.94442
252	63 504	15.87451	50.19960	292	85 264	17.08801	54.03702
253	64 009	15.90597	50.29911	293	85 849	17.11724	54.12947
254	64 516	15.93738	50.39841	294	86 436	17.14643	54.22177
255	65 025	15.96872	50.49752	295	87 025	17.17556	54.31390
256	65 536	16.00000	50.59644	296	87 616	17.20465	54.40588
257	66 049	16.03122	50.69517	297	88 209	17.23369	54.49771
258	66 564	16.06238	50.79370	298	88 804	17.26268	54.58938
259	67 081	16.09348	50.89204	299	89 401	17.29162	54.68089

n	n^2	$\sqrt{n}$	$\sqrt{10n}$	n	n^2	$\sqrt{n}$	$\sqrt{10n}$
300	90 000	17.32051	54.77226	**340**	115 600	18.43909	58.30952
301	90 601	17.34935	54.86347	341	116 281	18.46619	58.39521
302	91 204	17.37815	54.95453	342	116 964	18.49324	58.48077
303	91 809	17.40690	55.04544	343	117 649	18.52026	58.56620
304	92 416	17.43560	55.13620	344	118 336	18.54724	58.65151
305	93 025	17.46425	55.22681	345	119 025	18.57418	58.73670
306	93 636	17.49286	55.31727	346	119 716	18.60108	58.82176
307	94 249	17.52142	55.40758	347	120 409	18.62794	58.90671
308	94 864	71.54993	55.49775	348	121 104	18.65476	58.99152
309	95 481	17.57840	55.58777	349	121 801	18.68154	59.07622
310	96 100	17.60682	55.67764	**350**	122 500	18.70829	59.16080
311	96 721	17.63519	55.76737	351	123 201	18.73499	59.24525
312	97 344	17.66352	55.85696	352	123 904	18.76166	59.32959
313	97 969	17.69181	55.94640	353	124 609	18.78829	59.41380
314	98 596	17.72005	56.03570	354	125 316	18.81489	59.49790
315	99 225	17.74824	56.12486	355	126 025	18.84144	59.58188
316	99 856	17.77639	56.21388	356	126 736	18.86796	59.66574
317	100 489	17.80449	56.30275	357	127 449	18.89444	59.74948
318	101 124	17.83255	56.39149	358	128 164	18.92089	59.83310
319	101 761	17.86057	56.48008	359	128 881	18.94730	59.91661
320	102 400	17.88854	56.56854	**360**	129 600	18.97367	60.00000
321	103 041	17.91647	56.65686	361	130 321	19.00000	60.08328
322	103 684	17.94436	56.74504	362	131 044	19.02630	60.16644
323	104 329	17.97220	56.83309	363	131 769	19.05256	60.24948
324	104 976	18.00000	56.92100	364	132 496	19.07878	60.33241
325	105 625	18.02776	57.00877	365	133 225	19.10497	60.41523
326	106 276	18.05547	57.09641	366	133 956	19.13113	60.49793
327	106 929	18.08314	57.18391	367	134 689	19.15724	60.58052
328	107 584	18.11077	57.27128	368	135 424	19.18333	60.66300
329	108 241	18.13836	57.35852	369	136 161	19.20937	60.74537
330	108 900	18.16590	57.44563	**370**	136 900	19.23538	60.82763
331	109 561	18.19341	57.53260	371	137 641	19.26136	60.90977
332	110 224	18.22087	57.61944	372	138 384	19.28730	60.99180
333	110 889	18.24829	57.70615	373	139 129	19.31321	61.07373
334	111 556	18.27567	57.79273	374	139 876	19.33908	61.15554
335	112 225	18.30301	57.87918	375	140 625	19.36492	61.23724
336	112 896	18.33030	57.96551	376	141 376	19.39072	61.31884
337	113 569	18.35756	58.05170	377	142 129	19.41649	61.40033
338	114 244	18.38478	58.13777	378	142 884	19.44222	61.48170
339	114 921	18.41195	58.22371	379	143 641	19.46792	61.56298

n	n^2	$\sqrt{n}$	$\sqrt{10n}$	n	n^2	$\sqrt{n}$	$\sqrt{10n}$
380	144 400	19.49359	61.64414	420	176 400	20.49390	64.80741
381	145 161	19.51922	61.72520	421	177 241	20.51828	64.88451
382	145 924	19.54482	61.80615	422	178 084	20.54264	64.96153
383	146 689	19.57039	61.88699	423	178 929	20.56696	65.03845
384	147 456	19.59592	61.96773	424	179 776	20.59126	65.11528
385	148 225	19.62142	62.04837	425	180 625	20.61553	65.19202
386	148 996	19.64688	62.12890	426	181 476	20.63977	65.26868
387	149 769	19.67232	62.20932	427	182 329	20.66398	65.34524
388	150 544	19.69772	62.28965	428	183 184	20.68816	65.42171
389	151 321	19.72308	62.36986	429	184 041	20.71232	65.49809
390	152 100	19.74842	62.44998	**430**	184 900	20.73644	65.57439
391	152 881	19.77372	62.52999	431	185 761	20.76054	65.65059
392	153 664	19.79899	62.60990	432	186 624	20.78461	65.72671
393	154 449	19.82423	62.68971	433	187 489	20.80865	65.80274
394	155 236	19.84943	62.76942	434	188 356	20.83267	65.87868
395	156 025	19.87461	62.84903	435	189 225	20.85665	65.95453
396	156 816	19.89975	62.92853	436	190 096	20.88061	66.03030
397	157 609	19.92486	63.00794	437	190 969	20.90454	66.10598
398	158 404	19.94994	63.08724	438	191 844	20.92845	66.18157
399	159 201	19.97498	63.16645	439	192 721	20.95233	66.25708
400	160 000	20.00000	63.24555	**440**	193 600	20.97618	66.33250
401	160 801	20.02498	63.32456	441	194 481	21.00000	66.40783
402	161 604	20.04994	63.40347	442	195 364	21.02380	66.48308
403	162 409	20.07486	63.48228	443	196 249	21.04757	66.55825
404	163 216	20.09975	63.56099	444	197 136	21.07131	66.63332
405	164 025	20.12461	63.63961	445	198 025	21.09502	66.70832
406	164 836	20.14944	63.71813	446	198 916	21.11871	66.78323
407	165 649	20.17424	63.79655	447	199 809	21.14237	66.85806
408	166 464	20.19901	63.87488	448	200 704	21.16601	66.93280
409	167 281	20.22375	63.95311	449	201 601	21.18962	67.00746
410	168 100	20.24864	64.03124	**450**	202 500	21.21320	67.08204
411	168 921	20.27313	64.10928	451	203 401	21.23676	67.15653
412	169 744	20.29778	64.18723	452	204 304	21.26029	67.23095
413	170 569	20.32240	54.26508	453	205 209	21.28380	67.30527
414	171 396	20.34699	64.34283	454	206 116	21.30728	67.37952
415	172 225	20.37155	64.42049	455	207 025	21.33073	67.45369
416	173 056	20.39608	64.49806	456	207 936	21.35416	67.52777
417	173 889	20.42058	64.57554	457	208 849	21.37756	67.60178
418	174 724	20.44505	64.65292	458	209 764	21.40093	67.67570
419	175 561	20.46949	64.73021	459	210 681	21.42429	67.74954

n	n^2	$\sqrt{n}$	$\sqrt{10n}$	n	n^2	$\sqrt{n}$	$\sqrt{10n}$
460	211 600	21.44761	67.82330	**500**	250 000	22.36068	70.71068
461	212 521	21.47091	67.89698	501	251 001	22.38303	70.78135
462	213 444	21.49419	67.97058	502	252 004	22.40536	70.85196
463	214 369	21.51743	68.04410	503	253 009	22.42766	70.92249
464	215 296	21.54066	68.11755	504	254 016	22.44994	70.99296
465	216 225	21.56386	68.19091	505	255 025	22.47221	71.06335
466	217 156	21.58703	68.26419	506	256 036	22.49444	71.13368
467	218 089	21.61018	68.33740	507	257 049	22.51666	71.20393
468	219 024	21.63331	68.41053	508	258 064	22.53886	71.27412
469	219 961	21.65641	68.48957	509	259 081	22.56103	71.34424
470	220 900	21.67948	68.55655	**510**	260 100	22.58318	71.41428
471	221 841	21.70253	68.62944	511	261 121	22.60531	71.48426
472	222 784	21.72556	68.70226	512	262 144	22.62742	71.55418
473	223 729	21.74856	68.77500	513	263 169	22.64950	71.62402
474	224 676	21.77154	68.84766	514	264 196	22.67157	71.69379
475	225 625	21.79449	68.92024	515	265 225	22.69361	71.76350
476	226 576	21.81742	68.99275	516	266 256	22.71563	71.83314
477	227 529	21.84033	69.06519	517	267 289	22.73763	71.90271
478	228 484	21.86321	69.13754	518	268 324	22.75961	71.97222
479	229 441	21.88607	69.20983	519	269 361	22.78157	72.04165
480	230 400	21.90890	69.28203	**520**	270 400	22.80351	72.11103
481	231 361	21.93171	69.35416	521	271 441	22.82542	72.18033
482	232 324	21.95450	69.42622	522	272 484	22.84732	72.24957
483	233 289	21.97726	69.49820	523	273 529	22.86919	72.31874
484	234 256	22.00000	69.57011	524	274 576	22.89105	72.38784
485	235 225	22.02272	69.64194	525	275 625	22.91288	72.45688
486	236 196	22.04541	69.71370	526	276 676	22.93469	72.52586
487	237 169	22.06808	69.78539	527	277 729	22.95648	72.59477
488	238 144	22.09072	69.85700	528	278 784	22.97825	72.66361
489	239 121	22.11334	69.92853	529	279 841	23.00000	72.73239
490	240 100	22.13594	70.00000	**530**	280 900	23.02173	72.80110
491	241 081	22.15852	70.07139	531	281 961	23.04344	72.86975
492	242 064	22.18107	70.14271	532	283 024	23.06513	72.93833
493	243 049	22.20360	70.21396	533	284 089	23.08679	73.00685
494	244 036	22.22611	70.28513	534	285 156	23.10844	73.07530
495	245 025	22.24860	70.35624	535	286 225	23.13007	73.14369
496	246 016	22.27106	70.42727	536	287 296	23.15167	73.21202
497	247 009	22.29350	70.49823	537	288 369	23.17326	73.28028
498	248 004	22.31591	70.56912	538	289 444	23.19483	73.34848
499	249 001	22.33831	70.63993	539	290 521	23.21637	73.41662

n	n^2	$\sqrt{n}$	$\sqrt{10n}$	n	n^2	$\sqrt{n}$	$\sqrt{10n}$
540	291 600	23.23790	73.48469	**580**	336 400	24.08319	76.15773
541	292 681	23.25941	73.55270	581	337 561	24.10394	76.22336
542	293 764	23.28089	73.62065	582	338 724	24.12468	76.28892
543	294 849	23.30236	73.68853	583	339 889	24.14539	76.35444
544	295 936	23.32381	73.75636	584	341 056	24.16609	76.41989
545	297 025	23.34524	73.82412	585	342 225	24.18677	76.48529
546	298 116	23.36664	73.89181	586	343 396	24.20744	76.55064
547	299 209	23.38803	73.95945	587	344 569	24.22808	76.61593
548	300 304	23.40940	74.02702	588	345 744	24.24871	76.68116
549	301 401	23.43075	74.09453	589	346 921	24.26932	76.74634
550	302 500	23.45208	74.16198	**590**	348 100	24.28992	76.81146
551	303 601	23.47339	74.22937	591	349 281	24.31049	76.87652
552	304 704	23.49468	74.29670	592	350 464	24.33105	76.94154
553	305 809	23.51595	74.36397	593	351 649	24.35159	77.00649
554	306 916	23.53720	74.43118	594	352 836	24.37212	77.07140
555	308 025	23.55844	74.49832	595	354 025	24.39262	77.13624
556	309 136	23.57965	74.56541	596	355 216	24.41311	77.20104
557	310 249	23.60085	74.63243	597	356 409	24.43358	87.26578
558	311 364	23.62202	74.69940	598	357 604	24.45404	77.33046
559	312 481	23.64318	74.76630	599	358 801	24.47448	77.39509
560	313 600	23.66432	74.83315	**600**	360 000	24.49490	77.45967
561	314 721	23.68544	74.89993	601	361 201	24.51530	77.52419
562	315 844	23.70654	74.96666	602	362 404	24.53569	77.58866
563	316 969	23.72762	75.03333	603	363 609	24.55606	77.65307
564	318 096	23.74868	75.09993	604	364 816	24.57641	77.71744
565	319 225	23.76973	75.16648	605	366 025	24.59675	77.78175
566	320 356	23.79075	75.23297	606	367 236	24.61707	77.84600
567	321 489	23.81176	75.29940	607	368 449	24.63737	77.91020
568	322 624	23.83275	75.36577	608	369 664	24.65766	77.97435
569	323 761	23.85372	75.43209	609	370 881	24.67793	78.03845
570	324 900	23.87467	75.49834	**610**	372 100	24.69818	78.10250
571	326 041	23.89561	75.56454	611	373 321	24.71841	78.16649
572	327 184	23.91652	75.63068	612	374 544	24.73863	78.23043
573	328 329	23.93742	75.69676	613	375 769	24.75884	78.29432
574	329 476	23.95830	75.76279	614	376 996	24.77902	78.35815
575	330 625	23.97916	75.82875	615	378 225	24.79919	78.42194
576	331 776	24.00000	75.89466	616	379 456	24.81935	78.48567
577	332 929	24.02082	75.96052	617	380 689	24.83948	78.54935
578	334 084	24.04163	76.02631	618	381 924	24.85961	78.61298
579	335 241	24.06242	76.09205	619	383 161	24.87971	78.67655

n	n^2	$\sqrt{n}$	$\sqrt{10n}$	n	n^2	$\sqrt{n}$	$\sqrt{10n}$
620	384 400	24.89980	78.74008	**660**	435 600	25.69047	81.24038
621	385 641	24.91987	78.80355	661	436 921	25.70992	81.30191
622	386 884	24.93993	78.86698	662	438 244	25.72936	81.36338
623	388 129	24.95997	78.93035	663	439 569	25.74879	81.42481
624	389 376	24.97999	78.99367	664	440 896	25.76820	81.48620
625	390 625	25.00000	79.05694	665	442 225	25.78759	81.54753
626	391 876	25.01999	79.12016	666	443 556	25.80698	81.60882
627	393 129	25.03997	79.18333	667	444 889	25.82634	81.67007
628	394 384	25.05993	79.24645	668	446 224	25.84570	81.73127
629	395 641	25.07987	79.30952	669	447 561	25.86503	81.79242
630	396 900	25.09980	79.37254	**670**	448 900	25.88436	81.85353
631	398 161	25.11971	79.43551	671	450 241	25.90367	81.91459
632	399 424	25.13961	79.49843	672	451 584	25.92296	81.97561
633	400 689	25.15949	79.56130	673	452 929	25.94224	82.03658
634	401 956	25.17936	79.62412	674	454 276	25.96151	82.09750
635	403 225	25.19921	79.68689	675	455 625	25.98076	82.15838
636	404 496	25.21904	79.74961	676	456 976	26.00000	82.21922
637	405 769	25.23886	79.81228	677	458 329	26.01922	82.28001
638	407 044	25.25866	79.87490	678	459 684	26.03843	82.34076
639	408 321	25.27845	79.93748	679	461 041	26.05763	82.40146
640	409 600	25.29822	80.00000	**680**	462 400	26.07681	82.46211
641	410 881	25.31798	80.06248	681	463 761	26.09598	82.52272
642	412 164	25.33772	80.12490	682	465 124	26.11513	82.58329
643	413 449	25.35744	80.18728	683	466 489	26.13427	82.64381
644	414 736	25.37716	80.24961	684	467 856	26.15339	82.70429
645	416 025	25.39685	80.31189	685	469 225	26.17250	82.76473
646	417 316	25.41653	80.37413	686	470 596	26.19160	82.82512
647	418 609	25.43619	80.43631	687	471 969	26.21068	82.88546
648	419 904	25.45584	80.49845	688	473 344	26.22975	82.94577
649	421 201	25.47548	80.56054	689	474 721	26.24881	83.00602
650	422 500	25.49510	80.62258	**690**	476 100	26.26785	83.06624
651	423 801	25.51470	80.68457	691	477 481	26.28688	83.12641
652	425 104	25.53429	80.74652	692	478 864	26.30589	83.18654
653	426 409	25.55386	80.80842	693	480 249	26.32489	83.24662
654	427 716	25.57342	80.87027	694	481 636	26.34388	83.30666
655	429 025	25.59297	80.93207	695	483 025	26.36285	83.36666
656	430 336	25.61250	80.99383	696	484 416	26.38181	83.42661
657	431 649	25.63201	81.05554	697	485 809	26.40076	83.48653
658	432 964	25.65151	81.11720	698	487 204	26.41969	83.54639
659	434 281	25.67100	81.17881	699	488 601	26.43861	83.60622

n	n^2	$\sqrt{n}$	$\sqrt{10n}$	n	n^2	$\sqrt{n}$	$\sqrt{10n}$
700	490 000	26.45751	83.66600	**740**	547 600	27.20294	86.02325
701	491 401	26.47640	83.72574	741	549 081	27.22132	86.08136
702	492 804	26.49528	83.78544	742	550 564	27.23968	86.13942
703	494 209	26.51415	83.84510	743	552 049	27.25803	86.19745
704	495 616	26.53300	83.90471	744	553 536	27.27636	86.25543
705	497 025	26.55184	83.96428	745	555 025	27.29469	86.31338
706	498 436	26.57066	84.02381	746	556 516	27.31300	86.37129
707	499 849	26.58947	84.08329	747	558 009	27.33130	86.42916
708	501 264	26.60827	84.14274	748	559 504	27.34959	86.48699
709	502 681	26.62705	84.20214	749	561 001	27.36786	86.54479
710	504 100	26.64583	84.26150	**750**	562 500	27.38613	86.60254
711	505 521	26.66458	84.32082	751	564 001	27.40438	86.66026
712	506 944	26.68333	84.38009	752	565 504	27.42262	86.71793
713	508 369	26.70206	84.43933	753	567 009	27.44085	86.77557
714	509 796	26.72078	84.49852	754	568 516	27.45906	86.83317
715	511 225	26.73948	84.55767	755	570 025	27.47726	86.89074
716	512 656	26.75818	84.61678	756	571 536	27.49545	86.94826
717	514 089	26.77686	84.67585	757	573 049	27.51363	87.00575
718	515 524	26.79552	84.73488	758	574 564	27.53180	87.06320
719	516 961	26.81418	84.79387	759	576 081	27.54995	87.12061
720	518 400	26.83282	84.85281	**760**	577 600	27.56810	87.17798
721	519 841	26.85144	84.91172	761	579 121	27.58623	87.23531
722	521 284	26.87006	84.97058	762	580 644	27.60435	87.29261
723	522 729	26.88866	85.02941	763	582 169	27.62245	87.34987
724	524 176	26.90725	85.08819	764	583 696	27.64055	87.40709
725	525 625	26.92582	85.14693	765	585 225	27.65863	87.46428
726	527 076	26.94439	85.20563	766	586 756	27.67671	87.52143
727	528 529	26.96294	85.26429	767	588 289	27.69476	87.57854
728	529 984	26.98148	85.32292	768	589 824	27.71281	87.63561
729	531 441	27.00000	85.38150	769	591 361	27.73085	87.69265
730	532 900	27.01851	85.44004	**770**	592 900	27.74887	87.74964
731	534 361	27.03701	85.49854	771	594 441	27.76689	87.80661
732	535 824	27.05550	85.55700	772	595 984	27.78489	87.86353
733	537 289	27.07397	85.61542	773	597 529	27.80288	87.92042
734	538 756	27.09243	85.67380	774	599 076	27.82086	87.97727
735	540 225	27.11088	85.73214	775	600 625	27.83882	88.03408
736	541 696	27.12932	85.79044	776	602 176	27.85678	88.09086
737	543 169	27.14774	85.84870	777	603 729	27.87472	88.14760
738	544 644	27.16616	85.90693	778	605 284	27.89265	88.20431
739	546 121	27.18455	85.96511	779	606 841	27.91057	88.26098

n	n^2	$\sqrt{n}$	$\sqrt{10n}$	n	n^2	$\sqrt{n}$	$\sqrt{10n}$
780	608 400	27.92848	88.31761	**820**	672 400	28.63564	90.55385
781	609 961	27.94638	88.37420	821	674 041	28.65310	90.60905
782	611 524	27.96426	88.43076	822	675 684	28.67054	90.66422
783	613 089	27.98214	88.48729	823	677 329	28.68798	90.71935
784	614 656	28.00000	88.54377	824	678 976	28.70540	90.77445
785	616 225	28.01785	88.60023	825	680 625	28.72281	90.82951
786	617 796	28.03569	88.65664	826	682 726	28.74022	90.88454
787	619 369	28.05352	88.71302	827	683 929	28.75761	90.93954
788	620 944	28.07134	88.76936	828	685 584	28.77499	90.99451
789	622 521	28.08914	88.82567	829	687 241	28.79236	91.04944
790	624 100	28.10694	88.88194	**830**	688 900	28.80972	91.10434
791	625 681	28.12472	88.93818	831	690 561	28.82707	91.15920
792	627 264	28.14249	88.99428	832	692 224	28.84441	91.21403
793	628 849	28.16026	89.05055	833	693 889	28.86174	91.26883
794	630 436	28.17801	89.10668	834	695 556	28.87906	91.32360
795	632 025	28.19574	89.16277	835	697 225	28.89637	91.37833
796	633 616	28.21347	89.21883	836	698 896	28.91366	91.43304
797	635 209	28.23119	89.27486	837	700 569	28.93095	91.48770
798	636 804	28.24889	89.33085	838	702 244	28.94823	91.54234
799	638 401	28.26659	89.38680	839	703 921	28.96550	91.59694
800	640 000	28.28472	89.44272	**840**	705 600	28.98275	91.65151
801	641 601	28.30194	89.49860	841	707 281	29.00000	91.70605
802	643 204	28.31960	89.55445	842	708 964	29.01724	91.76056
803	644 809	28.33725	89.61027	843	710 649	29.03446	91.81503
804	646 416	28.35489	89.66605	844	712 336	29.05168	91.86947
805	648 025	28.37252	89.72179	845	714 025	29.06888	91.92388
806	649 636	28.39014	89.77750	846	715 716	29.08608	91.97826
807	651 249	28.40775	89.83318	847	717 409	29.10326	92.03260
808	652 864	28.42534	89.88882	848	719 104	29.12044	92.08692
809	654 481	28.44293	89.94443	849	720 801	29.13760	92.14120
810	656 100	28.46050	90.00000	**850**	722 500	29.15476	92.19544
811	657 721	28.47806	90.05554	851	724 201	29.17190	92.24966
812	659 344	28.49561	90.11104	852	725 904	29.18904	92.30385
813	660 969	28.51315	90.16651	853	727 609	29.20616	92.35800
814	662 596	28.53069	90.22195	854	729 316	29.22328	92.41212
815	664 225	28.54820	90.27735	855	731 025	29.24038	92.46621
816	665 856	28.56571	90.33272	856	732 736	29.25748	92.52027
817	667 489	28.58321	90.38805	857	734 449	29.27456	92.57429
818	669 124	28.60070	90.44335	858	736 164	29.29164	92.62829
819	670 761	28.61818	90.49862	859	737 881	29.30870	92.68225

n	n^2	$\sqrt{n}$	$\sqrt{10n}$	n	n^2	$\sqrt{n}$	$\sqrt{10n}$
860	739 600	29.32576	92.73618	**900**	810 000	30.00000	94.86833
861	741 321	29.34280	92.79009	901	811 801	30.01666	94.92102
862	743 044	29.35984	92.84396	902	813 604	30.03331	94.97368
863	744 769	29.37686	92.89779	903	815 409	30.04996	95.02631
864	746 496	29.39388	92.95160	904	817 216	30.06659	95.07891
865	748 225	29.41088	93.00538	905	819 025	30.08322	95.13149
866	749 956	29.42788	93.05912	906	820 836	30.09983	95.18403
867	751 689	29.44486	93.11283	907	822 649	30.11644	95.23655
868	753 424	29.46184	93.16652	908	824 464	30.13304	95.28903
869	755 161	29.47881	93.22017	909	826 281	30.14963	95.34149
870	756 900	29.49576	93.27379	**910**	828 100	30.16621	95.39392
871	758 641	29.51271	93.32738	911	829 921	30.18278	95.44632
872	760 384	29.52965	93.38094	912	831 744	30.19934	95.49869
873	762 129	29.54657	93.43447	913	833 569	30.21589	95.55103
874	763 876	29.56349	93.48797	914	835 396	20.23243	95.60335
875	765 625	29.58040	93.54143	915	837 225	30.24897	95.65563
876	767 376	29.59730	93.59487	916	839 056	30.26549	95.70789
877	769 129	29.61419	93.64828	917	840 889	30.28201	95.76012
878	770 884	29.63106	93.70165	918	842 724	30.29851	95.81232
879	772 641	29.64793	93.75500	919	844 561	30.31501	95.86449
880	774 400	29.66479	93.80832	**920**	846 400	30.33150	95.91663
881	776 161	29.68164	93.86160	921	848 241	30.34798	95.96874
882	777 924	29.69848	93.91486	922	850 084	30.36445	96.02083
883	779 689	29.71532	93.96808	923	851 929	30.38092	96.07289
884	781 456	29.73214	94.02127	924	853 776	30.39737	96.12492
885	783 225	29.74895	94.07444	925	855 625	30.41381	96.17692
886	784 996	29.76575	94.12757	926	857 476	30.43025	96.22889
887	786 769	29.78255	94.18068	927	859 329	30.44667	96.28084
888	788 544	29.79933	94.23375	928	861 184	30.46309	96.33276
889	790 321	29.81610	94.28680	929	863 041	30.47950	96.38465
890	792 100	29.83287	94.33981	**930**	864 900	30.49590	96.43651
891	793 881	29.84962	94.39280	931	866 761	30.51229	96.48834
892	795 664	29.86637	94.44575	932	868 624	30.52868	96.54015
893	797 449	29.88311	94.49868	933	870 489	30.54505	96.59193
894	799 236	29.89983	94.55157	934	872 356	30.56141	96.64368
895	801 025	29.91655	94.60444	935	874 225	30.57777	96.69540
896	802 816	29.93326	94.65728	936	876 096	30.59412	96.74709
897	804 609	29.94996	94.71008	937	877 969	30.61046	96.79876
898	806 404	29.96665	94.76286	938	879 844	30.62679	96.85040
899	808 201	29.98333	94.81561	939	881 721	30.64311	96.90201

n	n^2	$\sqrt{n}$	$\sqrt{10n}$	n	n^2	$\sqrt{n}$	$\sqrt{10n}$
940	883 600	30.65942	96.95360	**970**	940 900	31.14482	98.48858
941	885 481	30.67572	97.00515	971	942 841	31.16087	98.53933
942	887 364	30.69202	97.05668	972	944 784	31.17691	98.59006
943	889 249	30.70831	97.10819	973	946 729	31.19295	98.64076
944	891 136	30.72458	97.15966	974	948 676	31.20897	98.69144
945	893 025	30.74085	97.21111	975	950 625	31.22499	98.74209
946	894 916	30.75711	97.26253	976	952 576	31.24100	98.79271
947	896 809	30.77337	97.31393	977	954 529	31.25700	98.84331
948	898 704	30.78961	97.36529	978	956 484	31.27299	98.89388
949	900 601	30.80584	97.41663	979	958 441	31.28898	98.94443
950	902 500	30.82207	97.46794	**980**	960 400	31.30495	98.99495
951	904 401	30.83829	97.51923	981	962 361	31.32092	99.04544
952	906 304	30.85450	97.57049	982	964 324	31.33688	99.09591
953	908 209	30.87070	97.62172	983	966 289	31.35283	99.14636
954	910 116	30.88689	97.67292	984	968 256	31.36877	99.19677
955	912 025	30.90307	97.72410	985	970 225	31.38471	99.24717
956	913 936	30.91925	97.77525	986	972 196	31.40064	99.29753
957	915 849	30.93542	97.82638	987	974 169	31.41656	99.34787
958	917 764	30.95158	97.87747	988	976 144	31.43247	99.39819
959	919 681	30.96773	97.92855	989	978 121	31.44837	99.44848
960	921 600	30.98387	97.97959	990	980 100	31.46427	99.49874
961	923 521	31.00000	98.03061	991	982 081	31.48015	99.54898
962	925 444	31.01612	98.08160	992	984 064	31.49603	99.59920
963	927 369	31.03224	98.13256	993	986 049	31.51190	99.64939
964	929 296	31.04835	98.18350	994	988 036	31.52777	99.69955
965	931 225	31.06445	98.23441	995	990 025	31.54362	99.74969
966	933 156	31.08054	98.28530	996	992 016	31.55947	99.79980
967	935 089	31.09662	98.33616	997	994 009	31.57531	99.84989
968	937 024	31.11270	98.38699	998	996 004	31.59114	99.89995
969	938 961	31.12876	98.43780	999	998 001	31.60696	99.94999
				1000	1000 000	31.62278	100.00000

From "Handbook of Tables for Probability and Statistics," edited by William H. Beyer (Cleveland: The Chemical Rubber Company, 1966). Reproduced by permission of the publishers, The Chemical Rubber Company.

ANSWERS

Chapter 2

1. (a) 3, (b) 7, (c) 11, (d) -1, (e) -5, (f) $4a^2 + 3$, (g) $-4a + 3$, (h) $f(1 - y) = 7 - 4y$.

2. (a) 3/2, (b) $-8/3$, (c) 0, (d) $\dfrac{x^2 - 1}{x}$, (e) $\dfrac{a^2 - 2a}{a - 1}$.

3. (a) 7, (b) $a^2 + 2ab + b^2 - a - b + 1$.

4. (a) 0, (b) Undefined, (c) 3, (d) $-(a^2 + 1)$.

5. 1, $(1 - a)$.

6. (a) 1/4, (b) -6, (c) $\dfrac{3}{x^2} - \dfrac{3}{x} + 1$, (d) $3x^2 - 21x + 37$.

7. (a) 2, (b) 2, (c) 2.

8. 36.

9. 18.

10. 30.

11. $5(x^2 + 6)$.

12. $6x^2 + 55$.

13. $3(3 + 2i)$.

14. $10(y^2 + 1)$.

15. $y_1 + y_2 - 3$.

16. $\sum_{i=1}^{n} y_i - na$.

17. $\sum_{i=1}^{n} y_i^2 - 2a \sum_{i=1}^{n} y_i + na^2$.

Chapter 3

3. $\bar{y} = 3$, $s^2 = 6.8$, $s = 2.6$.

4. $\bar{y} = 2.28$, $s^2 = 3.9$, $s = 1.98$.

6. $\bar{y} = 2.65$, $s^2 = .252$, $s = .502$.

9. $\bar{y} \pm s = 2.15 - 3.15$, $\bar{y} \pm 2s = 1.65 - 3.65$.

10. $\bar{y} = 7.12$, $s^2 = .017$, $s = .13$.

11. $\bar{y} \pm s = 7.12 \pm .13 = 6.99 - 7.25$, $\bar{y} \pm 2s = 6.86 - 7.38$.

13. (a) $\begin{cases} \bar{y} \pm 2s = 600 \pm 140 \text{ at least } 3/4, \\ \bar{y} \pm 3s = 600 \pm 210 \text{ at least } 8/9; \end{cases}$

   (b) $\bar{y} \pm s = 530 - 670$, 68%; (c) $2\frac{1}{2}\%$.

14. 95%.

15. 16.15%.

17. $\bar{y} = 80.37$, $s^2 = 189.2$, $s = 13.75$.

18. (a) $66.62 - 94.12$, $23/30$; (b) $52.87 - 107.87$, $28/30$.

19. range $= 59$, ratio $= 4.29$, $4s$ to $6s$.

21. $1.9/4 = .48$; $s = .50$.

22. Ex. 3, $7/2.5 = 2.8$; $s = 2.6$.
    Ex. 10, $.3/2.5 = .12$; $s = .13$.

23. $.5/4 = .125 \le .263$; $s = .132$.

24. No.

Chapter 4

2. Let (L_2A_1) represent the outcome that the second LSD tablet was selected and then the first aspirin tablet was selected, etc. $A = \{(L_1A_1), (L_1A_2), (L_2A_1), (L_2A_2), (L_1L_2), (L_2L_1)\}$, etc.

3. Let $(I\ I\ F\ I)$ represent the outcome that T_3 was the only taster failing to identify the specimen from the latest batch, etc. $A = \{(I\ I\ I\ F),$ $(I\ I\ I\ I)\}$, etc.

4. (a) 1/6, (b) 1/2, (c) 0.

5. (a) 1/2, (b) 2/3, (c) 1/3, (d) 5/6.

6. 1/6.

7. 3/8, 1/2.

8. 1/15, 3/5.

9. 1/36, 1/6.

10. 5/21.

11. 36.

12. 8.

13. 12.

14. 2×10^4.

16. $\dfrac{5}{21}$.

17. (a) 6, (b) 15.

18. 30, 1/15, 3/5.

19. 12.

20. 120, 625.

21. 120, 180.

22. 30, 240.

23. 42.

24. 294.

25. $P(A) = 1/4$, $P(B) = 1/12$, $P(AB) = 0$, $P(A + B) = 1/3$.

26. $P(C) = 1/2$, $P(AC) = 1/4$, $P(BC) = 1/3$, $P(A + C) = 3/4$, $P(B + C) = 5/6$, $P(ABC) = 1/6$, $P(A + B + C) = \frac{11}{12}$.

27. (c) $\left(\frac{13}{52}\right)\left(\frac{12}{51}\right)\left(\frac{11}{50}\right)\left(\frac{10}{49}\right)\left(\frac{9}{48}\right)$;

    (d) $\left(\frac{20}{52}\right)\left(\frac{4}{51}\right)\left(\frac{3}{50}\right)\left(\frac{2}{49}\right)\left(\frac{1}{48}\right)$;

    (e) $\left(\frac{5}{52}\right)\left(\frac{4}{51}\right)\left(\frac{3}{50}\right)\left(\frac{2}{49}\right)\left(\frac{1}{48}\right)$;

    (f) $\dfrac{(13!/8!) + (4)\cdot(5!) - 5!}{52!/47!}$.

28. 1/2, 1/5, 2/5.

29. $P(A) = 1/2$, $P(B) = 2/3$, $P(AB) = 1/3$, $P(A + B) = 5/6$, $P(C) = 1/6$, $P(AC) = 0$, $P(A + C) = 2/3$

30. $P(A) = 3/81$, $P(B) = 8/81$, $P(AB) = 2/81$, $P(A + B) = 9/81$, $P(C) = 9/81$, $P(AC) = 3/81$, $P(A + C) = 9/81$.

31. $P(A/B) = 1/3$, $P(A/C) = 0$, $P(B/C) = 1/2$. *A* and *B* are dependent and not mutually exclusive. *B* and *C* are independent and not mutually exclusive.

32. $P(A/B) = 1/2$, $P(A/C) = 0$, $P(B/C) = 0$. *A* and *B* are independent and not mutually exclusive. *B* and *C* are dependent and mutually exclusive.

33. $P(A/B) = 1/4$, $P(A/C) = 1/3$, $P(B/C) = 8/9$. *A* and *B* are dependent and not mutually exclusive. *B* and *C* are dependent and not mutually exclusive.

35. $P(A/B) = 1/2$, $P(B/A) = 2/3$, $P(AB) = 1/3$, $P(A + B) = 5/6$.

36. $P(AB) = 0$, $P(A + B) = 1/3$.

37. 1/20.

38. (a) 56, (b) 6, (c) 3/28.

39. (a) .81, (b) .01, (c) .99.

40. .999999.

41. (a) $\frac{5}{6}$, (b) $\frac{25}{36}$, (c) $\frac{11}{36}$.

42. 0.432.

43. .4783, .00781.

44. 15.

45. 1/81.

46. $\dfrac{84!}{17!19!27!21!}$

47. $P \text{ (observed event)} = \dfrac{(4!)(3!)^4}{12!}.$

48. $P(B/A) = \dfrac{5!8!}{13!}, \ P(AB) = \dfrac{5!47!}{52!},$

$P(A + B) = \dfrac{(13!/8!) + (3)(5!)}{52!/47!}.$

49. .476

50. (a) 45, (b) 10, (c) 2/9.

51. .8704.

52. 4/25.

53. 44/105.

54. 1/16

55. 4.

56. (a) .128, (b) .488.

57. (a) 1/5, (b) 2/5, (c) 1/2.

Chapter 5

3. $P(0) = 1/5, \ P(1) = 3/5, \ P(2) = 1/5.$

4. 1.625, 47/64.

7. 1.

8. 2.92.

9. $\sigma^2 = 2/5.$

12. $P(0) = 0; \ P(1) = 3/10; \ P(2) = 6/10; \ P(3) = 1/10, \ 7/10.$

13. $8333.

14. $\mu = 1.8, \ \sigma^2 = .36.$

15. 297/625.

16. .992.

17. $P(y) = \dfrac{C_y^2 C_{3-y}^4}{C_3^6}$.

18. $\mu = 2.4$, $\sigma^2 = .48$.

19. e^{-2}.

20. e^{-1}, e^{-1}, $\dfrac{e^{-1}}{2}$, $1 - e^{-1}$.

21. \$120.

22. (a) $P(0) = (\tfrac{2}{3})^4$, $P(1) = 2(\tfrac{2}{3})^4$, $P(2) = (\tfrac{2}{3})^3$, $P(3) = \tfrac{1}{3}(\tfrac{2}{3})^3$, $P(4) = (\tfrac{1}{3})^4$.
    (b) 1/9, (c) 4/3, (d) 8/9.

23. (a) $P(0) = 8/27$, $P(1) = 4/9$, $P(2) = 2/9$, $P(3) = 1/27$,
    (b) 7/27, (c) 1, (d) 2/3.

24. (a) $P(0) = 125/216$, $P(1) = 75/216$, $P(2) = 15/216$, $P(3) = 1/216$.
    (b) 2/27, (c) 1/2, (d) 5/12.

25. (a) $P(0) = 1/42$, $P(1) = 10/42$, $P(2) = 20/42$, $P(3) = 10/42$, $P(4) = 1/42$
    (b) 11/42, (c) 2, (d) 2/3.

Chapter 6

2. (a) $P(0) = 1/8$, $P(1) = 3/8$, $P(2) = 3/8$, $P(3) = 1/8$; (c) $E(y) = 1.5$,
   $\sigma = .866$.

3. (a) $P(0) = .729$, $P(1) = .243$, $P(2) = .027$, $P(3) = .001$; (c) $E(y) = .3$,
   $\sigma = .520$.

4. .32805, .99999.

5. $E(y) = 100$, $V(y) = 90$, $81 \le y \le 119$ $(\mu + 2\sigma)$.

6. $P(0) = .9606$, $P(0) + P(1) = .9994$.

7. .6082.

8. $E(y) = 2$, $\sigma = 1.34$, 0 to 4.68 $(\mu \pm 2\sigma)$.

9. (a) .3875, (b) .6513, (c) .2638.

10. (a) .5905, (b) .1681, (c) .0312, (d) 1.000, (e) 0.

11. (a) .9186, (b) .5283, (c) .1874, (d) 1.000, (e) 0.

12. (a) .3487, (b) .0282, (c) .0010, (d) 1.000, (e) 0.

13. (a) .7362, (b) .1493, (c) .0108, (d) 1.000, (e) 0.

15. (a) $n = 25$, $a = 5$
    (b) $n = 25$, $a = 5$

16. (a) .1508, (b) .3016.

19. (a) .125, (b) .7518.

21. (b) 1/32, (c) .7378.

23. (a) $\dfrac{32}{32768}$, (b) .833.

24. (a) 242/32768, (b) .602.

25. (a) $p = 1/3$,   (b) 11/243,
    (c) 99/128,   (d) less.

Supplementary:

   5. .04.

   6. .987.

Chapter 7

1. $n = 126$, $p = 1/126$.

3. $\mu = 3.5$, s.d. $= .77$.

4. (a) .3849, (b) .3159.

5. (a) .4452, (b) .2734.

6. (a) .4279, (b) .1628.

7. (a) .4251, (b) .4778.

8. (a) .3227, (b) .1586.

9. (a) .0730, (b) .8623.

10. .7734.

11. .9115.

12. 0.

13. 1.10.

14. .2268.

15. -1.645.

16. 1.645.

17. 2.575.

18. .1596.

19. .2266.

20. .2661.

21. .0401.

22. 85.36.

23. (a) .578, (b) .5752.

24. (a) .421, (b) .4013.

25. .1601.

26. .9554.

27. Yes.

28. Yes.

29. $\mu = 7.301$.

30. $z = \pm 1.96$, $y = 28, 52$.

31. .117.

32. .9929.

33. (a) .0071, (b) .0571.

34. 383.65.

35. No.

36. (a) 141, (b) .04.

Chapter 8

2. 1280 ± 28.4.

3. .1587.

4. $.92 \pm .0172$.

5. $1256.64 < u < 1303.36$.

6. $.898 < p < .942$.

7. $.075 < p < .125$.

8. $5.4 \pm .277$.

9. $1.7 \pm .494$.

10. $1.294 < \mu_1 - \mu_2 < 2.106$.

11. $.11 \pm .09$.

12. $25.625 < \mu < 26.975$.

13. 2400.

14. $4751 < \mu < 4849$.

15. 40,000.

16. $-.04 \pm .104$.

17. 768.

18. .6170.

19. 100.

20. 44.

21. 72.

24. $z = -2.53$.

25. $z = 1.58$.

26. $z = 4.71$.

27. .1342.

28. $z = -1$.

29. $z = 7.02$.

31. $z = -3.12$.

32. $z = -1.41$.

33. $z = 6.88$.

34. $z = 1.68$.

35. 68.

36. $z = -2.5$.

37. .1151, .0228.

38. No. ($z = 1.5 < 1.645$).

39. $n = 309$.

Chapter 9

3. $t = -1.34$; do not reject.

4. 795 ± 7.95.

5. 31.

6. 24.7 ± 1.05.

7. $t = 2.635$; reject.

8. $7.1 \pm .0696$.

9. 11.3 ± 1.437.

10. $t = -1.4$; do not reject.

11. 3.68 ± 1.56.

12. $t = -1.95$; do not reject.

13. $2.43 \pm .85$.

14. 19.

16. $t = 1.861$; reject.

17. 4.9 ± 4.54.

18. $t = 1.570$; do not reject.

19. Yes. $(t = 2.2 > 1.638)$.

20. $t = -1.71$; do not reject.

21. $t = 2.50$; reject.

22. $-.75 \pm .771$.

23. $.875 \pm .83$.

24. $.875 \pm .965$.

25. $t = 9.57$; reject.

26. unpaired: $.259 \pm .047$; paired: $.259 \pm .050$.

28. $t = 2.573$; reject.

29. $.01 \pm .0099$.

30. $t = 1.581$; do not reject.

31. 3.03 ± 3.47.

32. $n_1 = n_2 = 238$.

33. $29.35 < \sigma^2 < 391.31$.

34. $X^2 = 12.6$; do not reject.

35. $.00896 < \sigma^2 < .05814$.

38. $F = 1.922$; do not reject $(\alpha = .05)$.

39. $.775 < \dfrac{\sigma_2^2}{\sigma_1^2} < 4.77$.

40. $1.676 < \sigma^2 < 8.314$.

41. $X^2 = 22.47$; reject.

42. $1.41 < \sigma^2 < 31.28$.

43. $F = 2.1$; do not reject.

44. Yes $(F = 2.41 > 2.22)$.

Chapter 10

5. $\hat{y} = 1.00 + .70x$.

6. $\hat{y} = 2.643 + .554x$.

7. $.3666$.

8. $.6553$.

9. $t = 3.656$.

10. $t = 3.618$.

13. $\hat{y} = 307.92 + 34.58x$.

14. $t = 5.68$.

15. $21.03 < \beta_1 < 48.14$.

16. $.25 < \beta_1 < 1.15$.

17. $.160 < \beta_1 < .947$.

18. $1.7 \pm .78$.

19. $2.089 \pm .884$.

20. 515.417 ± 33.12.

21. 411.667 ± 102.846.

22. 3.750 ± 1.823.

26. $.902$.

27. $.850$.

28. 72.25%

29. $r = .8739$.

30. $\hat{y} = 46.00 - .317x$;
    $s^2 = 19.036$.

31. $-.419 < \beta_1 < -.215$.

32. 30.165 ± 2.500.

33. 30.165 ± 8.290.

34. $r = -.8718$.

35. $\hat{y} = -.333 + 1.400x$;
    $s^2 = 1.241$.

36. $t = 3.974$.

37. $\hat{y} = -5.497 + .066x$;
    $s^2 = .180$.

38. Yes; $t = 3.38$.

39. $.73$.

40. $2.01 < E(y/x = 120) < 2.56$.

41. $1.47 < y < 3.10$.

Chapter 11

2. $X^2 = 24.48$; Reject H_0 ($\chi^2_{.05} = 7.81$).

3. $X^2 = 10.40$; Do not reject H_0 ($\chi^2_{.05} = 11.1$).

4. (a) $z = -2.30$; Reject H_0,
   (b) Formulate H_0 before collecting data.

5. $X^2 = 18.53$; Reject H_0 ($\chi^2_{.05} = 3.84$).

6. $X^2 = 27.17$; Reject H_0 ($\chi^2_{.10} = 6.25$).

7. $X^2 = 2.87$; Do not reject H_0 ($\chi^2_{.05} = 5.99$).

8. $X^2 = 11.62$; Reject H_0 ($\chi^2_{.05} = 9.49$).

9. $X^2 = 5.02$; Do not reject H_0 ($\chi^2_{.05} = 5.99$).

10. $X^2 = 7.19$; Reject H_0 ($\chi^2_{.05} = 5.99$).

11. $X^2 = 12.91$; Do not reject H_0 ($\chi^2_{.05} = 15.5$).

12. $X^2 = 4.40$; Do not reject H_0 ($\chi^2_{.05} = 9.49$).

13. $X^2 = 54.11$; Reject H_0 ($\chi^2_{.05} = 15.5$).

Supplementary:

2. $\hat{p} = 1/2$, $X^2 = 8.56$; Reject H_0 ($\chi^2_{.05} = 7.81$).

Chapter 12

1. $F = 91.6$; reject.

4. $SSE = .0201$; $F = 1.98$; do not reject.

5. $2.20 < \mu_A < 2.30$; $-.01 < \mu_A - \mu_B < .18$.

6. $SSE = 498.67$; yes.

7. $67.9 < \mu_A < 84.1$; $55.8 < \mu_B < 76.8 - 3.6 < \mu_A - \mu_B < 23.0$; No, they are not independent.

8. $SSE = .0051$; yes; yes; yes.

9. $.02 < \mu_A - \mu_B < .14$; No.

10. No, it is a completely randomized design; completely randomized design with nine treatments and two observations per treatment.

11. 16; 135; 14.1.

12. $SSE = 4.99$; No; No.

13. $F = 5.14$; yes; Blocking causes a loss of degrees of freedom for estimating σ^2. Blocking may produce a slight loss of information if the block-to-block variation is small.

14. Randomized block design; 21; $SSE = 58.91$; $F = 3.10$; yes; No, the judge's responses may have been determined by a teaching characteristic other than the one under study.

15. At least 49.

16. At least 22.

Chapter 13

1. $.014$, $y \le 6$ and $y \ge 19$; $.044$, $y \le 7$ and $y \ge 18$; $.108$, $y \le 8$ and $y \ge 17$.

2. Rejection region: $y = 0$; $\alpha = 1/32$.   Rejection region: $y \le 1$; $\alpha = 7/32$. Do not reject in either case.

3. (a) Rejection region: $y \le 1$; $\alpha = .039$.   Rejection region: $y \le 2$; $\alpha = .180$.   Hence, we may reject H_0 at $\alpha = .180$, but not at $\alpha = .039$.

   (b) $|t| = .30 < 1.746$; do not reject.

4. (a) Rejection region: $y \le 1$; $\alpha = .0215$. Rejection region: $y \le 2$; $\alpha = .1094$. Do not reject.

 (b) Rejection region: $y \le 2$; $\alpha = .0547$. Do not reject.

5. Rejection region: $U \le 7$; $\alpha = .094$. Sample $U = 9$. Do not reject.

6. Rejection region: $R \le 4$; $\alpha = .067$. Rejection region: $R < 5$; $\alpha = .175$. Sample $R = 8$. Do not reject.

7. Rejection region: $U \le 21$; $\alpha = .094$. Sample $U = 32$. Do not reject.

8. Rejection region: $R \le 7$; $\alpha = .109$. Sample $R = 13$. Do not reject.

9. (a) Rejection region: $T \le 8$. Sample $T = 6$. Reject.

 (b) Rejection region: $T \le 11$. Sample $T = 6$. Reject,

10. (a) Rejection region: $y \le 1$; $\alpha = .039$. Do not reject.

 (b) Rejection region: $|t| \ge 2.306$ has $\alpha = .05$. $t = -1.65$. Do not reject.

11. Rejection region: $T \le 6$. Sample $T = 10.5$. Do not reject.

12. Rejection region: $R \le 2$; $\alpha = .029$.
 Rejection region: $R \le 3$; $\alpha = .114$.
 Sample $R = 3$. Reject at $\alpha = .114$ but not at $\alpha = .029$.

13. (a) Rejection region: $z = \dfrac{U - 112.5}{24.1} \le -1.645$; $\alpha = .05$.

 Sample $z = -1.805$. Reject H_0.

 (b) Reduction of the expected number of runs. Rejection region:

 $$z = \frac{R - 16}{2.69} \le -1.645; \alpha = .05.$$

 Sample $z = -.37$. Do not reject.

14. Rejection region: $R \le 3$; $\alpha = .040$.
 Rejection region: $R \le 4$; $\alpha = .167$.
 Sample $R = 5$. Do not reject.

15. (a) .0256.

 (b) An unusually small number of runs (judged at $\alpha = .05$) would imply a clustering of defective items in time.

16. (a) Rejection region: $R \le 6$; $\alpha = .100$. Sample $R = 7$; do not reject at $\alpha = .100$.

 (b) $t = .57$. Do not reject.

17. (a) Rejection region: $U \leq 3$; $\alpha = .056$. Sample $U = 3$; reject at $\alpha = .056$.

   (b) Rejection region: $F = s_A^2/s_B^2 \geq 9.12$; $\alpha = .05$. Sample $F = 4.91$; do not reject.

18. $-.845$.

19. Rejection region: $r_s \leq -.564$; $\alpha = .05$; reject H_0.

20. $-.593$.

21. Rejection region: $r_s \leq -.497$; $\alpha = .05$; reject H_0.

Supplementary: consult the appropriate table.

INDEX

Q

R

S

T

U

V